MUSIC EDUCATION SERIES

INTERMEDIATE MUSIC

BY

THADDEUS P. GIDDINGS

DIRECTOR OF SCHOOL MUSIC IN MINNEAPOLIS, MINNESOTA

WILL EARHART

DIRECTOR OF SCHOOL MUSIC IN PITTSBURGH, PENNSYLVANIA

RALPH L. BALDWIN

DIRECTOR OF SCHOOL MUSIC IN HARTFORD, CONNECTICUT

ELBRIDGE W. NEWTON

MANAGING EDITOR

GINN AND COMPANY

BOSTON · NEW YORK · CHICAGO · LONDON
ATLANTA · DALLAS · COLUMBUS · SAN FRANCISCO

𝕿𝖍𝖊 𝕬𝖙𝖍𝖊𝖓𝖆𝖊𝖚𝖒 𝕻𝖗𝖊𝖘𝖘

GINN AND COMPANY · PRO-
PRIETORS · BOSTON · U.S.A.

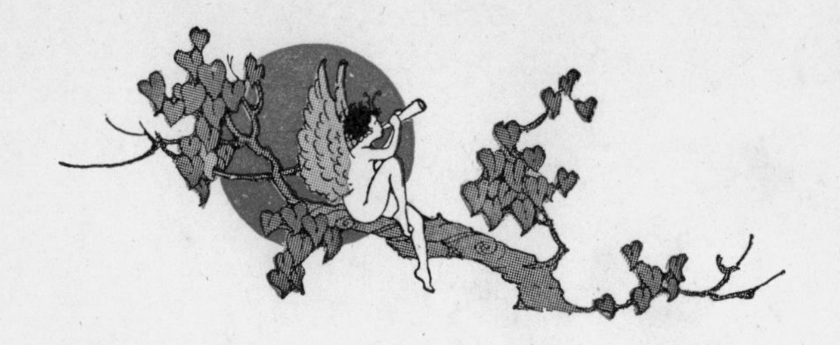

The wave that breaks upon the strand
  Has music mingled with its roar,
There's music in the breezes bland
  That breathe along the sheltered shore.

There's music in the mighty woods,
  And in the streams that wander through,
While desert sands and solitudes
  Send forth their own wild music, too.

Ah, let us not be blind to all
  The beauty in the world that dwells,
Nor deaf to that enchanting call —
  The song that from creation swells;

But, shaking off the slavish bond
  That binds us to the ways of strife,
Let music with its magic wand
  Awake us to the larger life.

                          DENIS A. McCARTHY

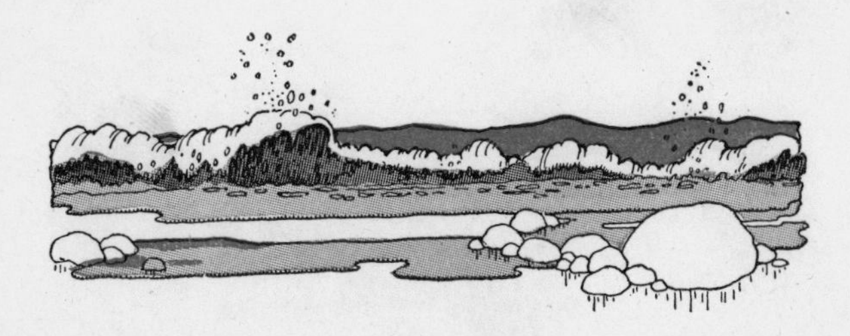

ACKNOWLEDGMENTS

In the preparation of this book the editors have received valuable assistance from Miss Helen S. Leavitt and gratefully acknowledge her service in musical and editorial contributions. They also wish to express their appreciation of the coöperation of the large group of editorial advisers who through constructive criticism and constant interest have contributed much to make this book effective.

Acknowledgment is also due to Houghton Mifflin Company for permission to use "Clouds," by Frank Dempster Sherman, and "The Poet's Friends," by William Dean Howells; to the C. W. Bardeen Company for permission to use "Planting the Tree," by Henry Abbey.

The illustrations are by Katherine G. Healey.

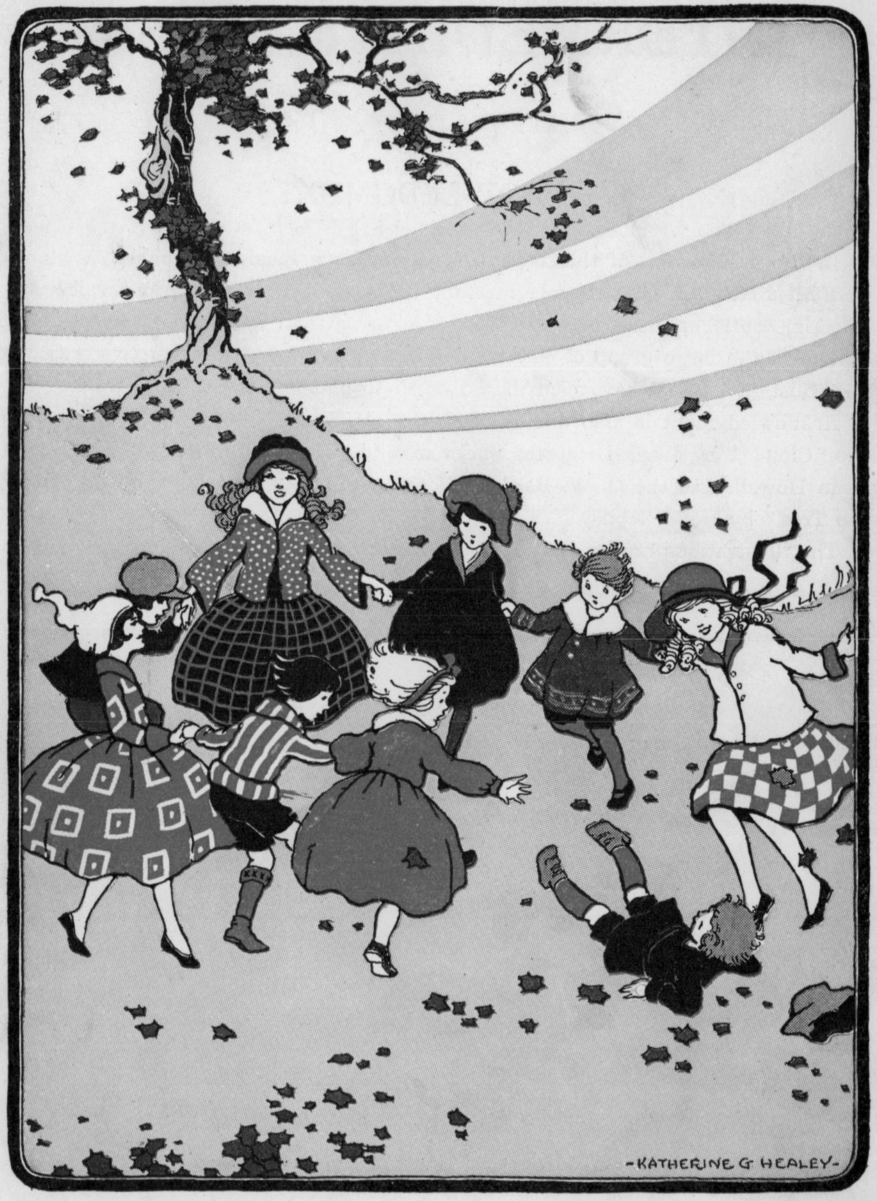
-KATHERINE G HEALEY-

INTERMEDIATE MUSIC

PART I

VOICES OF AUTUMN

ABBIE FARWELL BROWN

HARRY HARTS

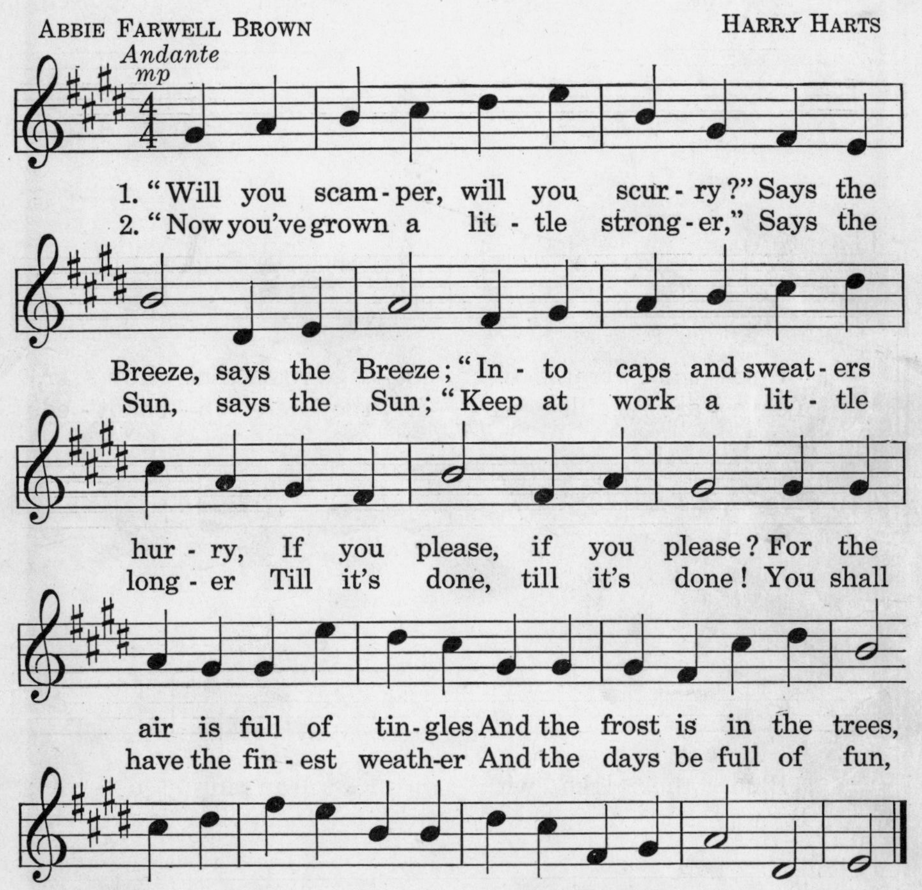

1. "Will you scam-per, will you scur-ry?" Says the
2. "Now you've grown a lit-tle strong-er," Says the

Breeze, says the Breeze; "In-to caps and sweat-ers
Sun, says the Sun; "Keep at work a lit-tle

hur-ry, If you please, if you please? For the
long-er Till it's done, till it's done! You shall

air is full of tin-gles And the frost is in the trees,
have the fin-est weath-er And the days be full of fun,

While a spic-y fra-grance min-gles With the au-tumn breeze."
While we work and play to-geth-er," Says the gold-en Sun.

7

AUTUMN DREAMS

MARY STANHOPE

LUDWIG VAN BEETHOVEN

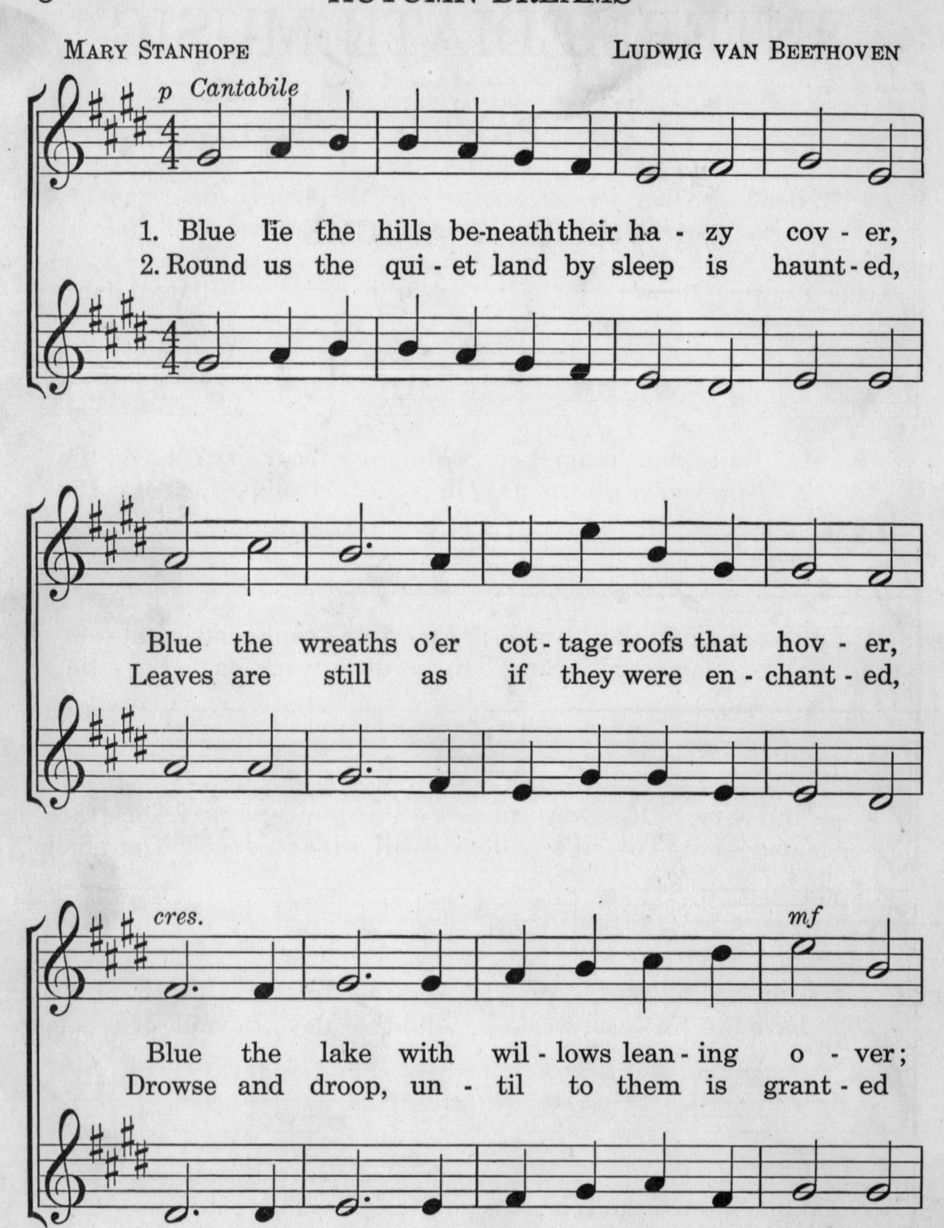

1. Blue lie the hills be-neath their ha - zy cov - er,
2. Round us the qui - et land by sleep is haunt - ed,

Blue the wreaths o'er cot - tage roofs that hov - er,
Leaves are still as if they were en - chant - ed,

Blue the lake with wil - lows lean - ing o - ver;
Drowse and droop, un - til to them is grant - ed

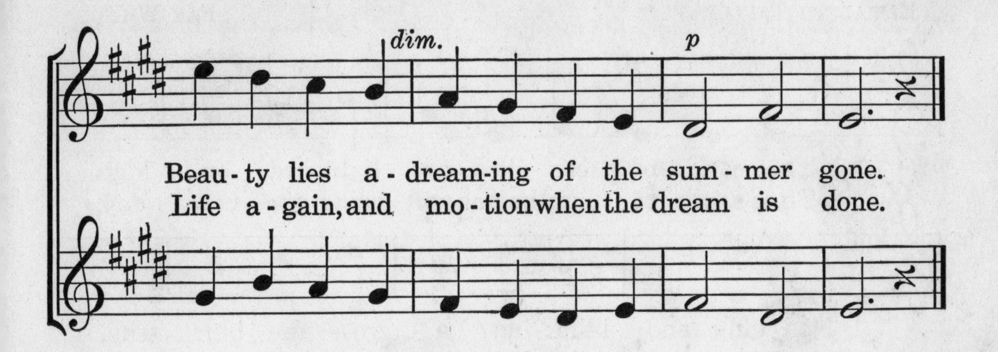

Beau-ty lies a-dream-ing of the sum-mer gone.
Life a-gain, and mo-tion when the dream is done.

WILD GRAPES

LOUISE STICKNEY

RUTH McCONN SPENCER

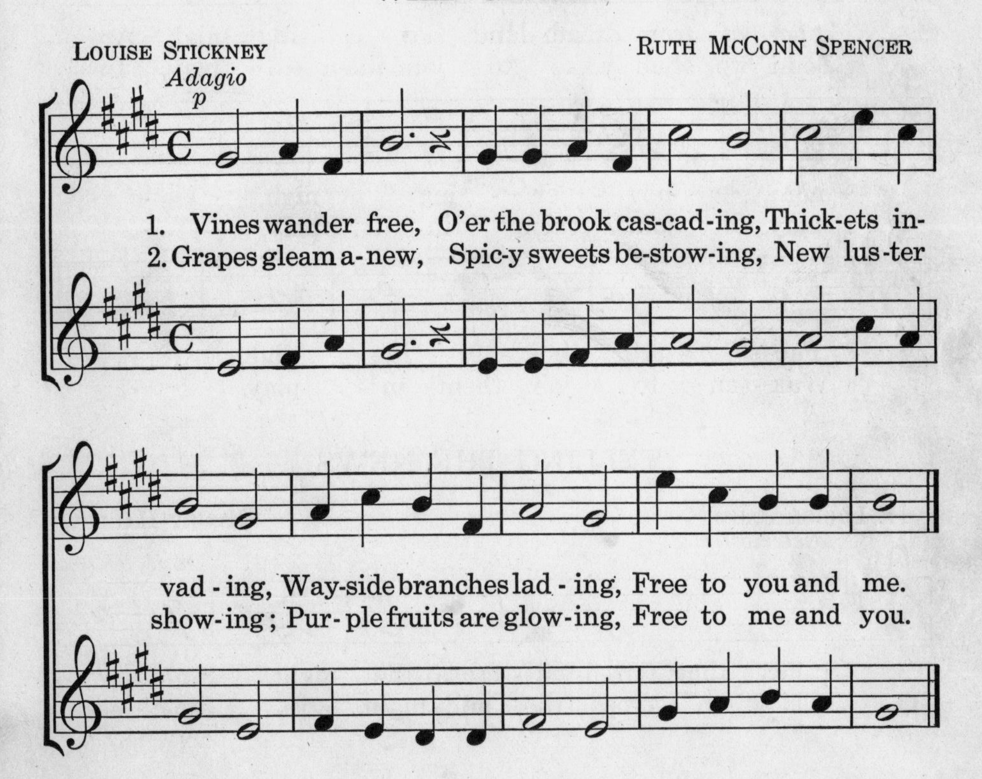

1. Vines wander free, O'er the brook cas-cad-ing, Thick-ets in-
2. Grapes gleam a-new, Spic-y sweets be-stow-ing, New lus-ter

vad-ing, Way-side branches lad-ing, Free to you and me.
show-ing; Pur-ple fruits are glow-ing, Free to me and you.

SKY CANDLES

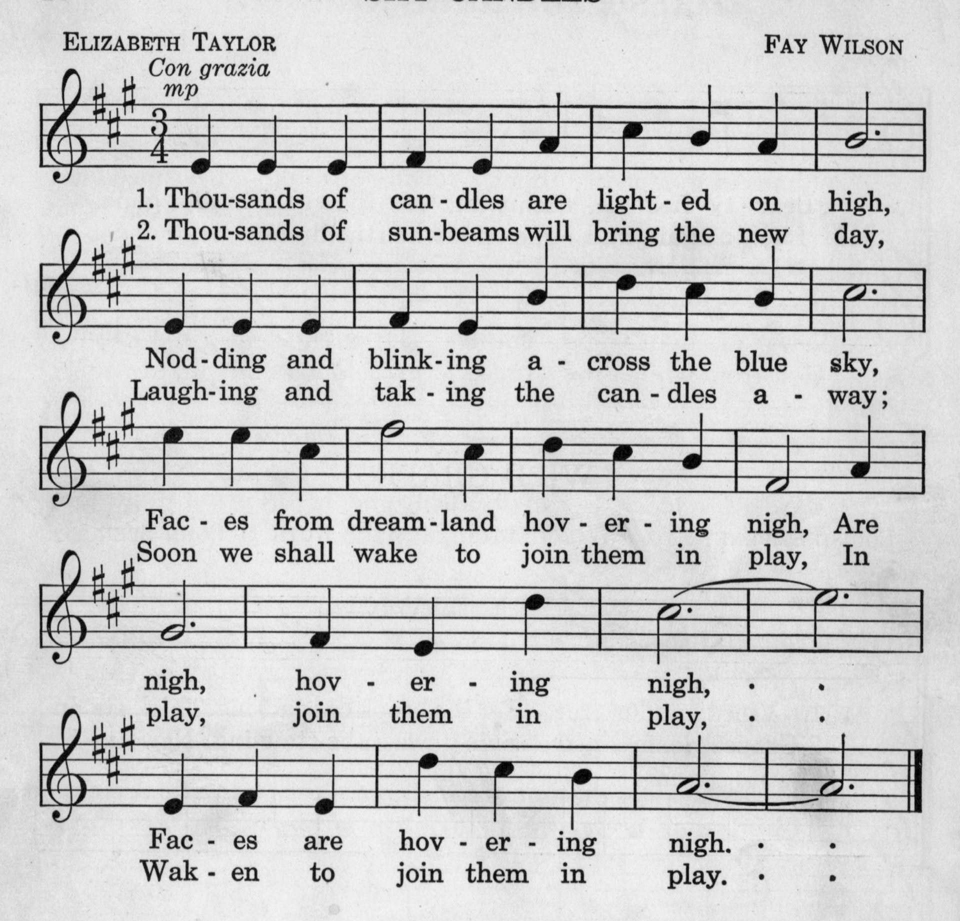

ELIZABETH TAYLOR

FAY WILSON

Con grazia
mp

1. Thou-sands of can - dles are light - ed on high,
2. Thou-sands of sun-beams will bring the new day,

Nod - ding and blink - ing a - cross the blue sky,
Laugh-ing and tak - ing the can - dles a - way;

Fac - es from dream-land hov - er - ing nigh, Are
Soon we shall wake to join them in play, In

nigh, hov - er - ing nigh, . .
play, join them in play, . .

Fac - es are hov - er - ing nigh. . .
Wak - en to join them in play. . .

TELLING THE NEWS

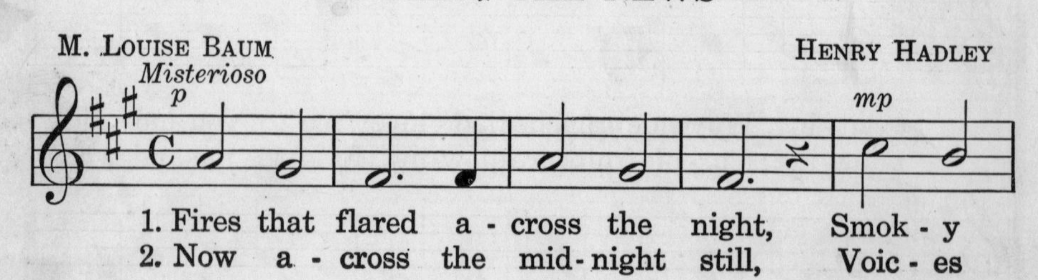

M. LOUISE BAUM

HENRY HADLEY

Misterioso
p
mp

1. Fires that flared a - cross the night, Smok - y
2. Now a - cross the mid-night still, Voic - es

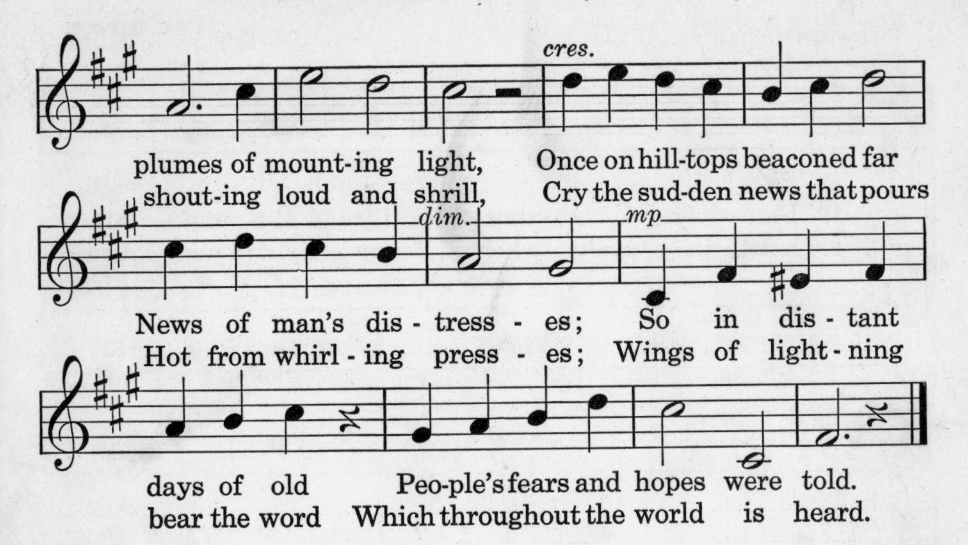

plumes of mount-ing light, Once on hill-tops beaconed far
shout-ing loud and shrill, Cry the sud-den news that pours

News of man's dis - tress - es; So in dis - tant
Hot from whirl - ing press - es; Wings of light - ning

days of old Peo-ple's fears and hopes were told.
bear the word Which throughout the world is heard.

EARLY DAWN

ABBIE FARWELL BROWN

WILL EARHART

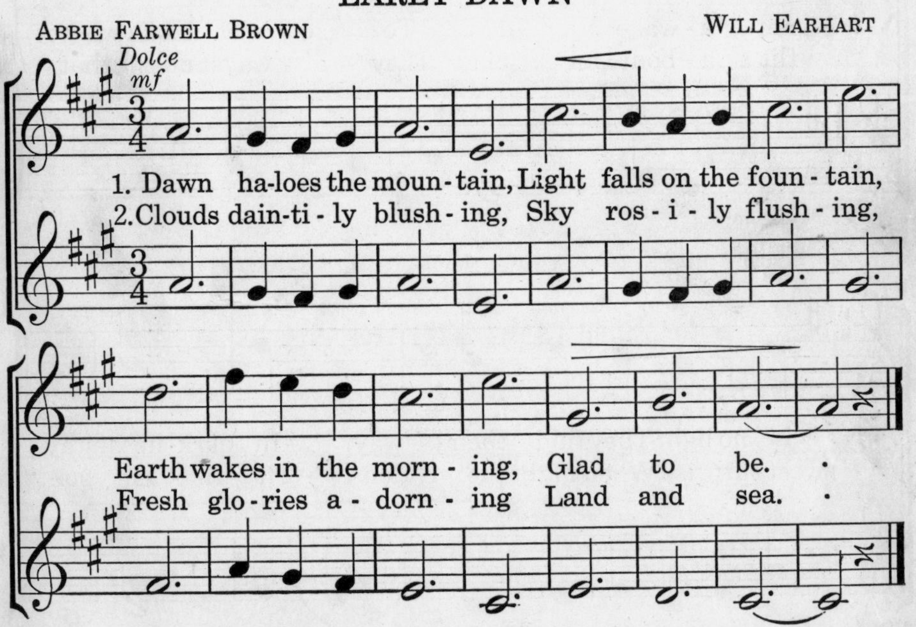

1. Dawn ha-loes the moun-tain, Light falls on the foun - tain,
2. Clouds dain-ti - ly blush-ing, Sky ros - i - ly flush-ing,

Earth wakes in the morn - ing, Glad to be.
Fresh glo-ries a - dorn - ing Land and sea.

FLUFFY OWLS

Frances Richardson

Evelyn Sprague

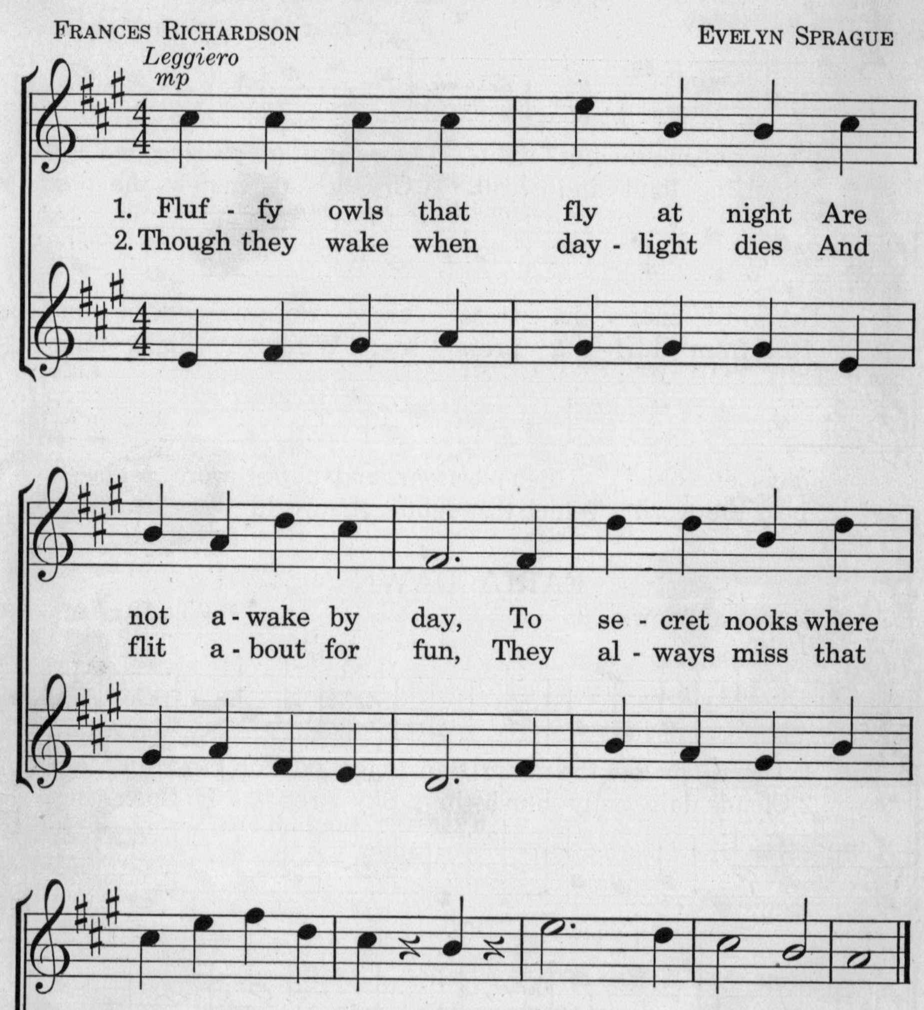

Leggiero
mp

1. Fluf - fy owls that fly at night Are
2. Though they wake when day - light dies And

not a - wake by day, To se - cret nooks where
flit a - bout for fun, They al - ways miss that

is no light They find their way, In dark - ness stay.
sweet surprise When night is done, — The ris - ing sun.

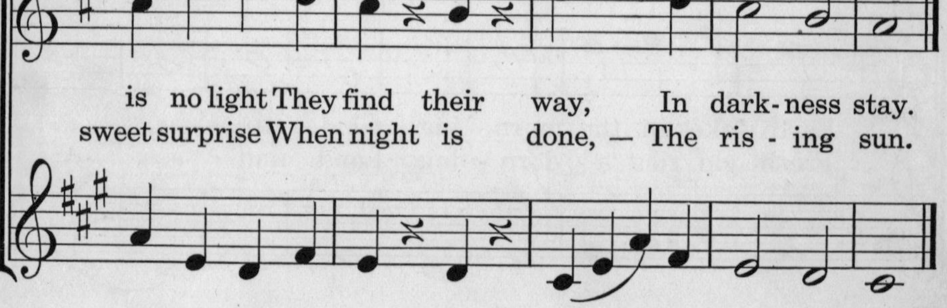

DENIS McCARTHY

CHARLES FONTEYN MANNEY

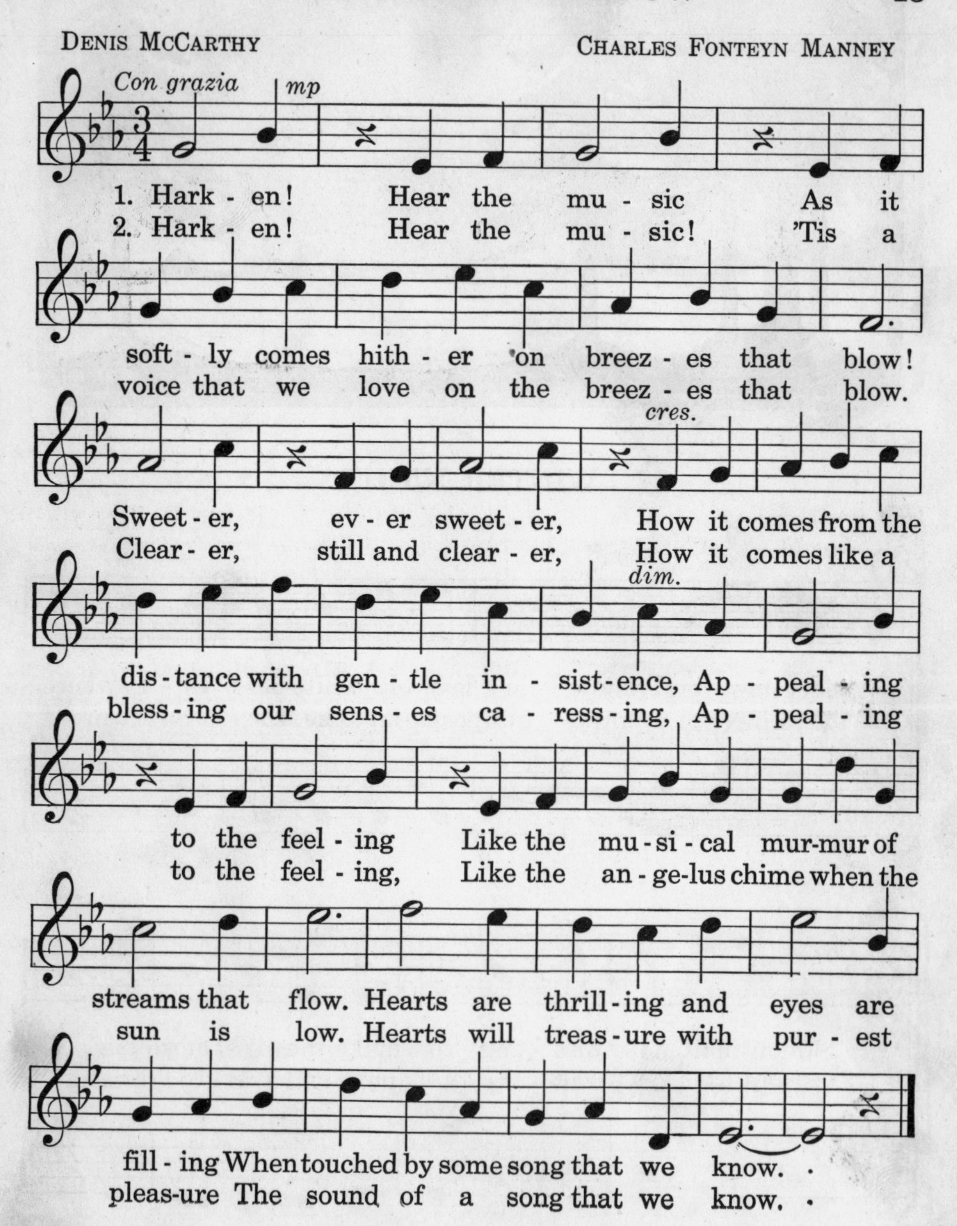

1. Hark - en! Hear the mu - sic As it
2. Hark - en! Hear the mu - sic! 'Tis a

soft - ly comes hith - er 'on breez - es that blow!
voice that we love on the breez - es that blow.

Sweet - er, ev - er sweet - er, How it comes from the
Clear - er, still and clear - er, How it comes like a

dis - tance with gen - tle in - sist - ence, Ap - peal - ing
bless - ing our sens - es ca - ress - ing, Ap - peal - ing

to the feel - ing Like the mu - si - cal mur-mur of
to the feel - ing, Like the an - ge-lus chime when the

streams that flow. Hearts are thrill - ing and eyes are
sun is low. Hearts will treas - ure with pur - est

fill - ing When touched by some song that we know. ·
pleas-ure The sound of a song that we know. ·

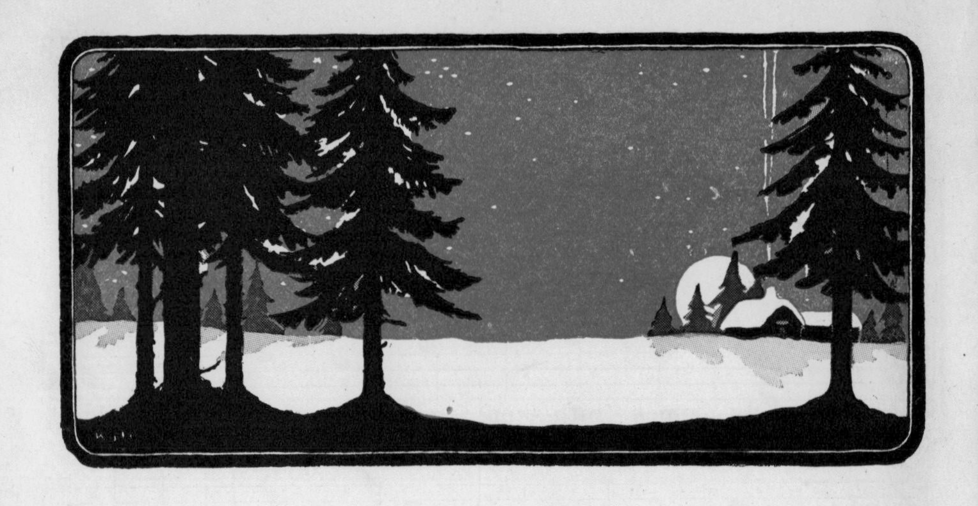

WINTER NIGHT

KATE FORMAN

RALPH L. BALDWIN

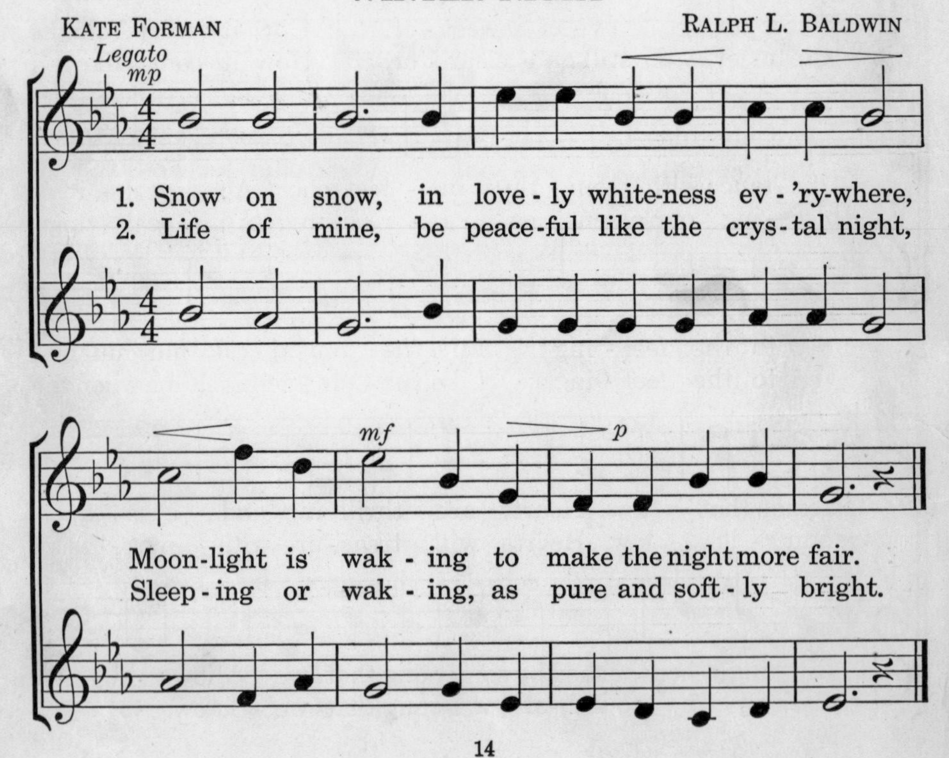

1. Snow on snow, in love-ly white-ness ev-'ry-where,
2. Life of mine, be peace-ful like the crys-tal night,

Moon-light is wak-ing to make the night more fair.
Sleep-ing or wak-ing, as pure and soft-ly bright.

ROBERT BRIGHAM

RUTH McCONN SPENCER

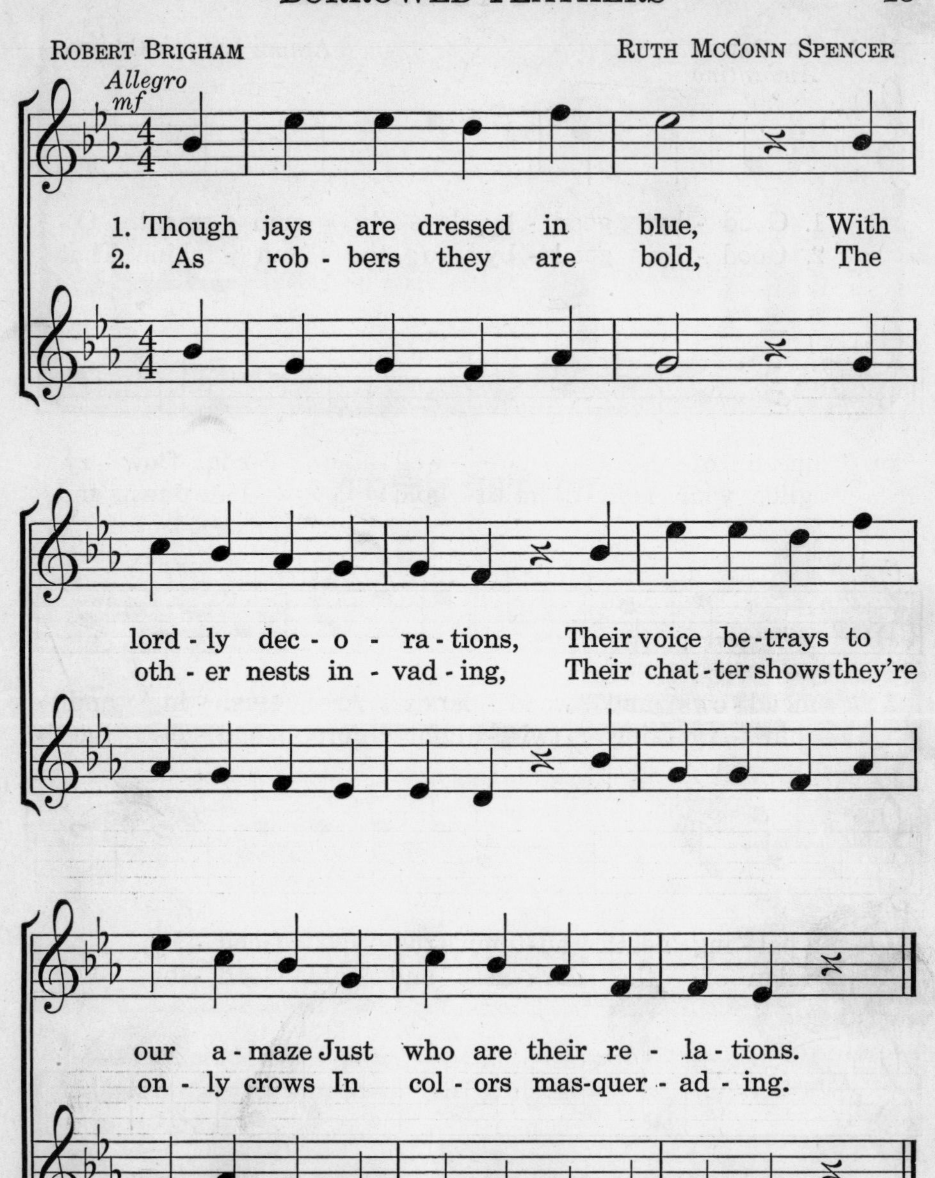

1. Though jays are dressed in blue, With
2. As rob - bers they are bold, The

lord - ly dec - o - ra - tions, Their voice be - trays to
oth - er nests in - vad - ing, Their chat - ter shows they're

our a - maze Just who are their re - la - tions.
on - ly crows In col - ors mas-quer - ad - ing.

GOOD-BY TO SUMMER

M. Louise Baum

André Ernest Grétry

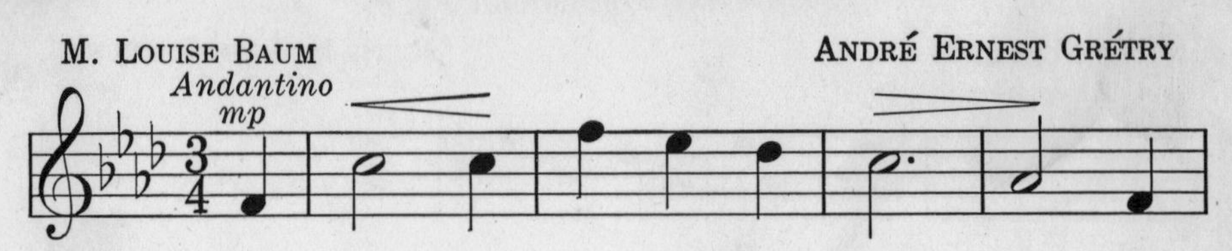

1. Good - by, good - by, love - ly sum - mer! O
2. Good - by, good - by to the sun - shine That

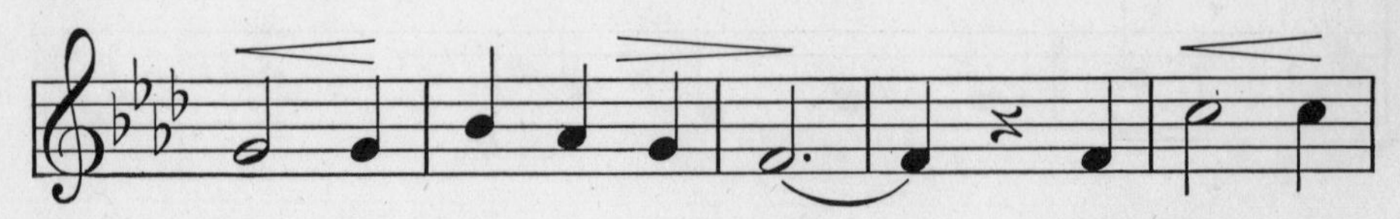

queen of beau - ty, fare - well! · Your flow - 'ry
gilds your man - tle with gold! · Late dawns and

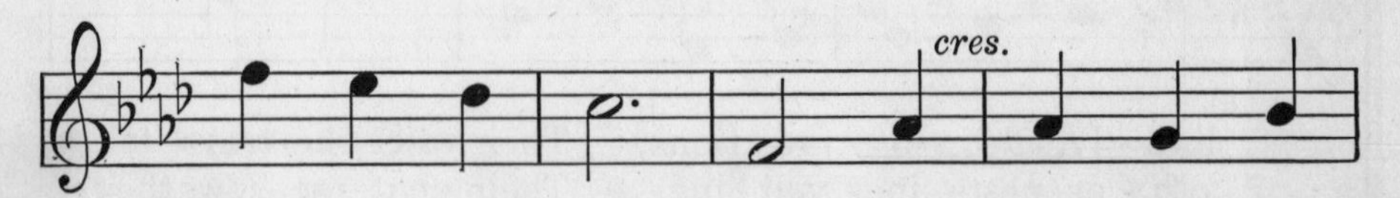

mead - ows and wood - lands Are flush - ing and
hur - ry - ing twi - light Fore - shad - ow the

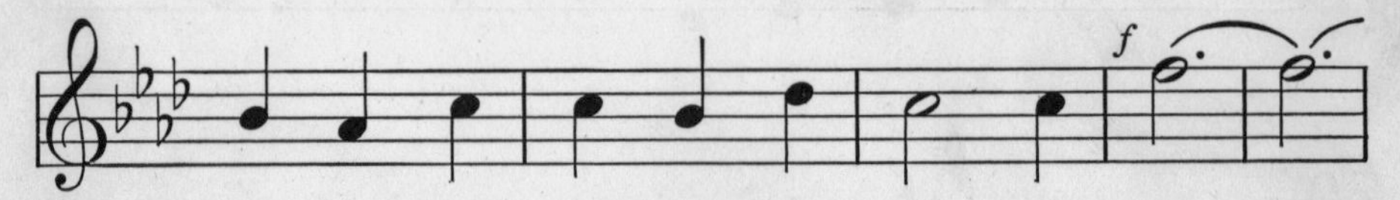

pal - ing 'neath au - tumn's rude spell. Good - by, · ·
reign of the dark - ness and cold. Good - by, · ·

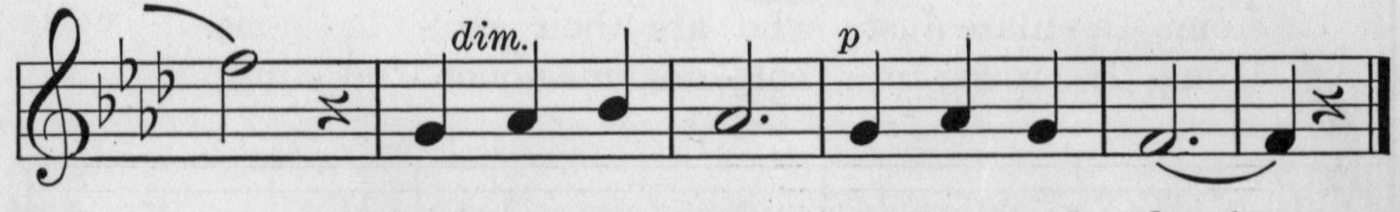

· · Queen of the year, ra - diant and dear! ·
· · Queen of the year, ra - diant and dear! ·

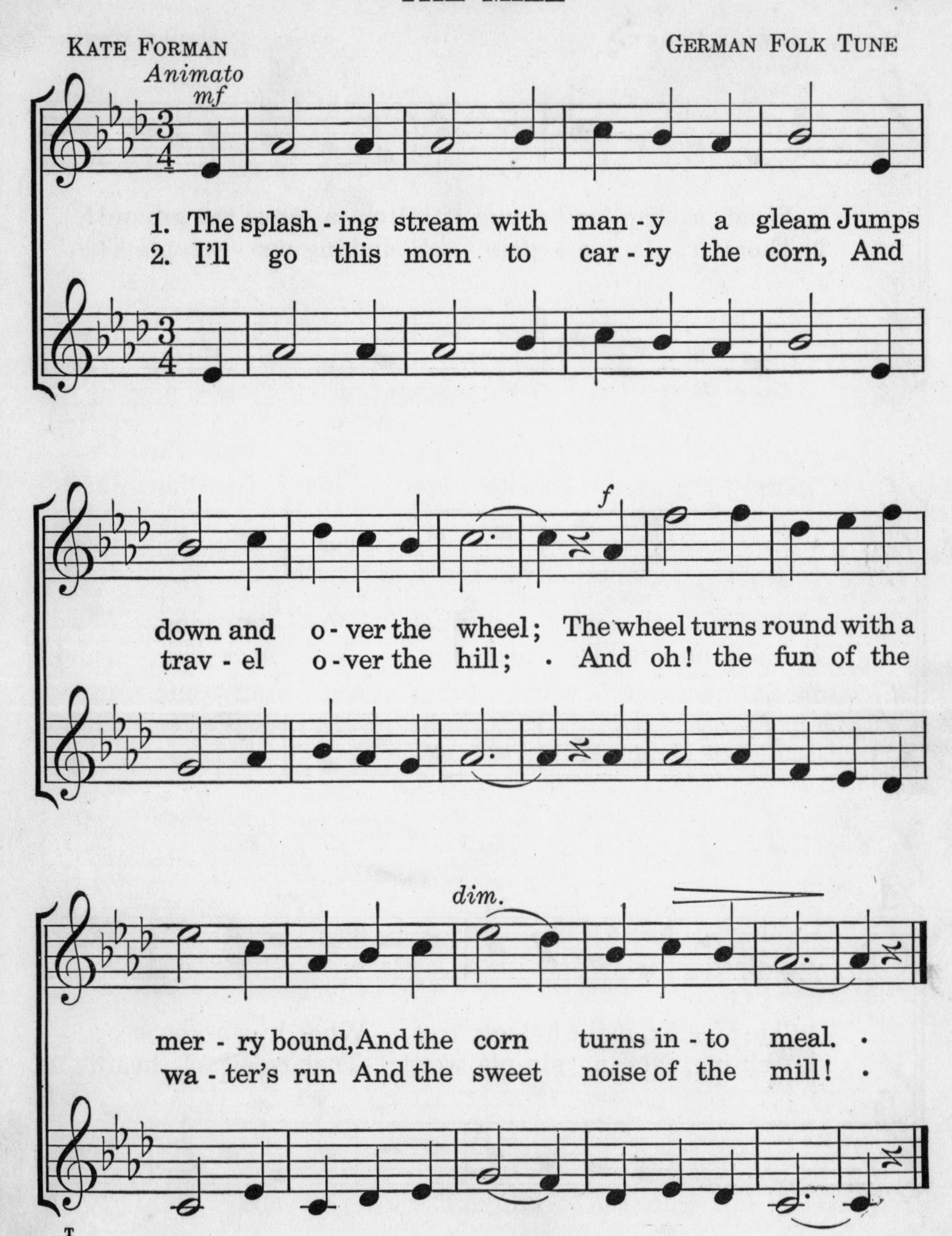

KATE FORMAN

GERMAN FOLK TUNE

Animato
mf

1. The splash - ing stream with man - y   a gleam Jumps
2. I'll   go this morn to   car - ry the corn, And

f

down and   o - ver the wheel; The wheel turns round with a
trav - el   o - ver the hill; . And oh! the fun of the

dim.

mer - ry bound, And the corn   turns in - to   meal. .
wa - ter's run And the sweet   noise of the   mill! .

THE WOODPECKER

ABBIE FARWELL BROWN

HARRY HARTS

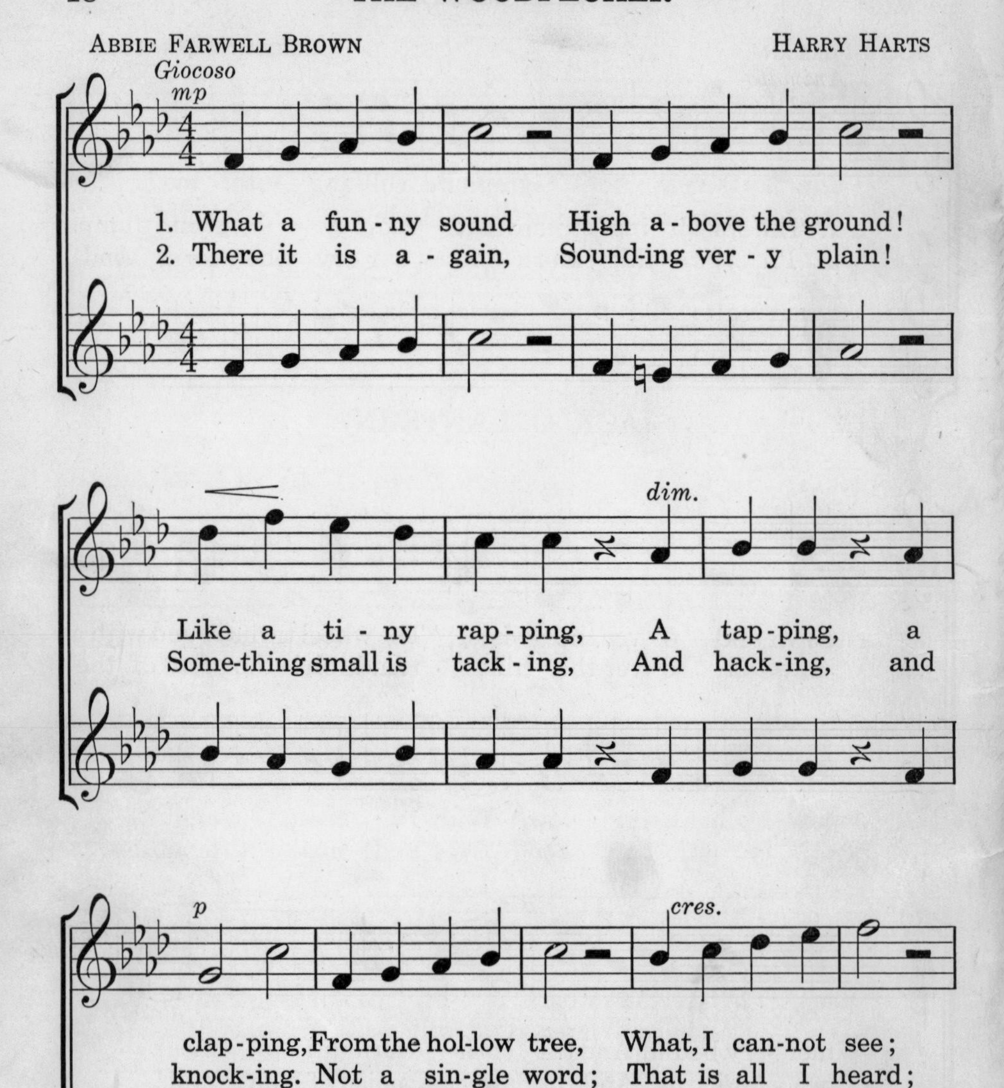

Giocoso
mp

1. What a fun-ny sound   High a-bove the ground!
2. There it is a-gain,   Sound-ing ver-y plain!

dim.

Like a ti-ny rap-ping,   A tap-ping,   a
Some-thing small is tack-ing,   And hack-ing,   and

p   *cres.*

clap-ping, From the hol-low tree,   What, I can-not see;
knock-ing. Not a sin-gle word;   That is all I heard;

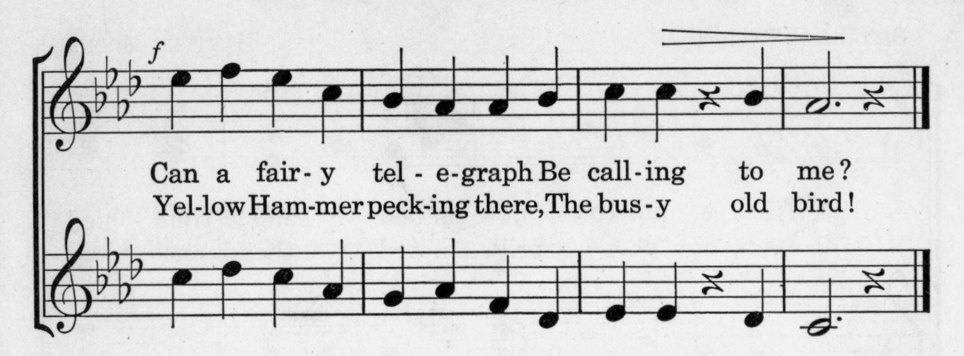

Can a fair-y tel-e-graph Be call-ing to me?
Yel-low Ham-mer peck-ing there, The bus-y old bird!

JACK O'LANTERN

JEAN NEAL

RALPH L. BALDWIN

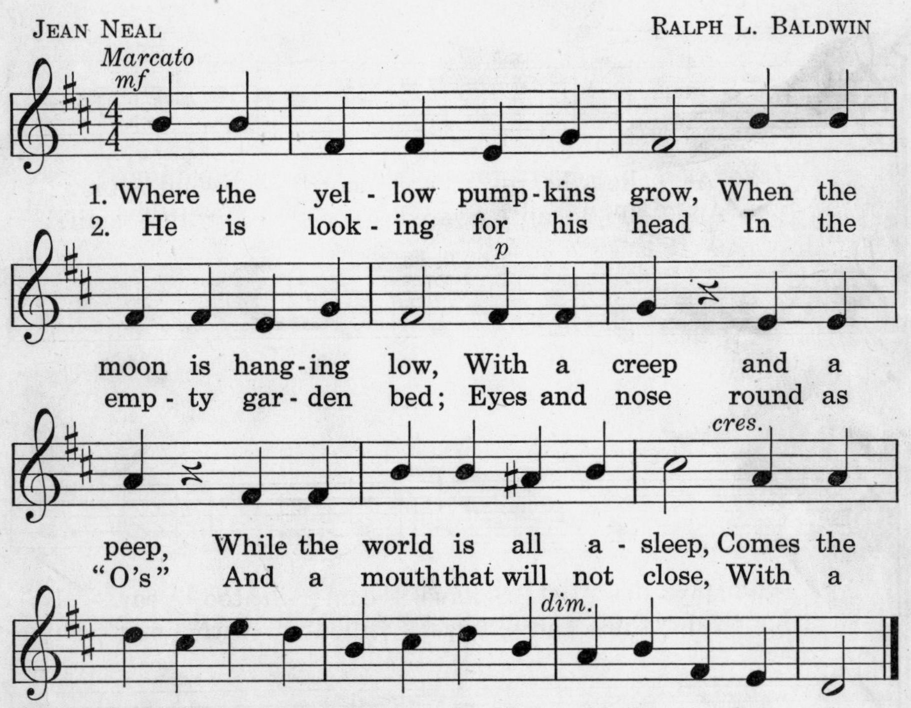

1. Where the yel-low pump-kins grow, When the
2. He is look-ing for his head In the

moon is hang-ing low, With a creep and a
emp-ty gar-den bed; Eyes and nose round as

peep, While the world is all a-sleep, Comes the
"O's" And a mouth that will not close, With a

Jack-o'-lan-tern steal-ing In the cold Oc-to-ber air.
light to make him bright-er And to fill all hearts with dread.

LADY APRIL

Elizabeth Taylor

Hartley Moore

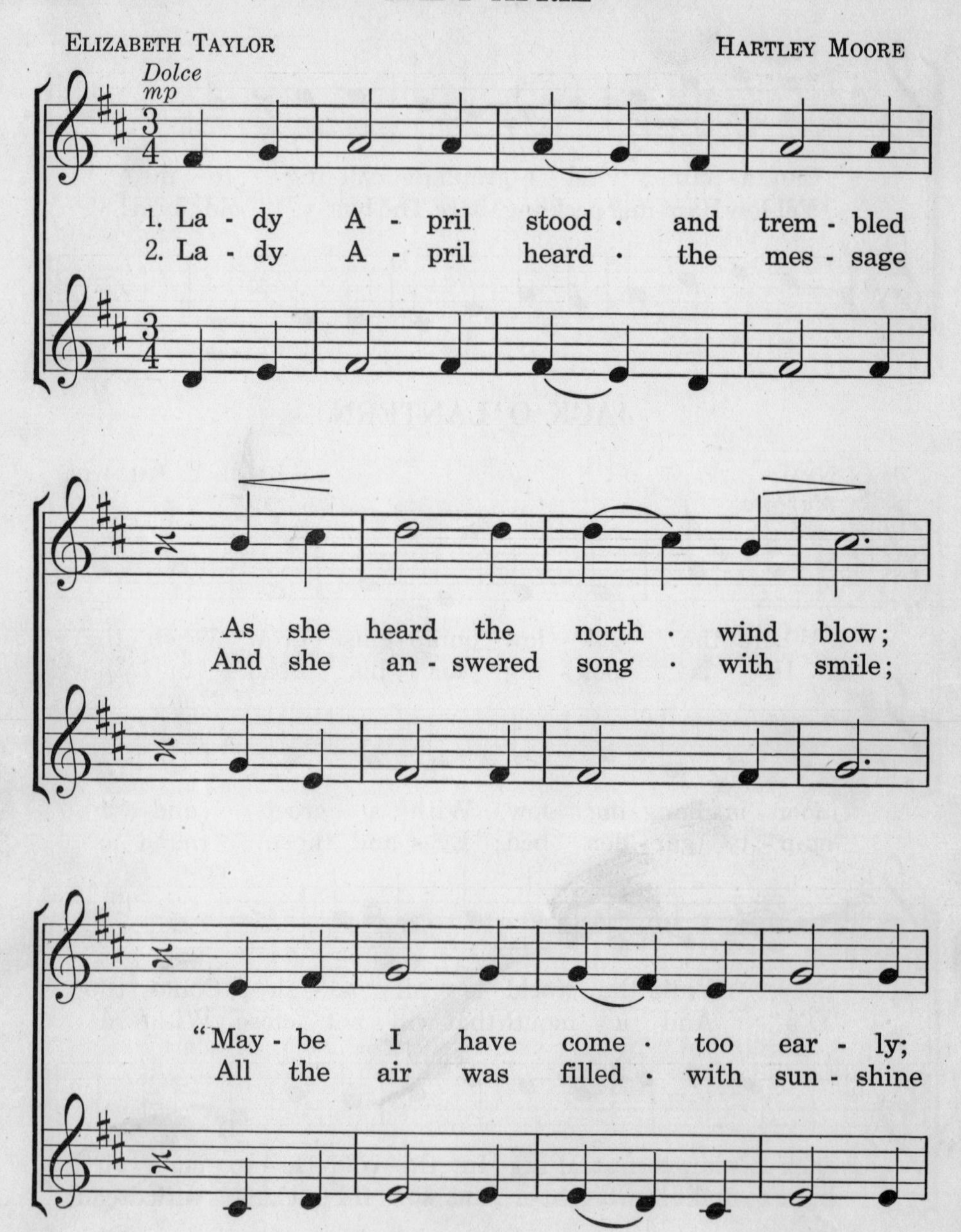

1. La - dy   A - pril   stood ·   and   trem - bled
2. La - dy   A - pril   heard ·   the   mes - sage

As   she   heard   the   north · wind   blow;
And   she   an - swered   song · with   smile;

"May - be   I   have   come · too   ear - ly;
All   the   air   was   filled · with   sun - shine

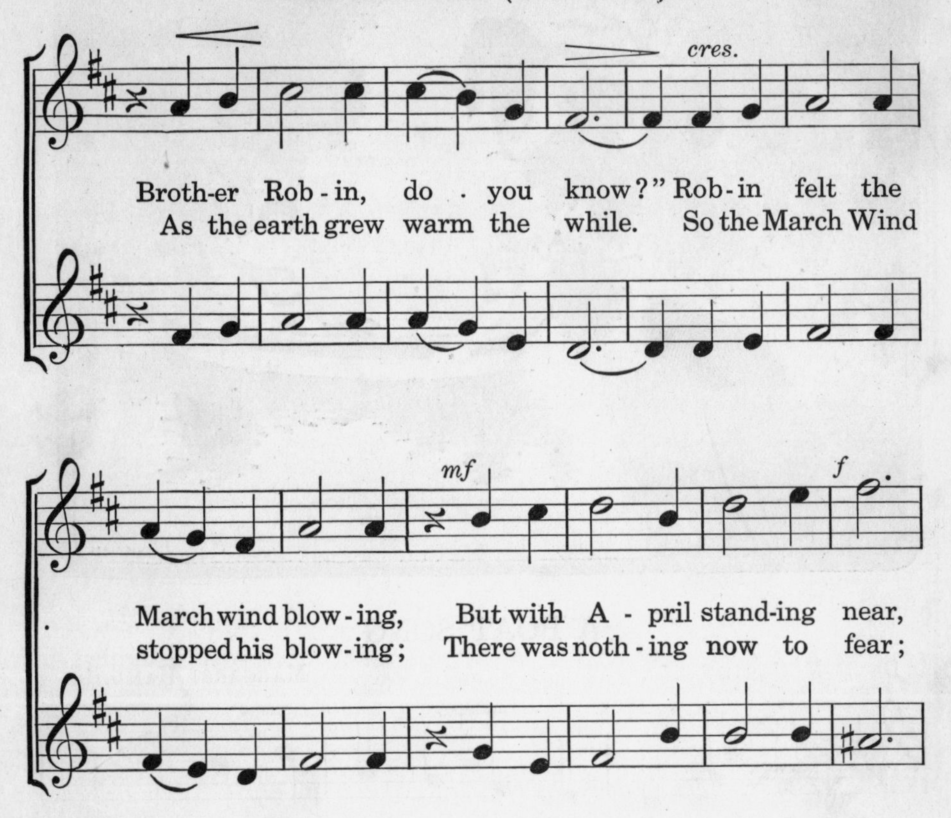

Broth-er Rob-in, do . you know?" Rob-in felt the
As the earth grew warm the while. So the March Wind

March wind blow-ing, But with A - pril stand-ing near,
stopped his blow-ing; There was noth - ing now to fear;

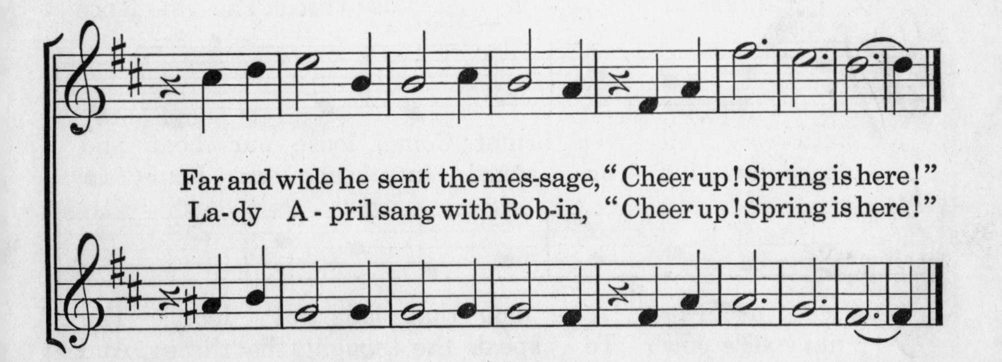

Far and wide he sent the mes-sage, "Cheer up! Spring is here!"
La-dy A - pril sang with Rob-in, "Cheer up! Spring is here!"

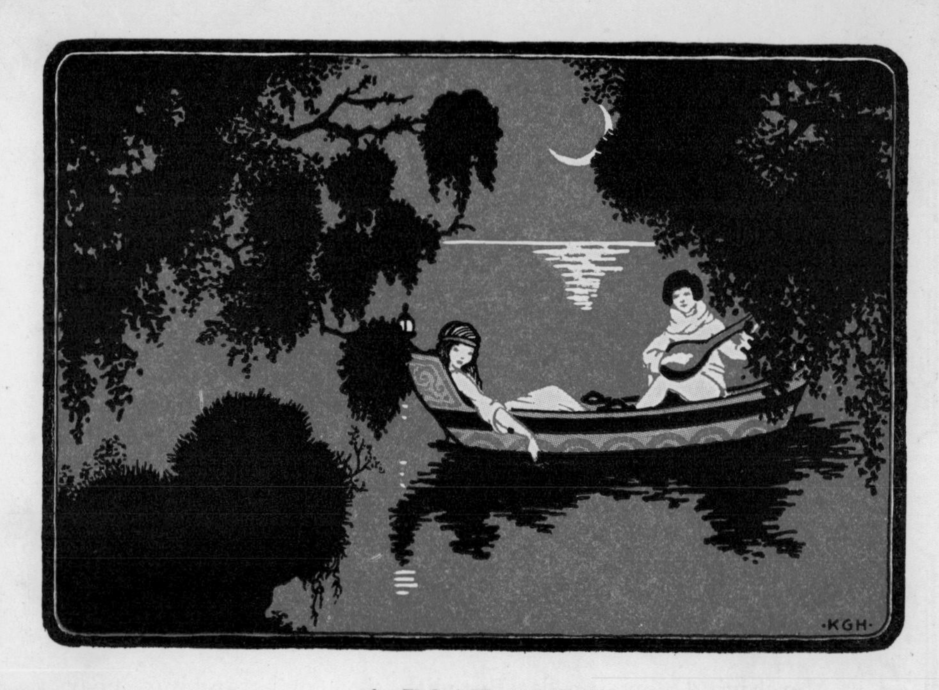

A BOAT SONG

DENIS McCARTHY

MARGARET HAMILTON

Legato

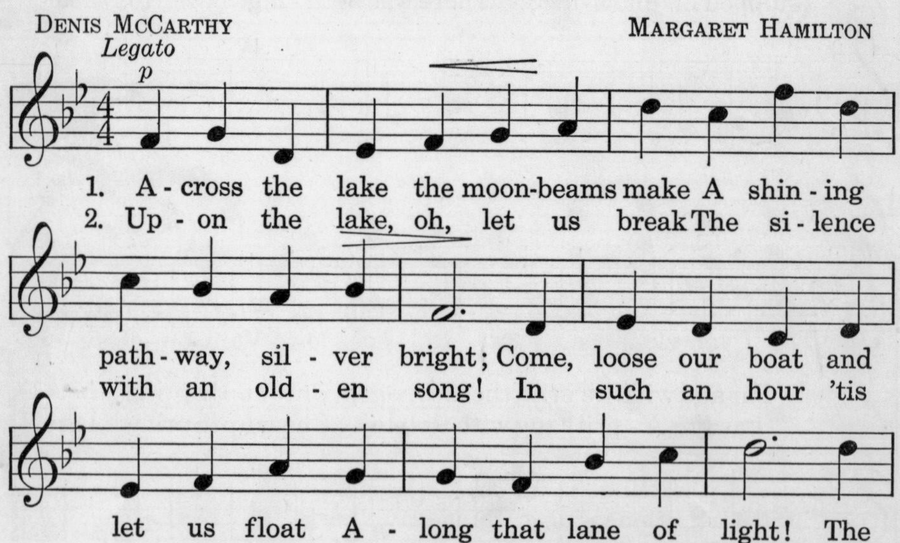

1. A - cross the lake the moon-beams make A shin - ing
2. Up - on the lake, oh, let us break The si - lence

path - way, sil - ver bright; Come, loose our boat and
with an old - en song! In such an hour 'tis

let us float A - long that lane of light! The
mu - sic's pow'r To speak the thoughts that throng. And

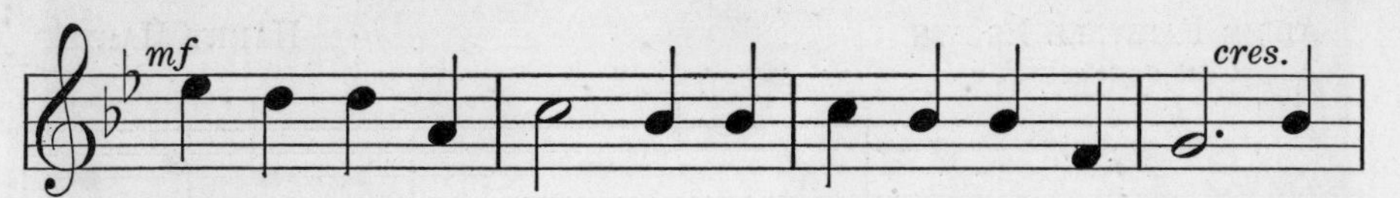

breez-es round us blow And the stars a-bove us glow, And
'tis in song a-lone That our deep-est thoughts are known, As

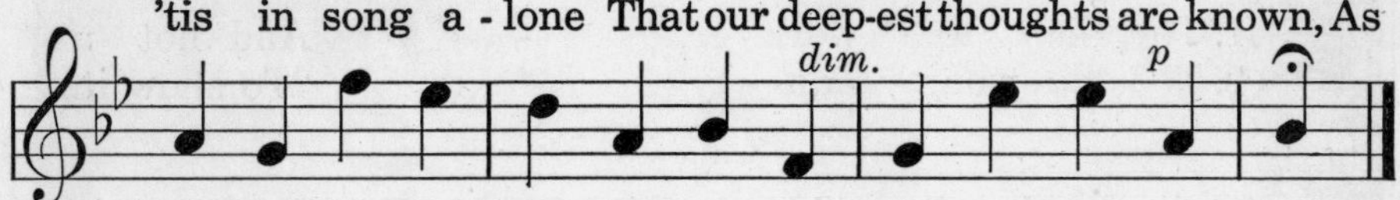

all the world en-chant-ed lies Be-neath the moon to-night.
'neath the mag-ic of the moon We soft-ly float a-long.

THE RUNAWAY

WILLIAM CORWIN　　　　　　　　　　　WILLIAM CORWIN

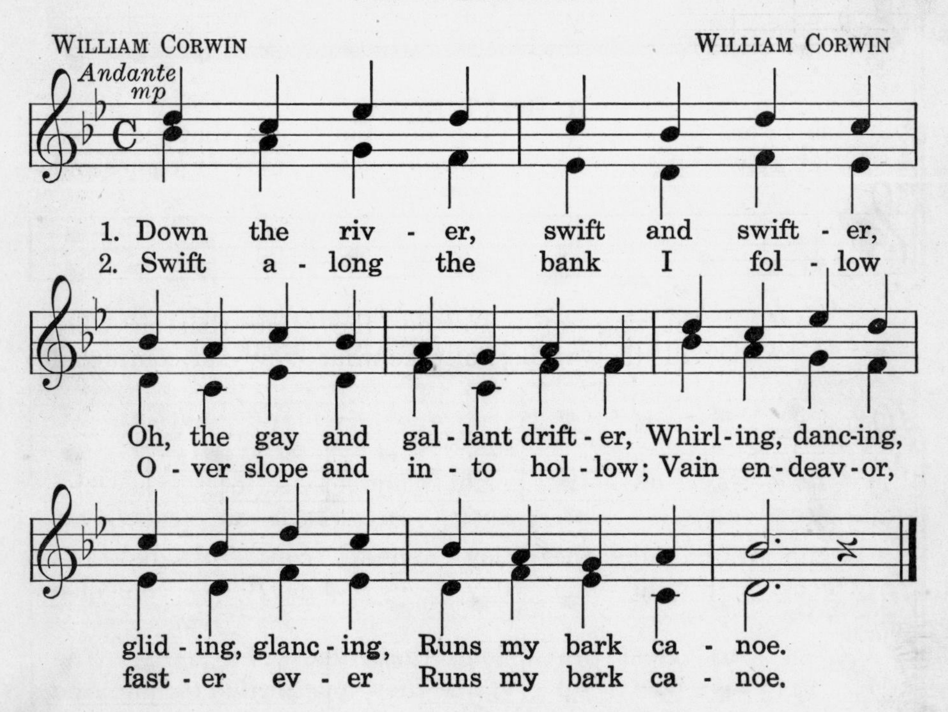

1. Down the riv - er, swift and swift - er,
2. Swift a - long the bank I fol - low

Oh, the gay and gal - lant drift - er, Whirl-ing, danc-ing,
O - ver slope and in - to hol - low; Vain en-deav-or,

glid - ing, glanc - ing, Runs my bark ca - noe.
fast - er ev - er Runs my bark ca - noe.

THE BEST WAY

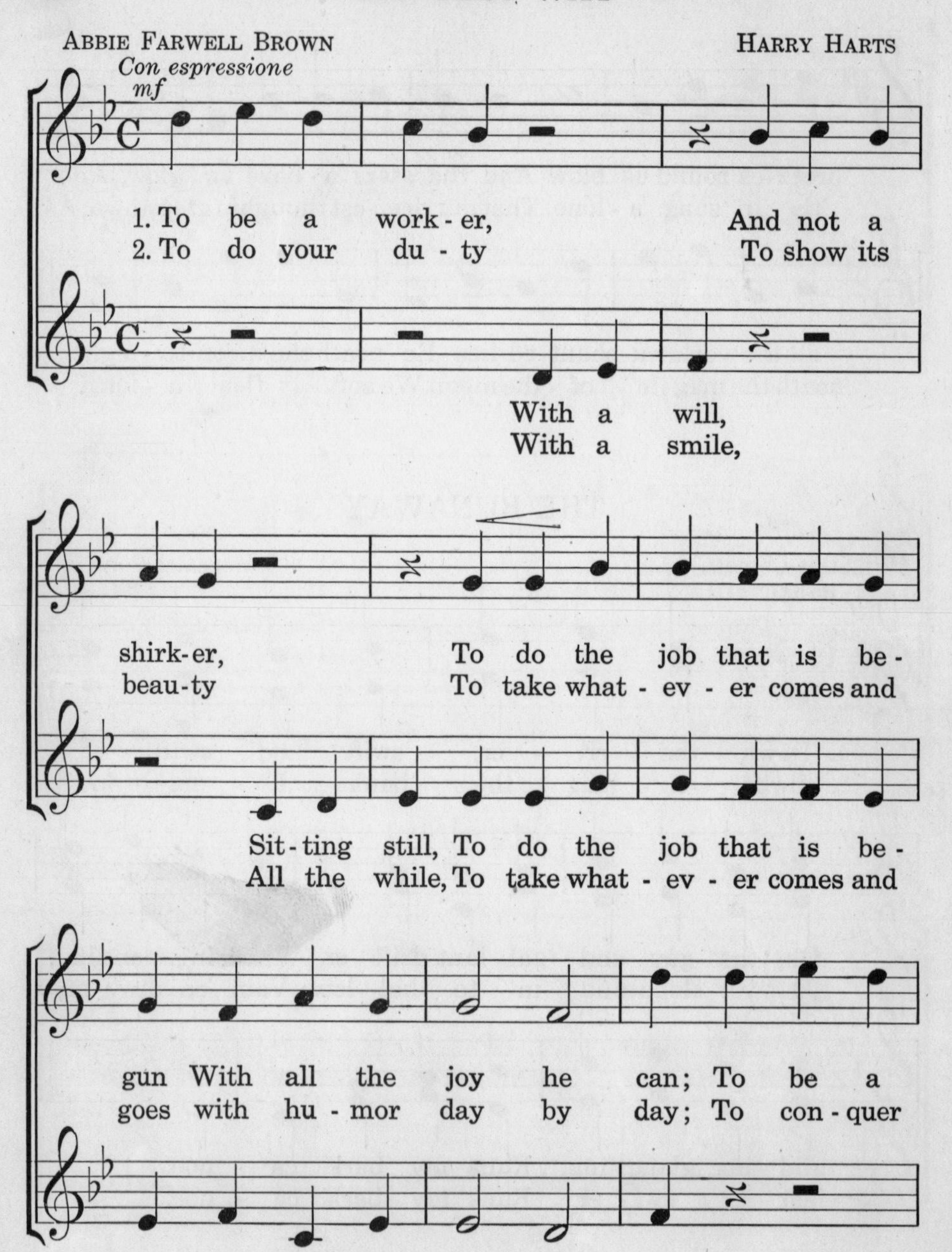

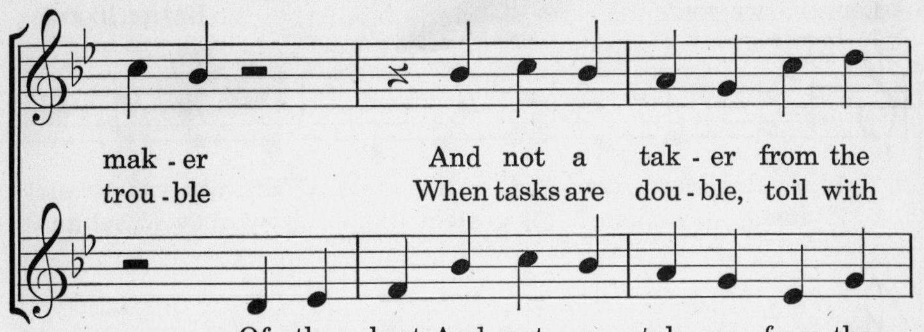

mak - er   And not a   tak - er from the
trou - ble   When tasks are   dou - ble, toil with

Of the   best, And not a   tak - er from the
With a   jest, When tasks are   dou - ble, toil with

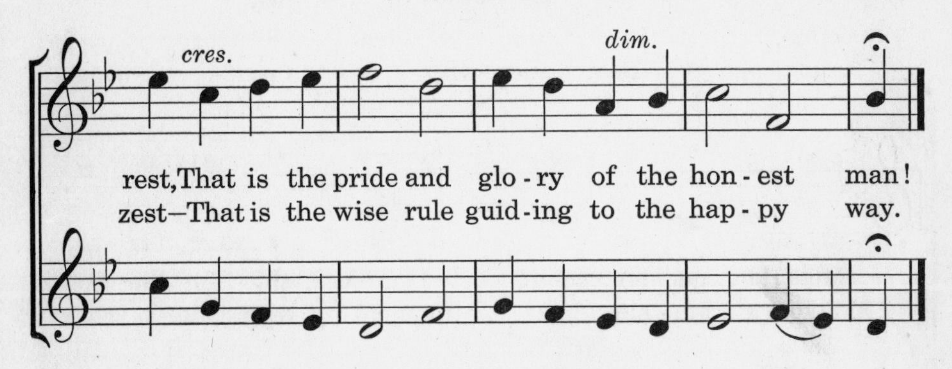

cres.   *dim.*

rest, That is the pride and glo - ry of the hon - est   man!
zest—That is the wise rule guid-ing to the hap - py   way.

WINTER

Frances Richardson   Ruth Maynard

Sostenuto
mp

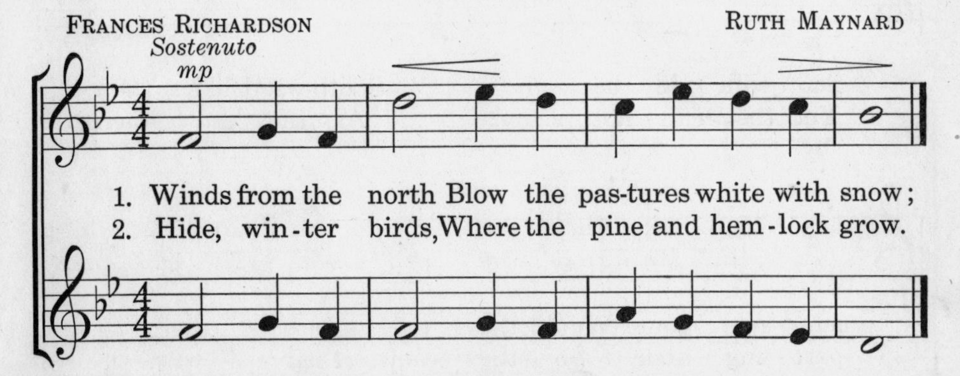

1. Winds from the   north Blow the pas-tures white with snow;
2. Hide, win - ter   birds, Where the   pine and hem-lock grow.

SWALLOWS

LOUISE STICKNEY

GASTON BORCH

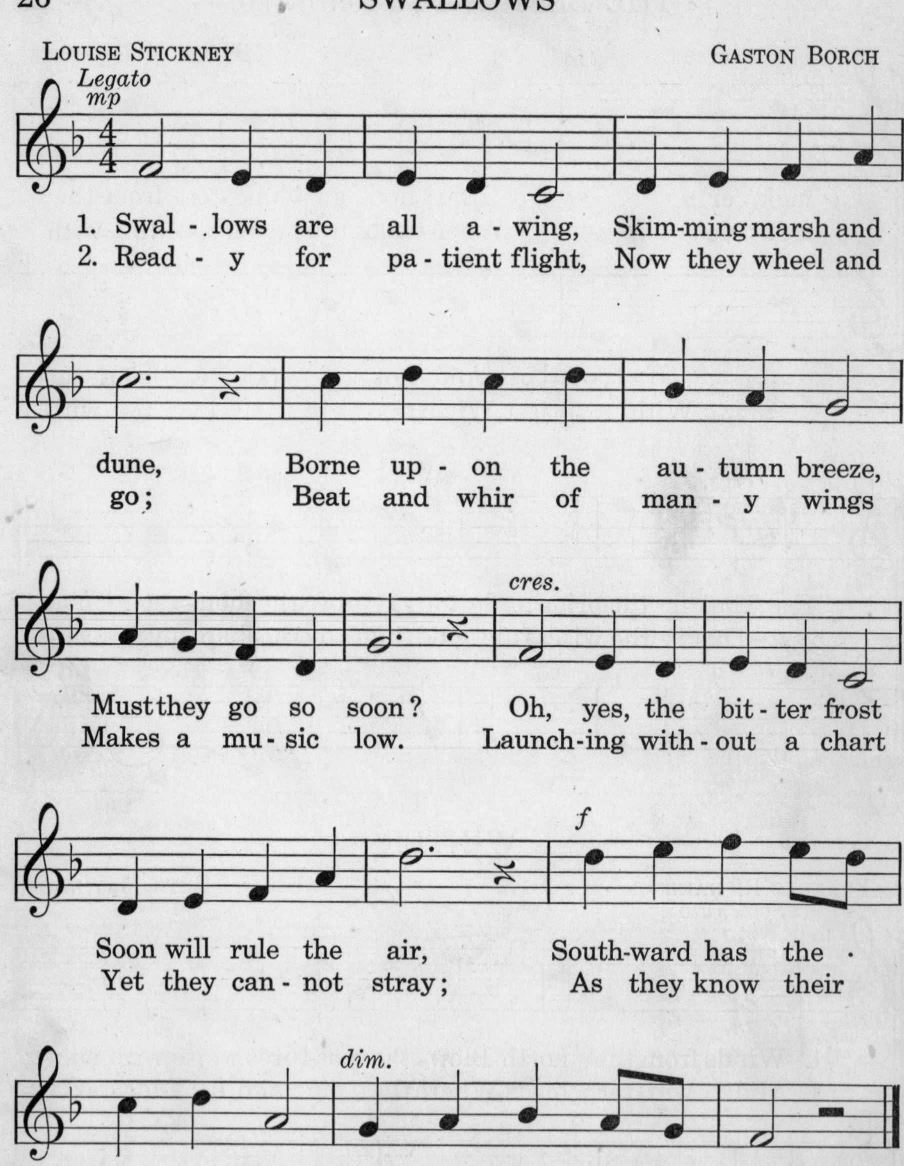

Legato
mp

1. Swal - lows are all a - wing, Skim-ming marsh and
2. Read - y for pa - tient flight, Now they wheel and

dune, Borne up - on the au - tumn breeze,
go; Beat and whir of man - y wings

cres.

Must they go so soon? Oh, yes, the bit - ter frost
Makes a mu - sic low. Launch-ing with - out a chart

f

Soon will rule the air, South-ward has the ·
Yet they can - not stray; As they know their

dim.

sum - mer gone. Would they too were · there!
part - ing hour So they know their · way.

MARGARET CONNOLLY

HENRY F. GILBERT

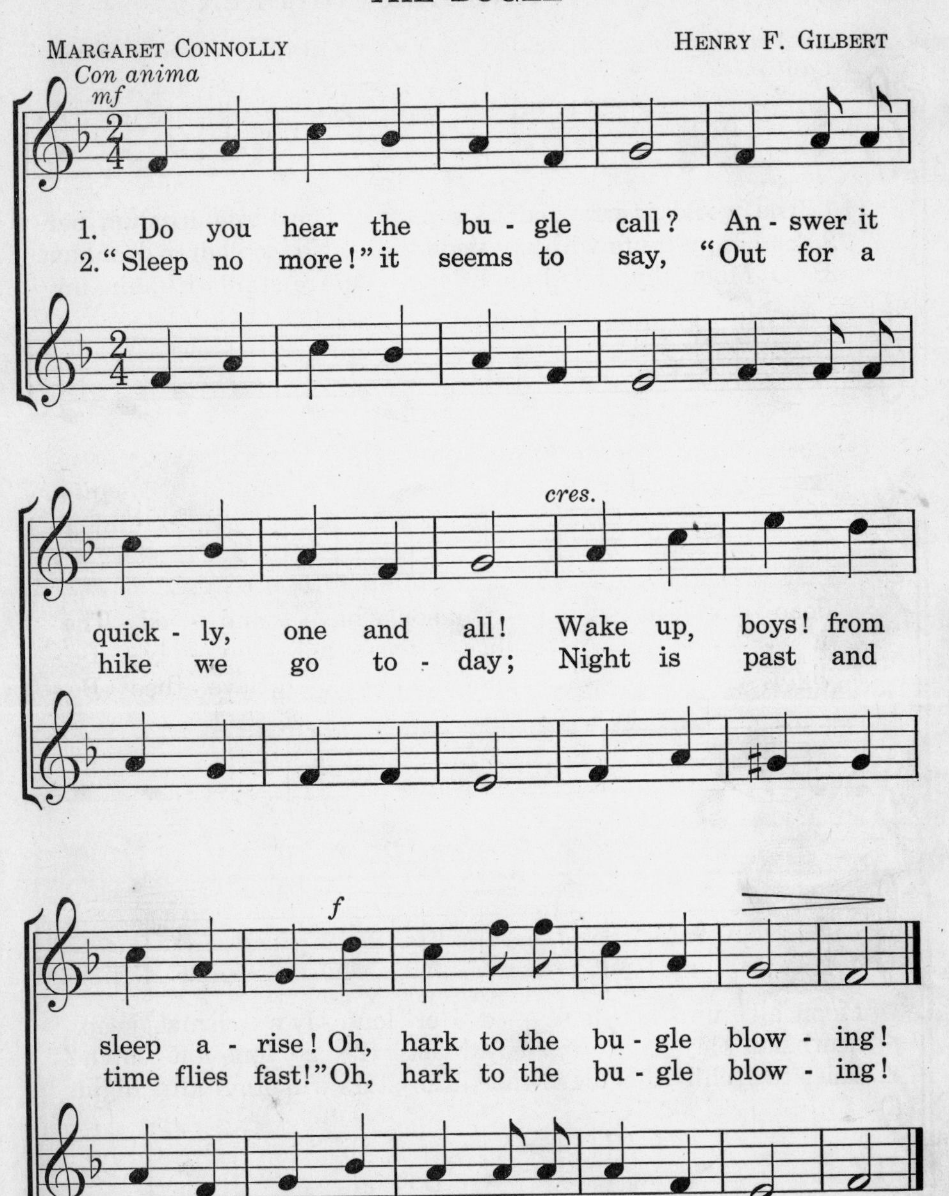

1. Do you hear the bu - gle call? An - swer it
2. "Sleep no more!" it seems to say, "Out for a

quick - ly, one and all! Wake up, boys! from
hike we go to - day; Night is past and

sleep a - rise! Oh, hark to the bu - gle blow - ing!
time flies fast!" Oh, hark to the bu - gle blow - ing!

THE MOON AND HER CHILDREN

NATHAN HASKELL DOLE

RUTH McCONN SPENCER

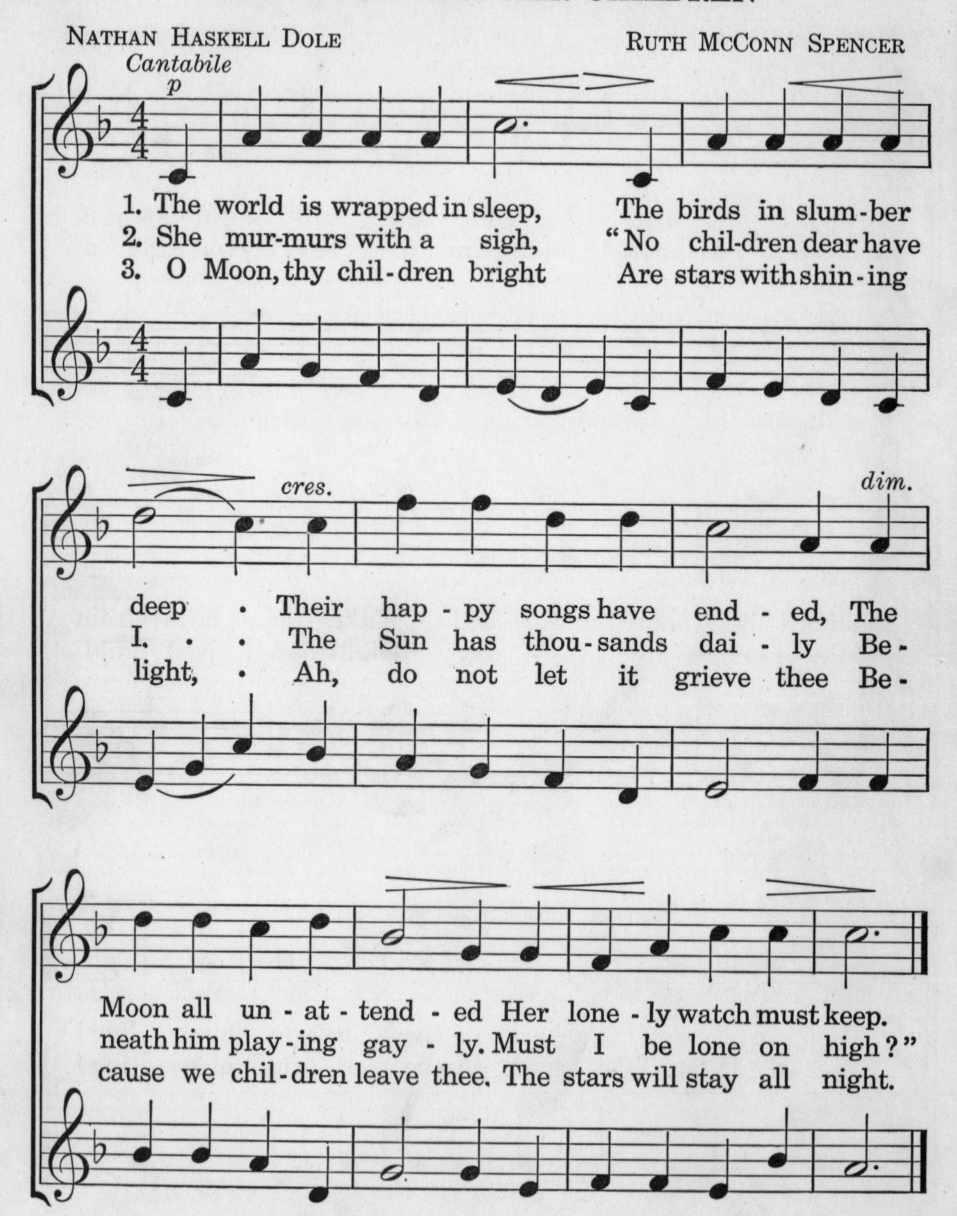

1. The world is wrapped in sleep, The birds in slum-ber
2. She mur-murs with a sigh, "No chil-dren dear have
3. O Moon, thy chil-dren bright Are stars with shin-ing

deep · Their hap-py songs have end-ed, The
I · · The Sun has thou-sands dai-ly Be-
light, · Ah, do not let it grieve thee Be-

Moon all un-at-tend-ed Her lone-ly watch must keep.
neath him play-ing gay-ly. Must I be lone on high?"
cause we chil-dren leave thee. The stars will stay all night.

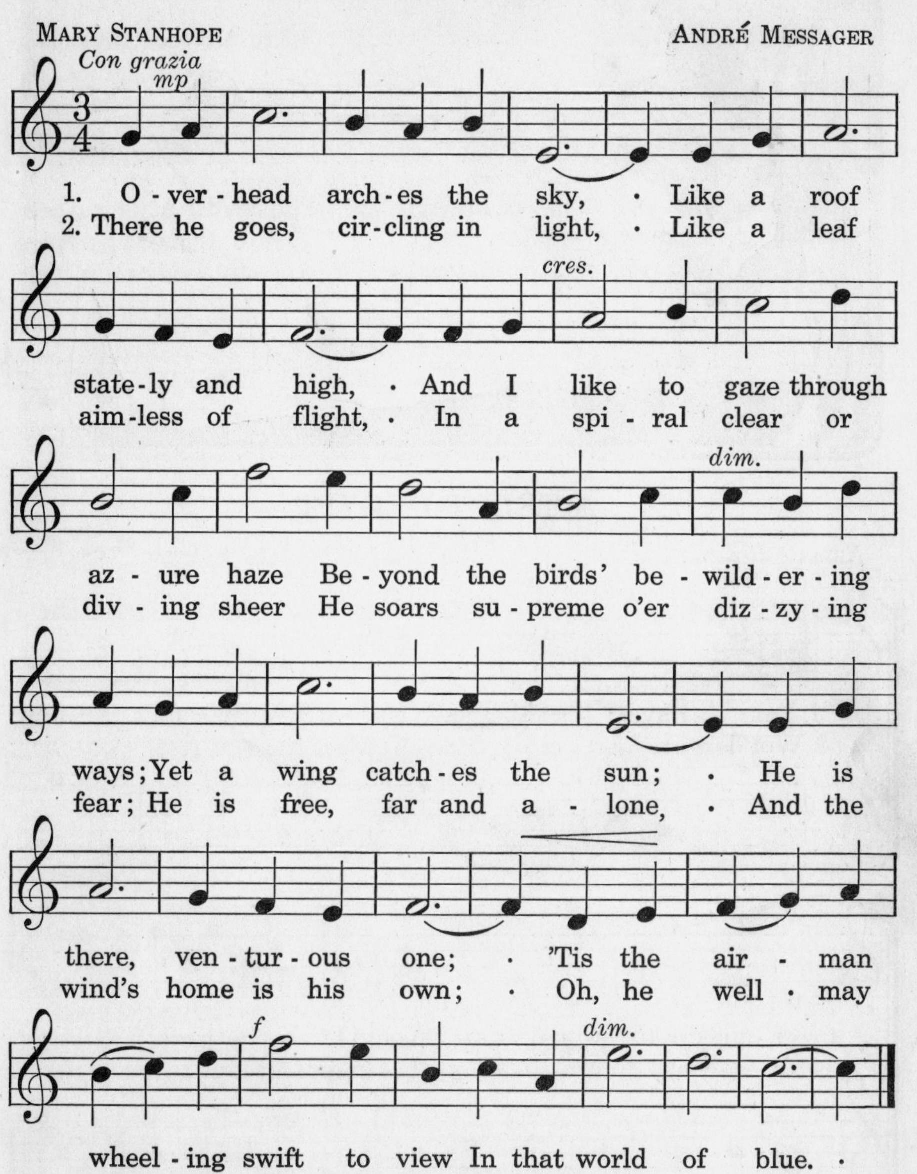

MARY STANHOPE

ANDRÉ MESSAGER

Con grazia
mp

1. O - ver - head arch - es the sky, · Like a roof
2. There he goes, cir - cling in light, · Like a leaf

cres.

state - ly and high, · And I like to gaze through
aim - less of flight, · In a spi - ral clear or

dim.

az - ure haze Be - yond the birds' be - wild - er - ing
div - ing sheer He soars su - preme o'er diz - zy - ing

ways; Yet a wing catch - es the sun; · He is
fear; He is free, far and a - lone, · And the

there, ven - tur - ous one; · 'Tis the air - man
wind's home is his own; · Oh, he well · may

f   dim.

wheel - ing swift to view In that world of blue. ·
scorn on soar - ing wings All the low - ly things.

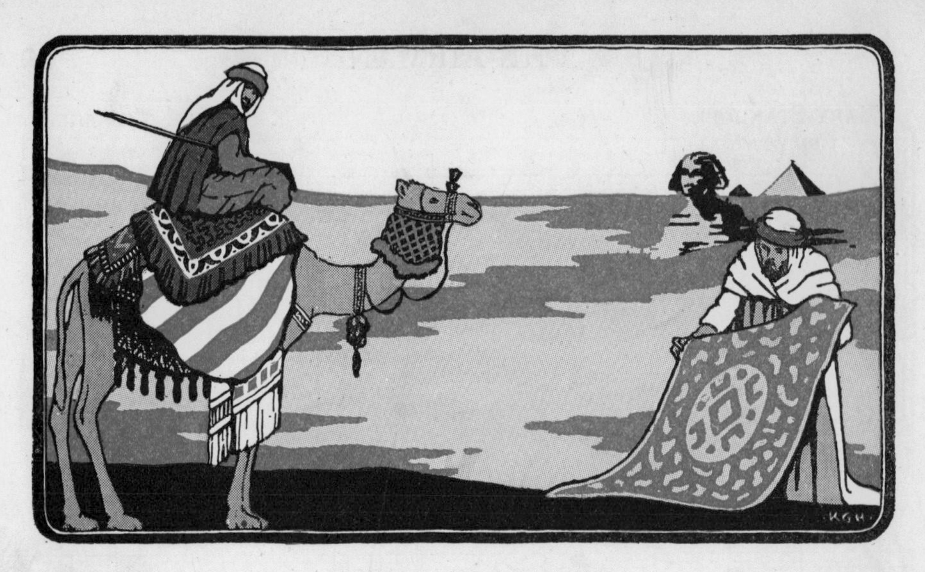

A TRIP TO EGYPT

ABBIE FARWELL BROWN   CHARLES FONTEYN MANNEY

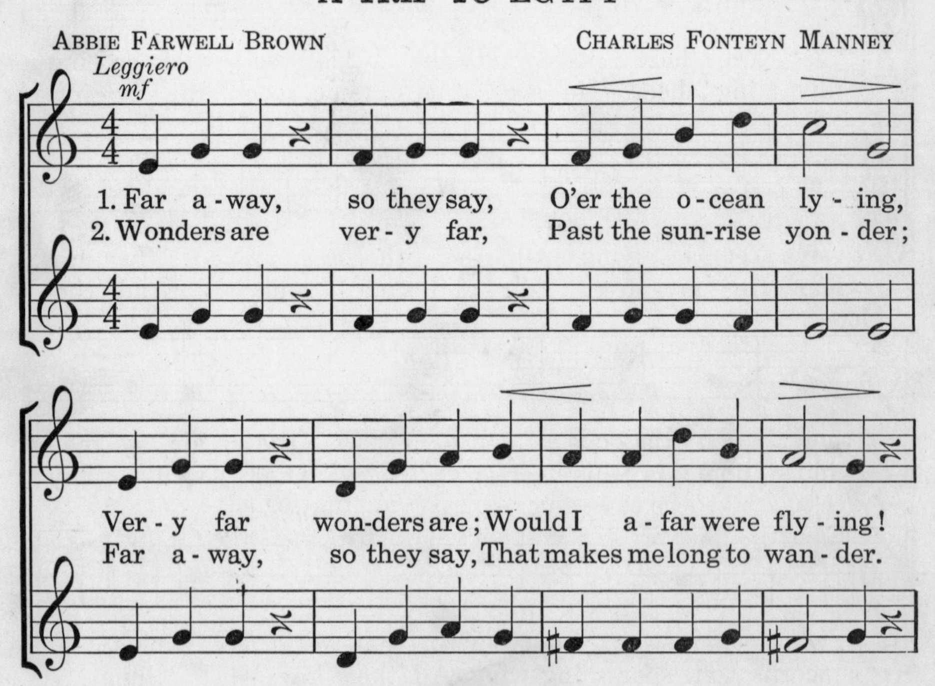

1. Far a-way, so they say, O'er the o-cean ly-ing,
2. Wonders are ver-y far, Past the sun-rise yon-der;

Ver-y far won-ders are; Would I a-far were fly-ing!
Far a-way, so they say, That makes me long to wan-der.

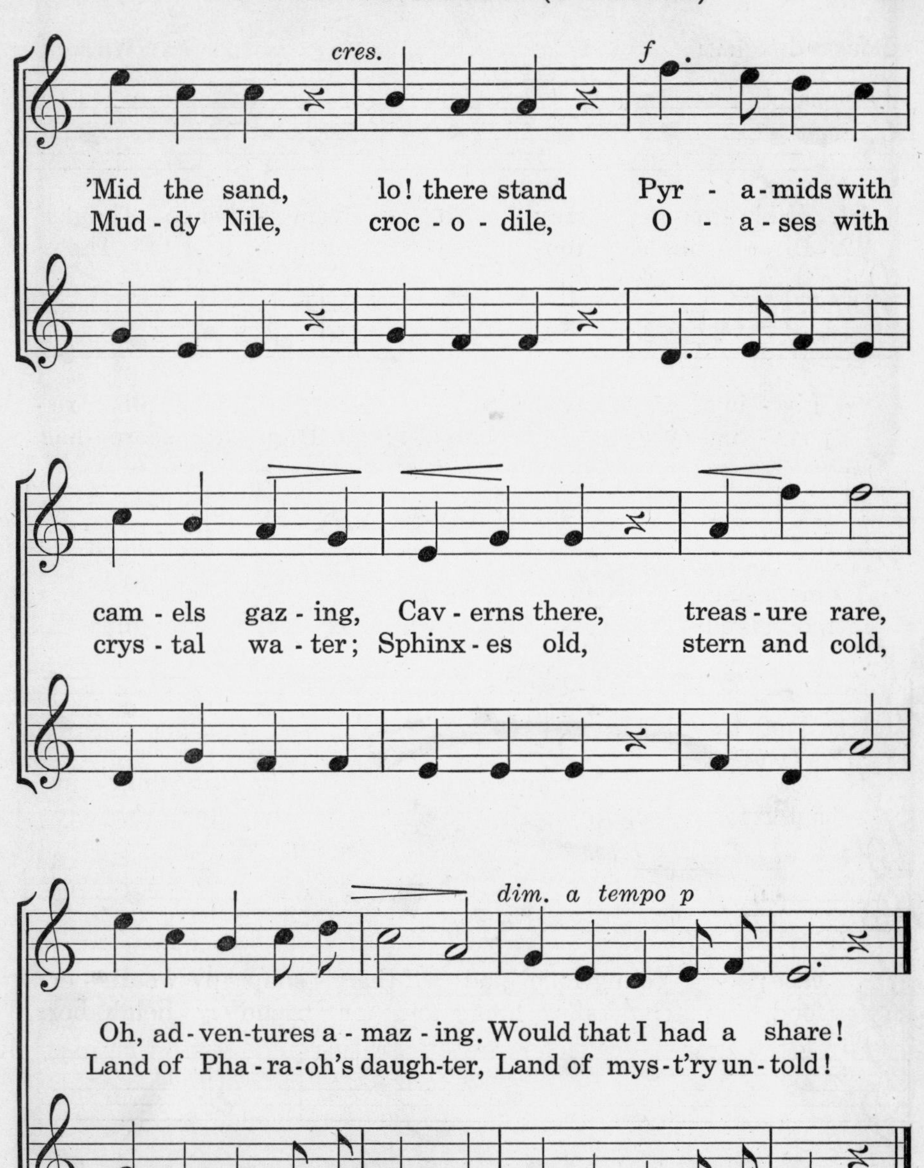

'Mid the sand, lo! there stand Pyr - a - mids with
Mud - dy Nile, croc - o - dile, O - a - ses with

cam - els gaz - ing, Cav - erns there, treas - ure rare,
crys - tal wa - ter; Sphinx - es old, stern and cold,

Oh, ad - ven-tures a - maz - ing. Would that I had a share!
Land of Pha - ra-oh's daugh-ter, Land of mys-t'ry un - told!

ROBERT BRIGHAM

FAY WILSON

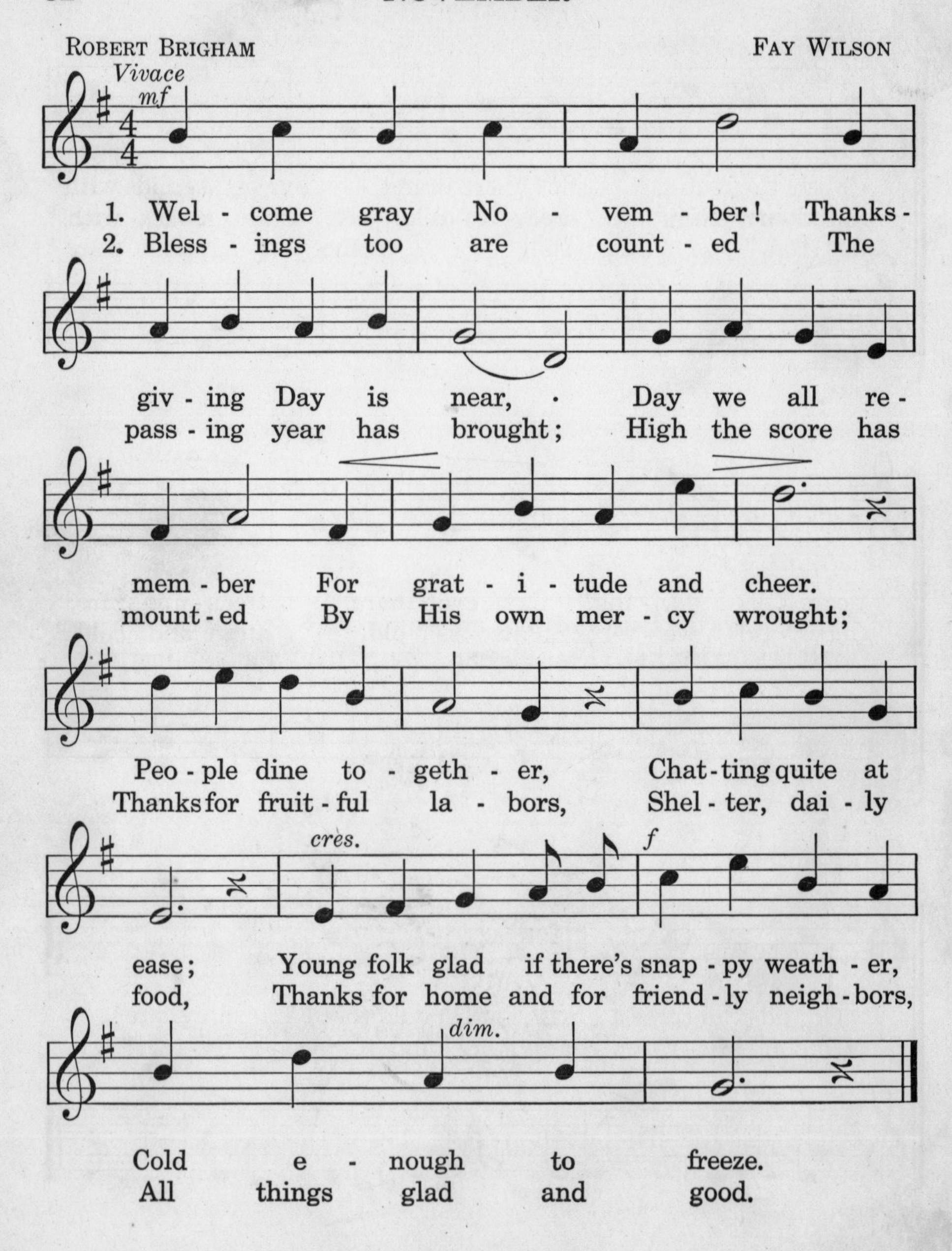

1. Wel - come gray No - vem - ber! Thanks -
2. Bless - ings too are count - ed The

giv - ing Day is near, · Day we all re -
pass - ing year has brought; High the score has

mem - ber For grat - i - tude and cheer.
mount - ed By His own mer - cy wrought;

Peo - ple dine to - geth - er, Chat - ting quite at
Thanks for fruit - ful la - bors, Shel - ter, dai - ly

ease; Young folk glad if there's snap - py weath - er,
food, Thanks for home and for friend - ly neigh - bors,

Cold e - nough to freeze.
All things glad and good.

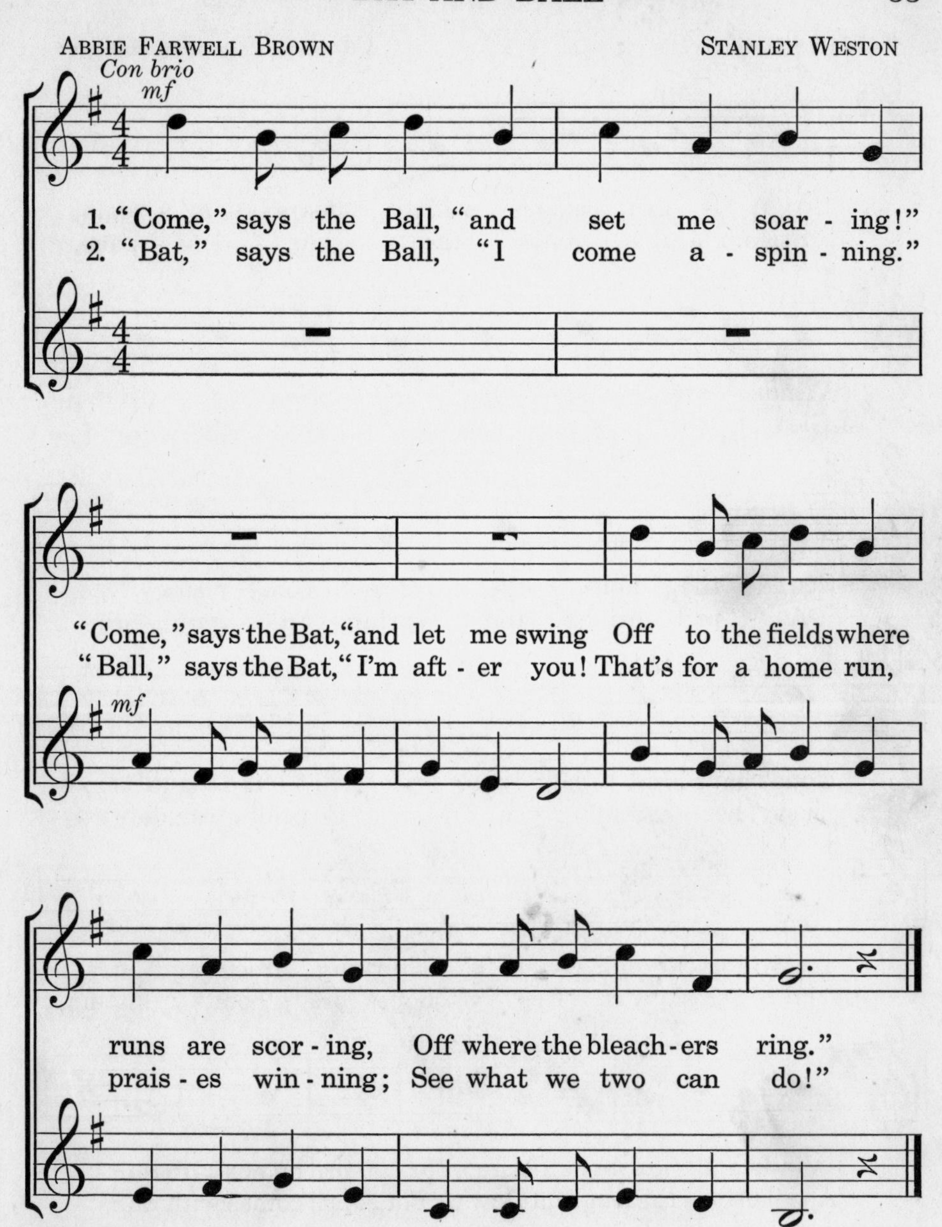

ABBIE FARWELL BROWN   STANLEY WESTON

Con brio

1. "Come," says the Ball, "and   set   me   soar - ing!"
2. "Bat," says the Ball, "I   come   a - spin - ning."

"Come," says the Bat, "and let   me swing   Off   to the fields where
"Ball," says the Bat, "I'm aft - er   you! That's for a home run,

runs   are   scor - ing,   Off where the bleach - ers   ring."
prais - es   win - ning; See what we two   can   do!"

T

APRIL COMES WITH RAIN

Kate Forman

Charles Fonteyn Manney

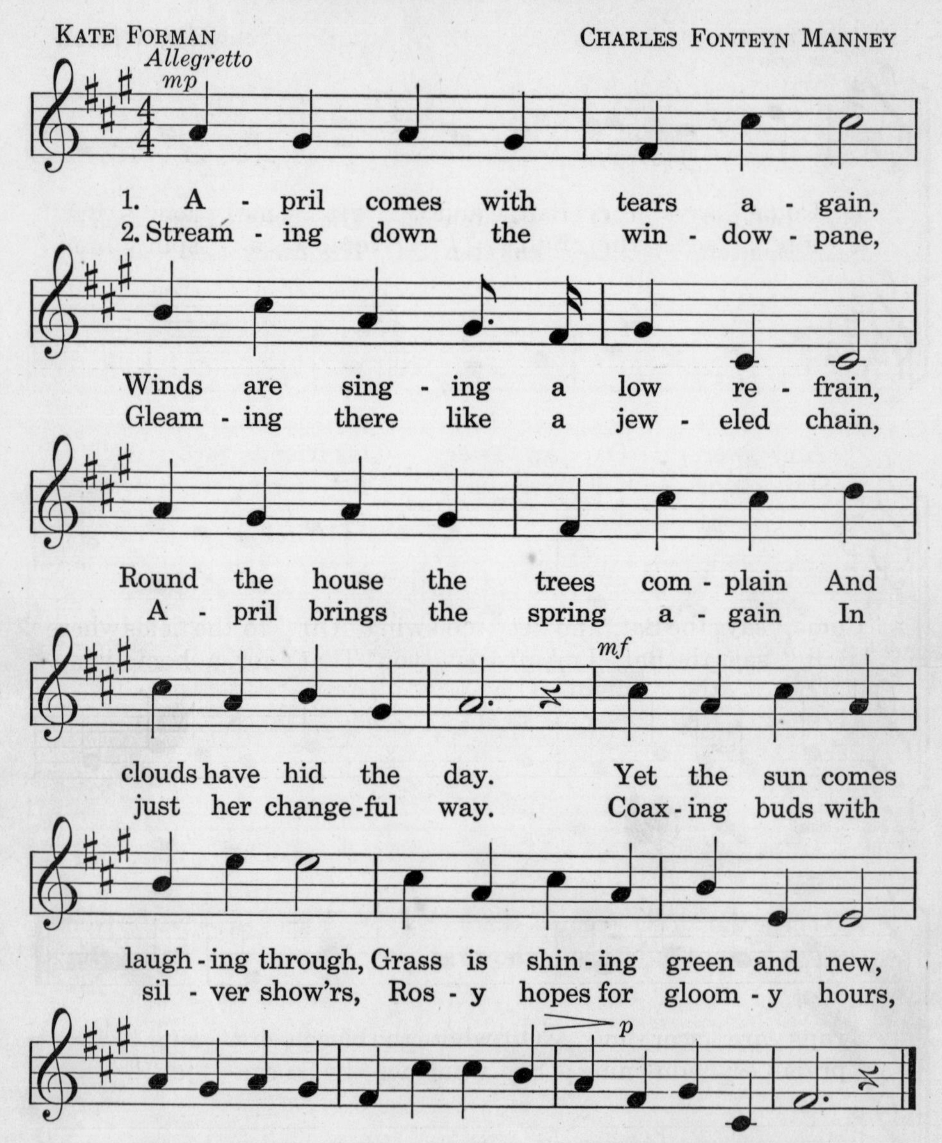

1. A - pril comes with tears a - gain,
2. Stream - ing down the win - dow - pane,

Winds are sing - ing a low re - frain,
Gleam - ing there like a jew - eled chain,

Round the house the trees com - plain And
A - pril brings the spring a - gain In

clouds have hid the day. Yet the sun comes
just her change - ful way. Coax - ing buds with

laugh - ing through, Grass is shin - ing green and new,
sil - ver show'rs, Ros - y hopes for gloom - y hours,

Vio-lets all are bud-ding, too, For A-pril comes with rain.
A-pril brings the fragrant flow'rs, For A-pril comes with rain.

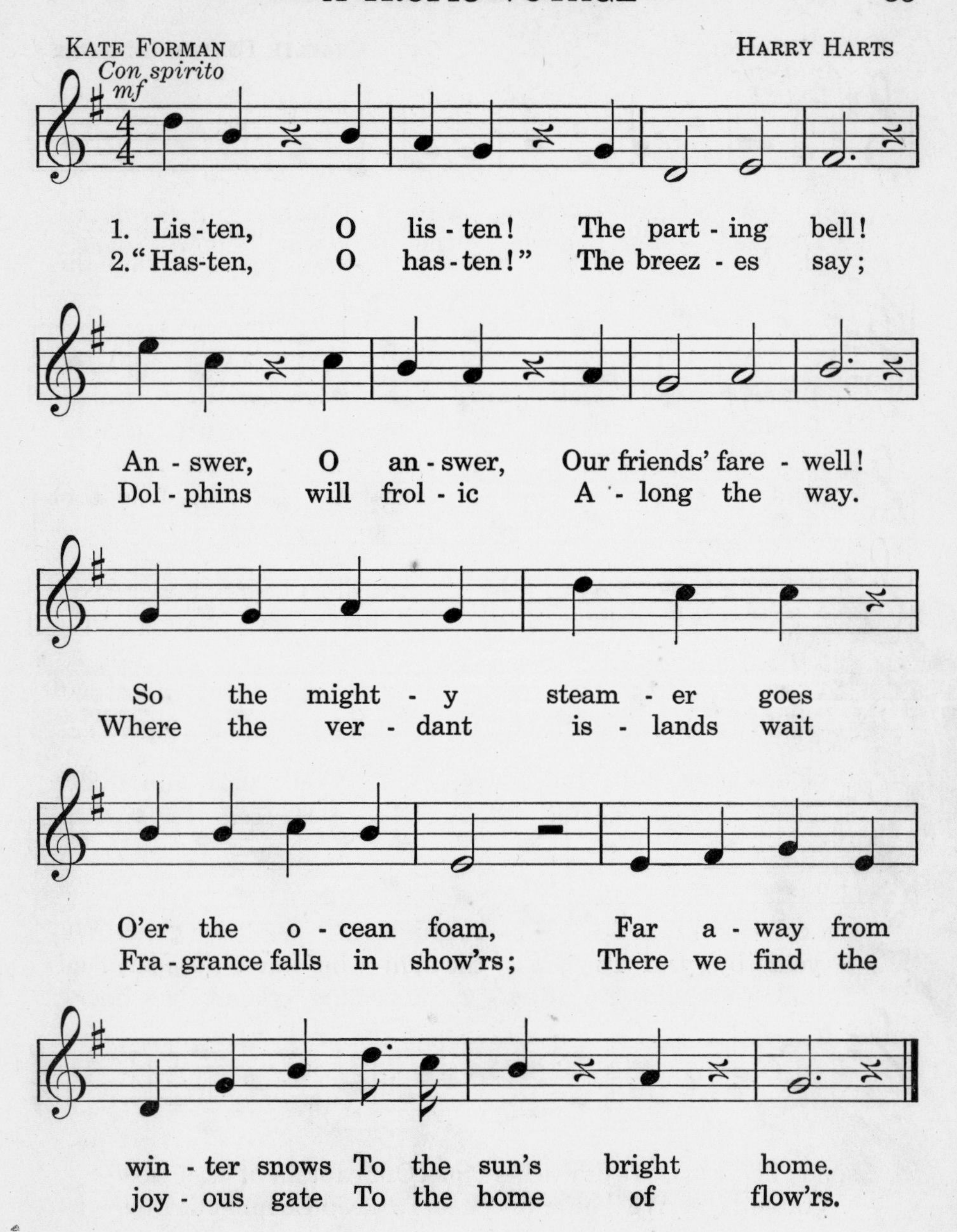

Kate Forman

Harry Harts

1. Lis - ten, O lis - ten! The part - ing bell!
2. "Has - ten, O has - ten!" The breez - es say;

An - swer, O an - swer, Our friends' fare - well!
Dol - phins will frol - ic A - long the way.

So the might - y steam - er goes
Where the ver - dant is - lands wait

O'er the o - cean foam, Far a - way from
Fra - grance falls in show'rs; There we find the

win - ter snows To the sun's bright home.
joy - ous gate To the home of flow'rs.

COLUMBUS DAY

DENIS MCCARTHY   H. CLOUGH-LEIGHTER.

Animato

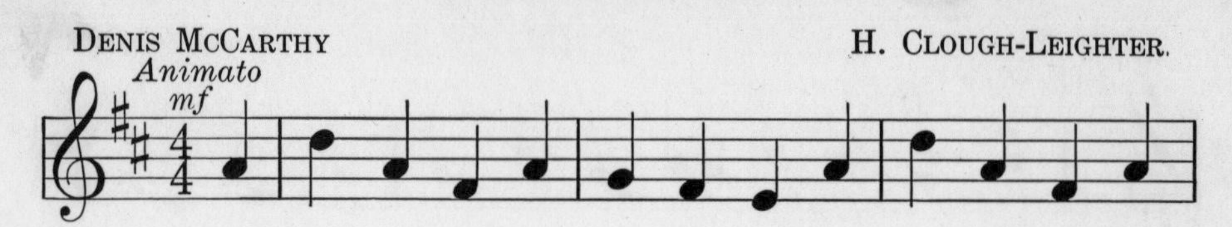

1. A - cross the wide mys - te-rious main Co - lum-bus sailed a-
2. A gift of gifts, a dower of dowers, He gave to man this

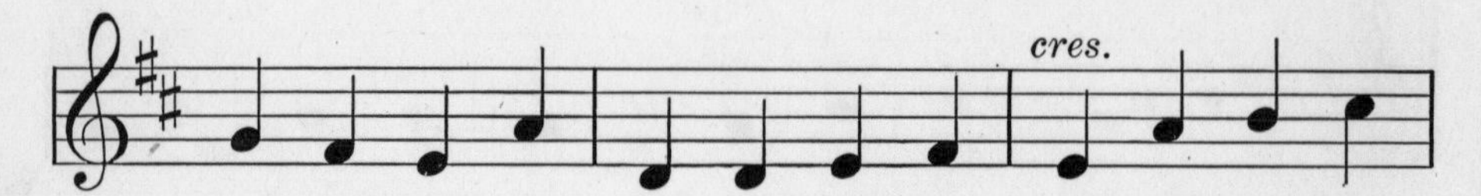

way from Spain, The first to brave the west - ern wave In
land of ours! To him is due a   trib - ute true That

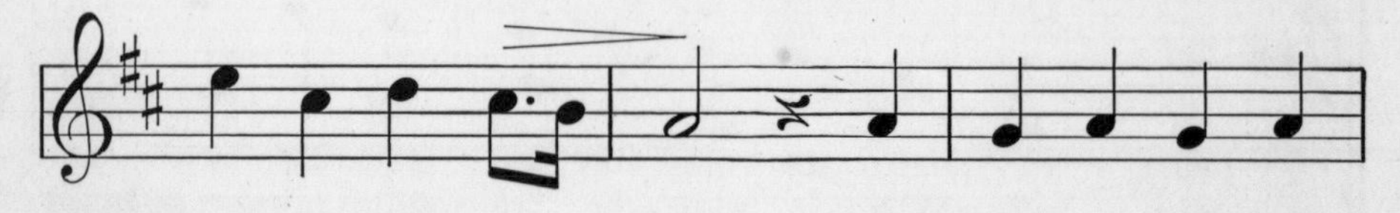

all   the world was   he.   And   so to - day we
glad - ly here we · pay.   So   let us gath - er

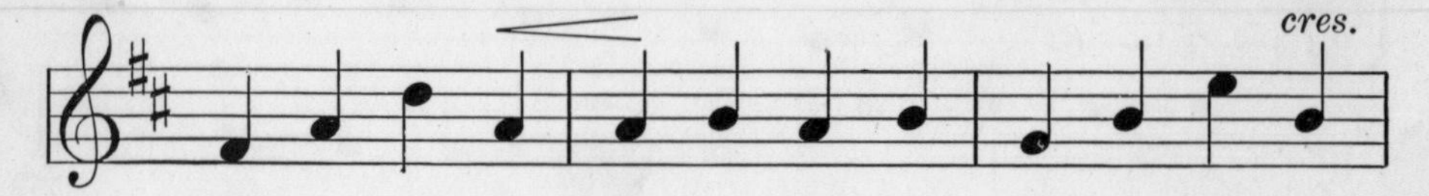

cel - e - brate A   he - ro high, a   sail - or great; We
year by year To   praise the man who knew no fear, And,

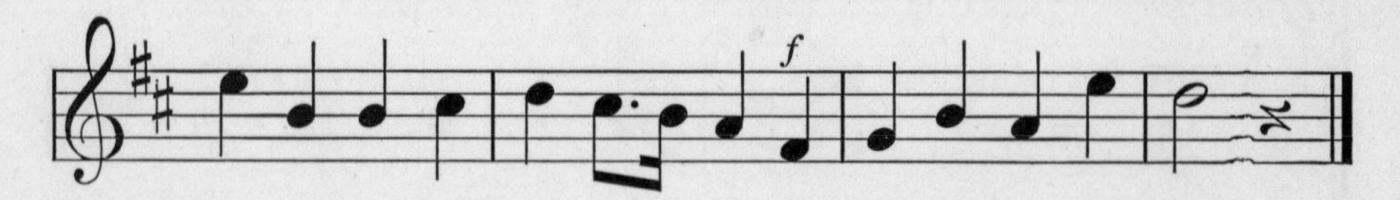

sound his name, We praise his fame, Our captain of the sea.
grate-ful yet, We'll ne'er for - get To keep Co-lum-bus Day.

ALICE BARD

RUTH McCONN SPENCER

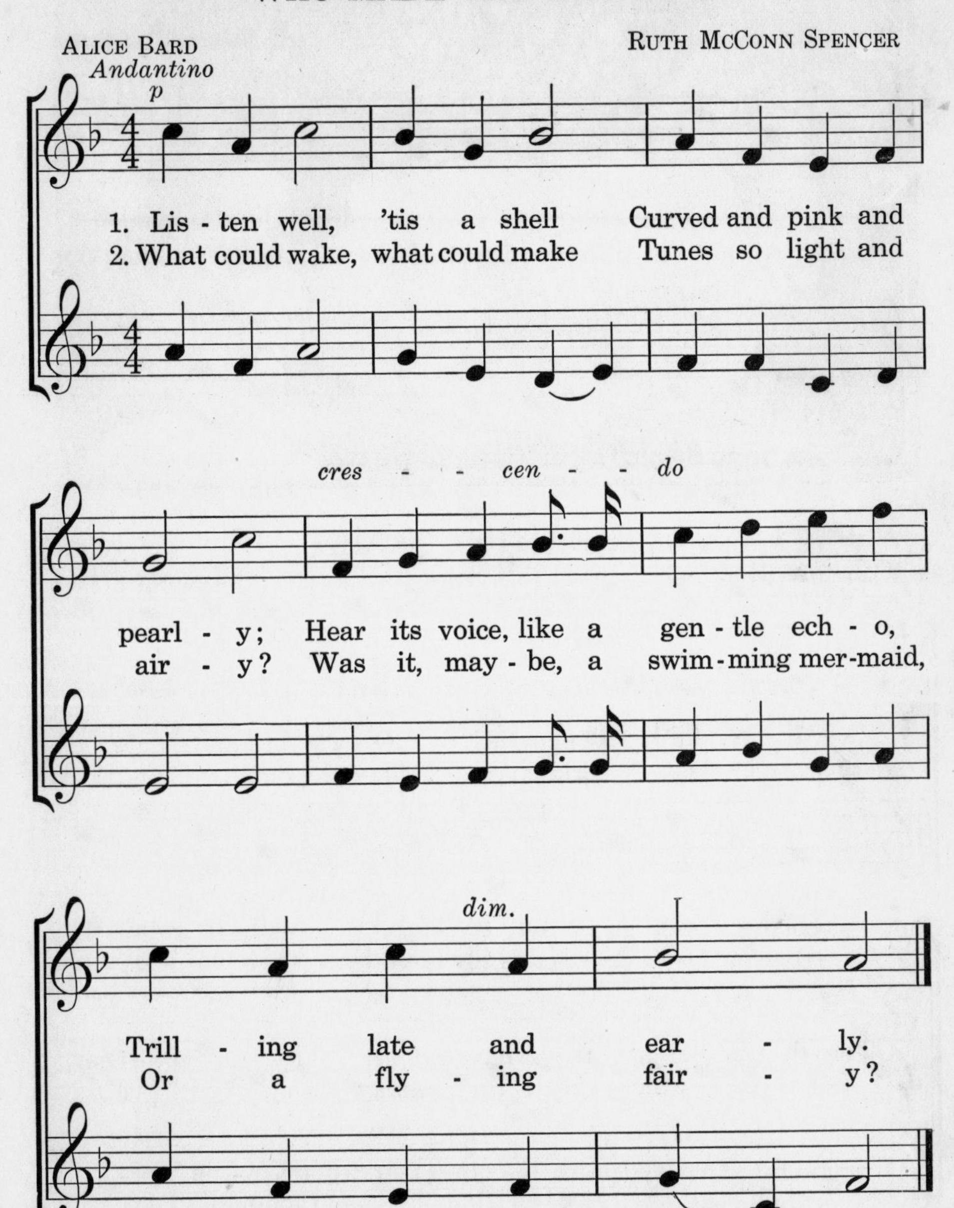

1. Lis - ten well, 'tis a shell Curved and pink and
2. What could wake, what could make Tunes so light and

cres - - cen - - do

pearl - y; Hear its voice, like a gen - tle ech - o,
air - y? Was it, may - be, a swim - ming mer - maid,

dim.

Trill - ing late and ear - ly.
Or a fly - ing fair - y?

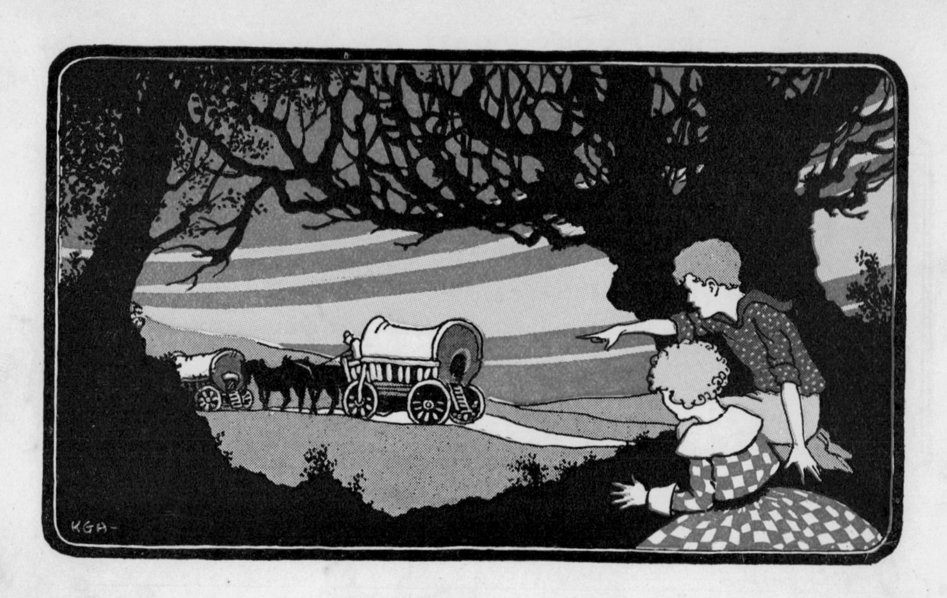

THE GYPSY TRAIL

Mary Stanhope

Raymond Ellis

Con moto
mf

1. I have fol-lowed gyp-sies   O - ver hill and   dale,
2. Grass or leaf - y branch-es,   Ma - ple, elm, or   vines,

cres.

Traced   the   signs   they   have   set   to   show   The
Tell   me   what   is   the   way   they   go,   The   For

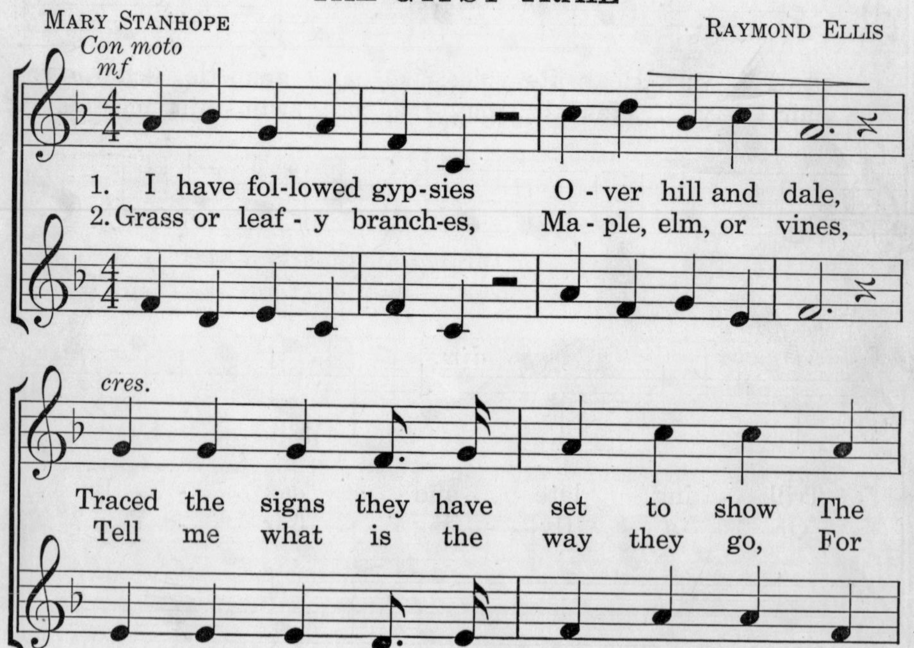

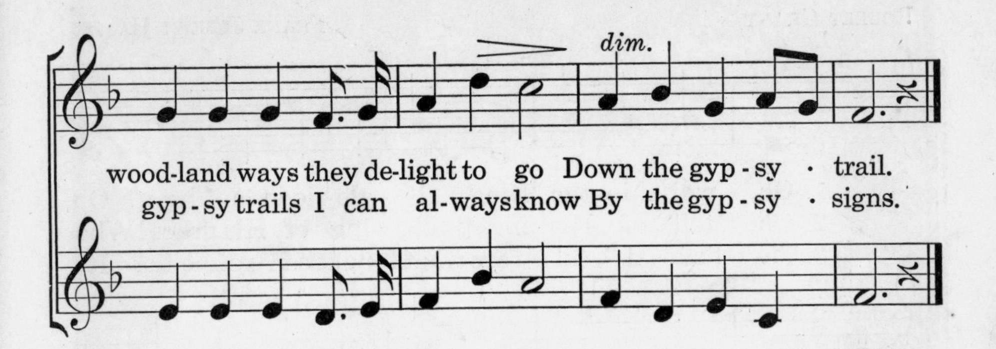

dim.

wood-land ways they de-light to go Down the gyp-sy · trail.
gyp-sy trails I can al-ways know By the gyp-sy · signs.

CHRISTMAS BELLS

KATE FORMAN   H. CLOUGH-LEIGHTER

Con anima
mf

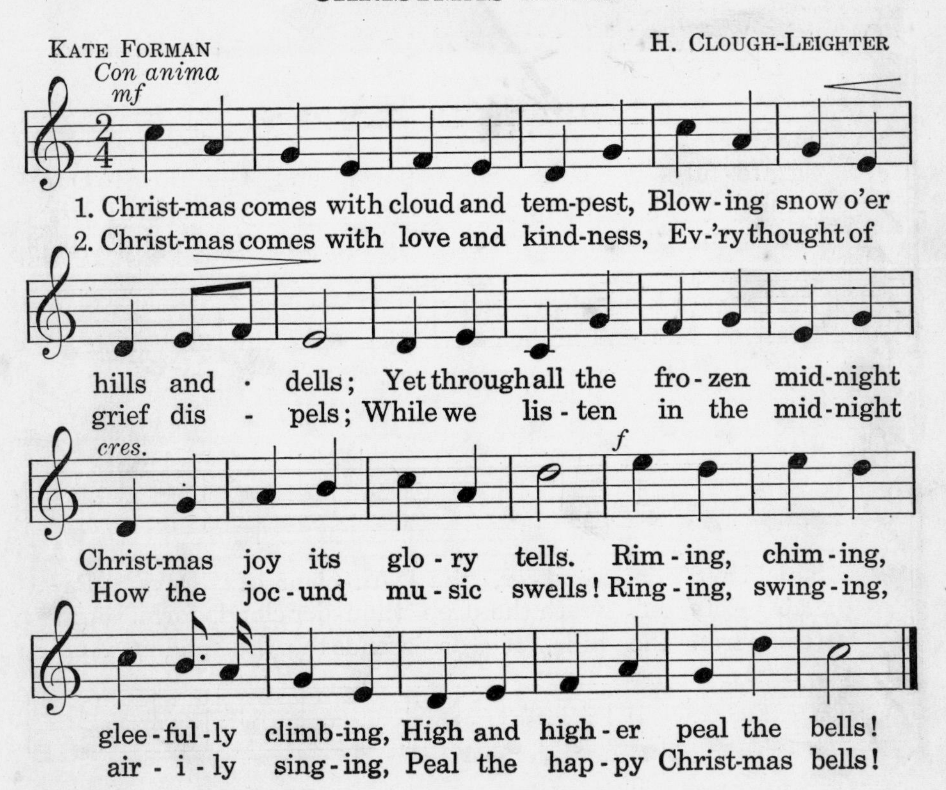

1. Christ-mas comes with cloud and tem-pest, Blow-ing snow o'er
2. Christ-mas comes with love and kind-ness, Ev-'ry thought of

hills and · dells; Yet through all the fro-zen mid-night
grief dis - pels; While we lis-ten in the mid-night

cres.   *f*

Christ-mas joy its glo-ry tells. Rim-ing, chim-ing,
How the joc-und mu-sic swells! Ring-ing, swing-ing,

glee-ful-ly climb-ing, High and high-er peal the bells!
air-i-ly sing-ing, Peal the hap-py Christ-mas bells!

40 OH, WORSHIP THE KING

ROBERT GRANT
Largo

FRANZ JOSEPH HAYDN

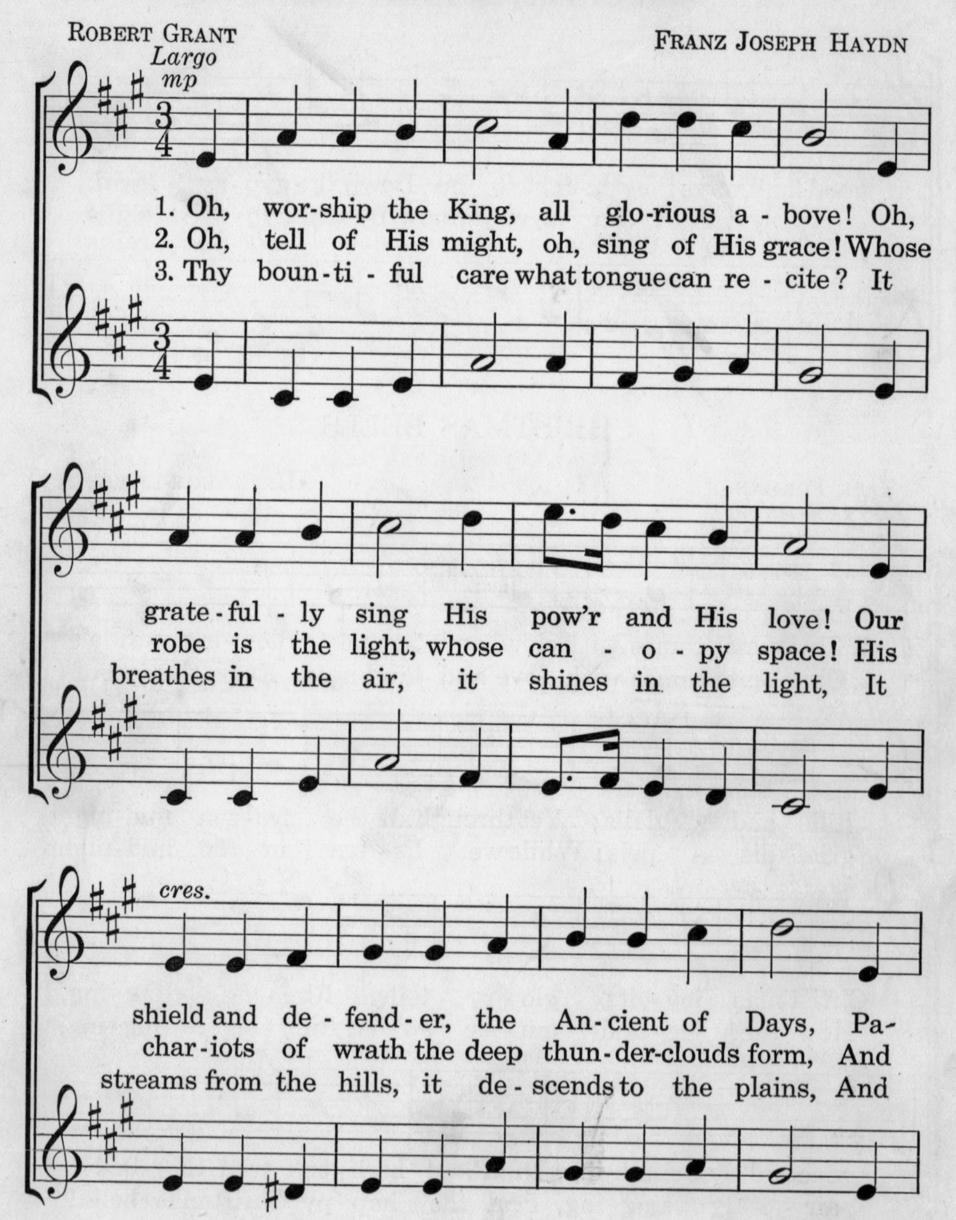

1. Oh, wor-ship the King, all glo-rious a-bove! Oh,
2. Oh, tell of His might, oh, sing of His grace! Whose
3. Thy boun-ti-ful care what tongue can re-cite? It

grate-ful-ly sing His pow'r and His love! Our
robe is the light, whose can-o-py space! His
breathes in the air, it shines in the light, It

shield and de-fend-er, the An-cient of Days, Pa-
char-iots of wrath the deep thun-der-clouds form, And
streams from the hills, it de-scends to the plains, And

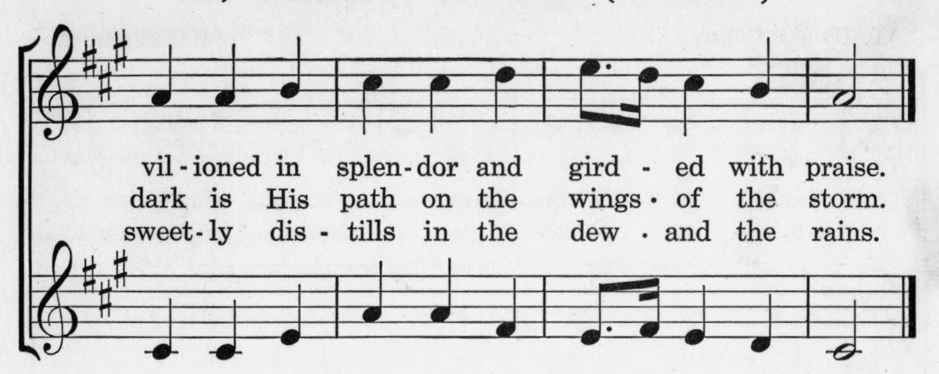

vil - ioned in splen - dor and gird - ed with praise.
dark is His path on the wings · of the storm.
sweet - ly dis - tills in the dew · and the rains.

SHADOW LEAVES

AGNES ROSS   EVELYN SPRAGUE

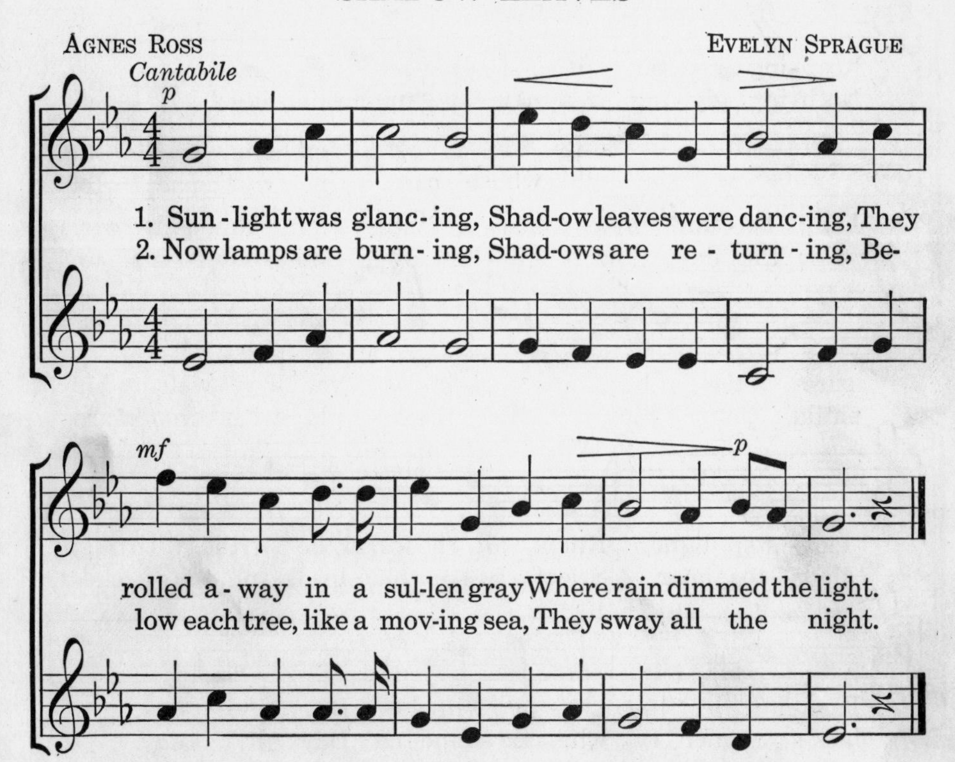

1. Sun - light was glanc - ing, Shad - ow leaves were danc - ing, They
2. Now lamps are burn - ing, Shad - ows are re - turn - ing, Be-

rolled a - way in a sul - len gray Where rain dimmed the light.
low each tree, like a mov - ing sea, They sway all the night.

THE WHISTLER

T. H. MacCrady

HARRY HARTS

Giocoso
mf

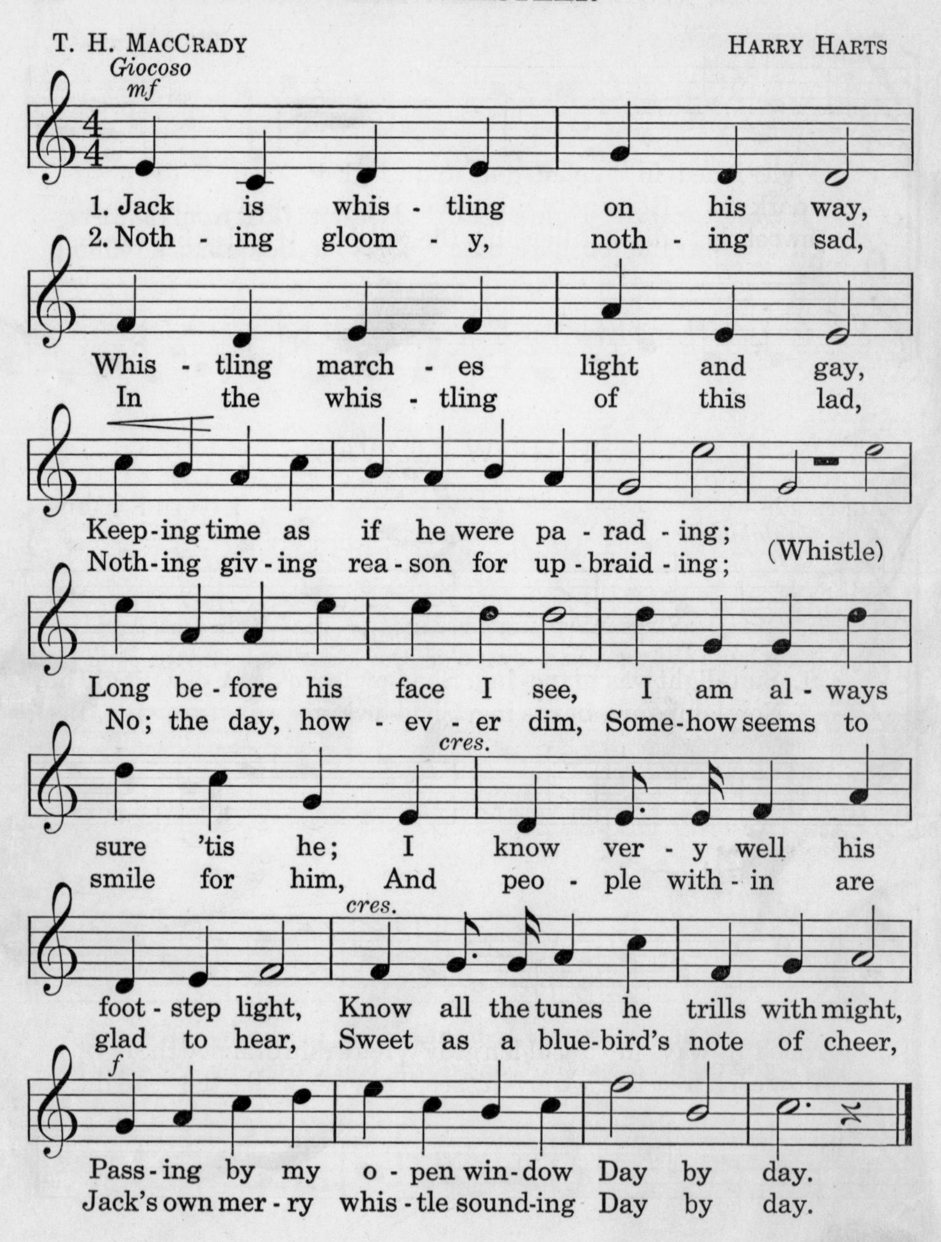

1. Jack is whis - tling on his way,
2. Noth - ing gloom - y, noth - ing sad,

Whis - tling march - es light and gay,
In the whis - tling of this lad,

Keep-ing time as if he were pa - rad - ing; (Whistle)
Noth-ing giv-ing rea-son for up-braid-ing;

Long be - fore his face I see, I am al - ways
No; the day, how - ev - er dim, Some-how seems to
cres.

sure 'tis he; I know ver - y well his
smile for him, And peo - ple with - in are
cres.

foot - step light, Know all the tunes he trills with might,
glad to hear, Sweet as a blue-bird's note of cheer,

Pass - ing by my o - pen win-dow Day by day.
Jack's own mer - ry whis - tle sound-ing Day by day.

MARGARET CONNOLLY

WILL EARHART

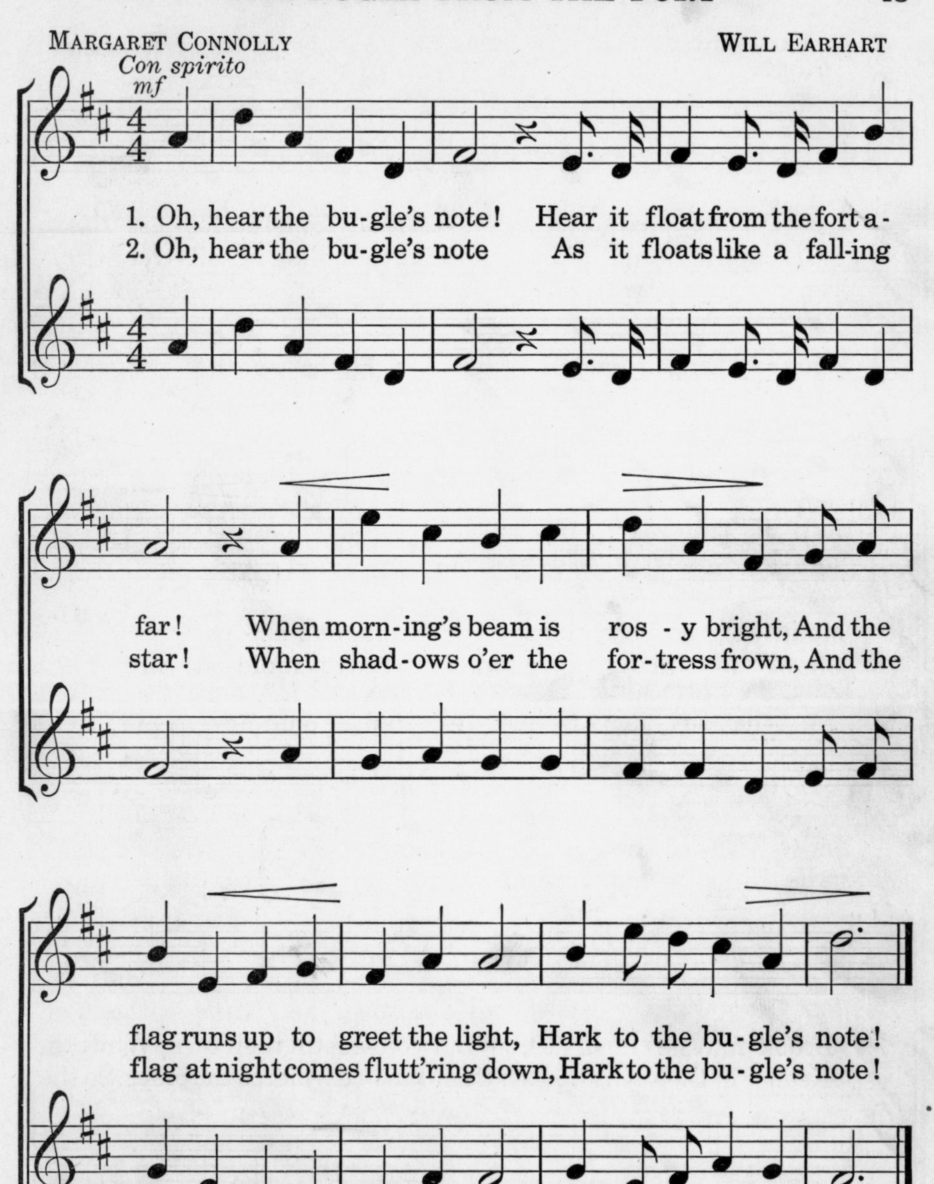

1. Oh, hear the bu-gle's note! Hear it float from the fort a-
2. Oh, hear the bu-gle's note As it floats like a fall-ing

far! When morn-ing's beam is ros - y bright, And the
star! When shad-ows o'er the for-tress frown, And the

flag runs up to greet the light, Hark to the bu-gle's note!
flag at night comes flutt'ring down, Hark to the bu-gle's note!

M. LOUISE BAUM

RALPH L. BALDWIN

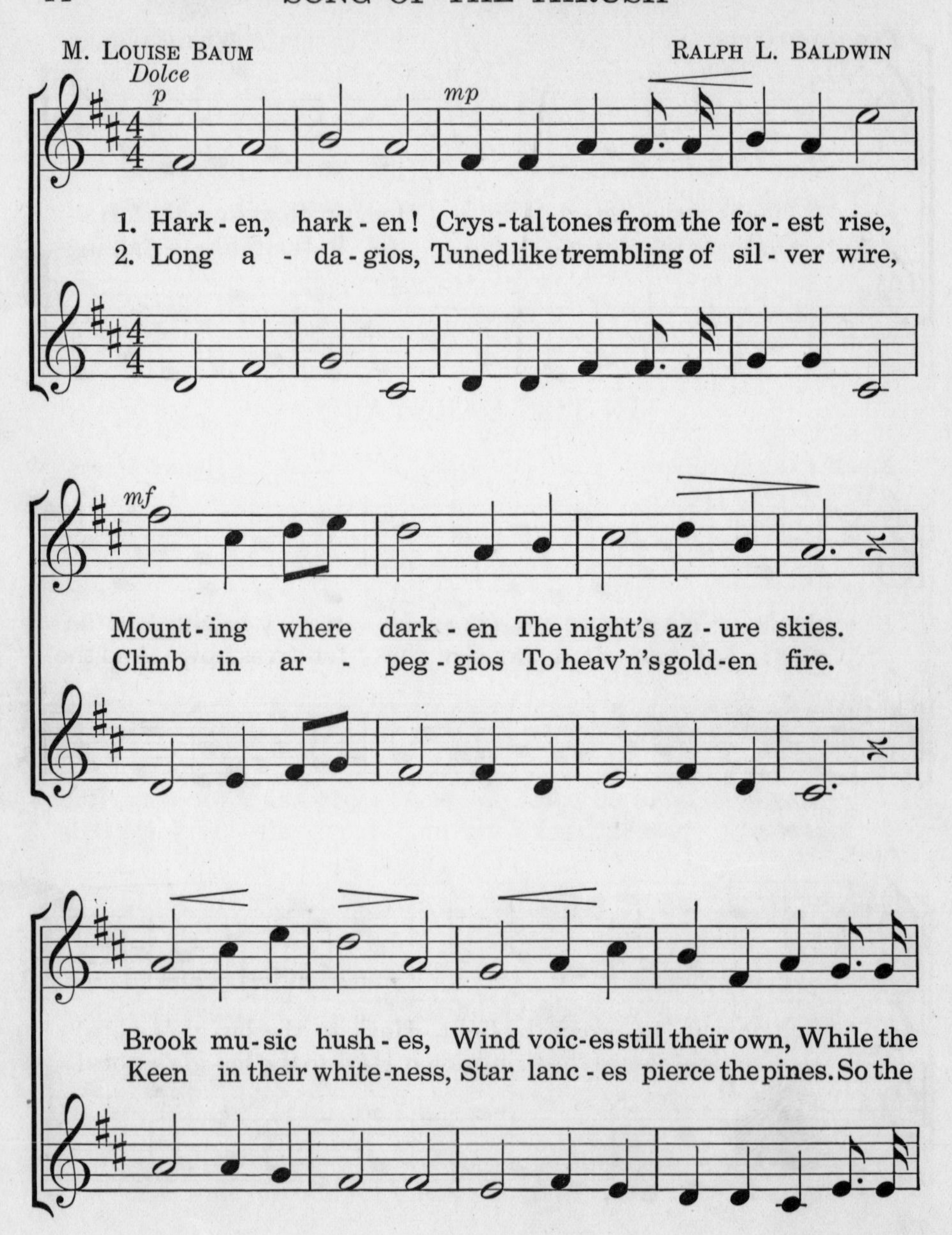

1. Hark - en, hark - en! Crys-tal tones from the for - est rise,
2. Long a - da - gios, Tuned like trembling of sil - ver wire,

Mount-ing where dark-en The night's az - ure skies.
Climb in ar - peg - gios To heav'n's gold-en fire.

Brook mu-sic hush-es, Wind voic-es still their own, While the
Keen in their white-ness, Star lanc - es pierce the pines. So the

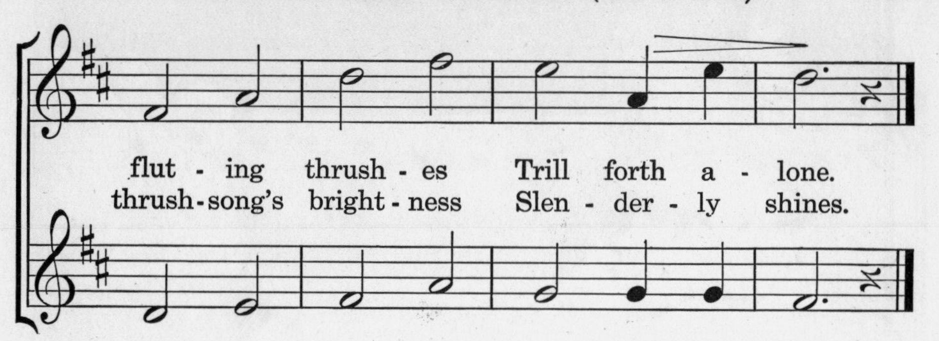

flut - ing   thrush - es   Trill   forth   a - lone.
thrush-song's   bright - ness   Slen - der - ly   shines.

IN THE BARNYARD

ABBIE FARWELL BROWN   HARRY HARTS

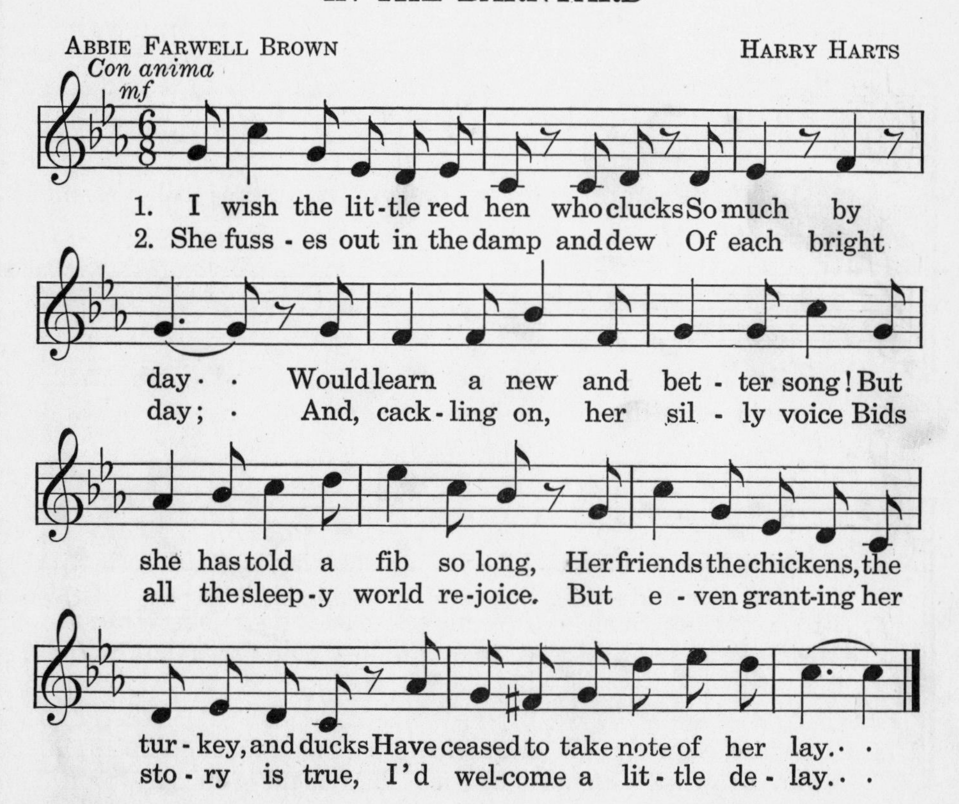

1. I wish the lit-tle red hen who clucks So much by
2. She fuss - es out in the damp and dew Of each bright

day · · Would learn a new and bet - ter song! But
day; · And, cack - ling on, her sil - ly voice Bids

she has told a fib so long, Her friends the chickens, the
all the sleep-y world re-joice. But e - ven grant-ing her

tur - key, and ducks Have ceased to take note of her lay. · ·
sto - ry is true, I'd wel-come a lit - tle de - lay. · ·

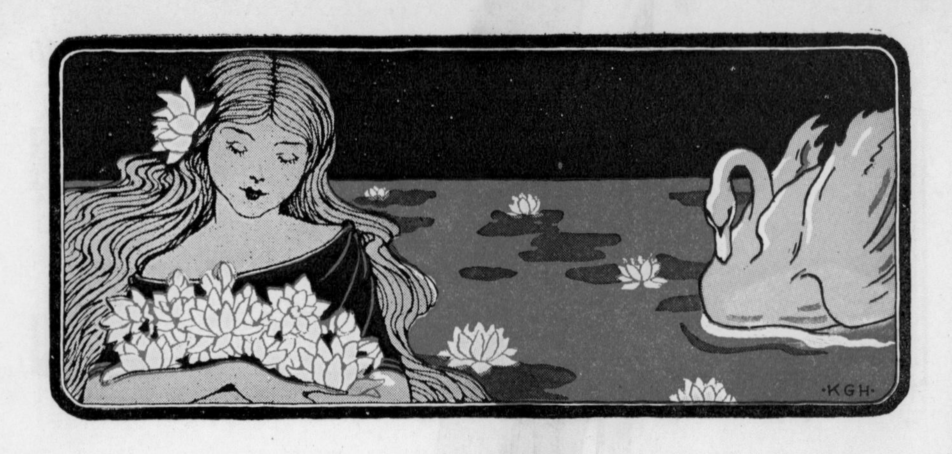

A PICTURE

LOUISE STICKNEY   MARTHA WHITE

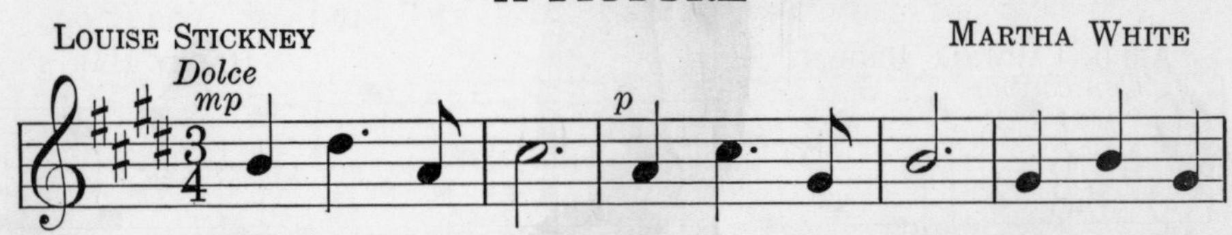

1. Wa - ters are   fair, moon-light is   there; Sil - ver the
2. Yon - der a   pool, shel - tered and cool, Mir - rors a

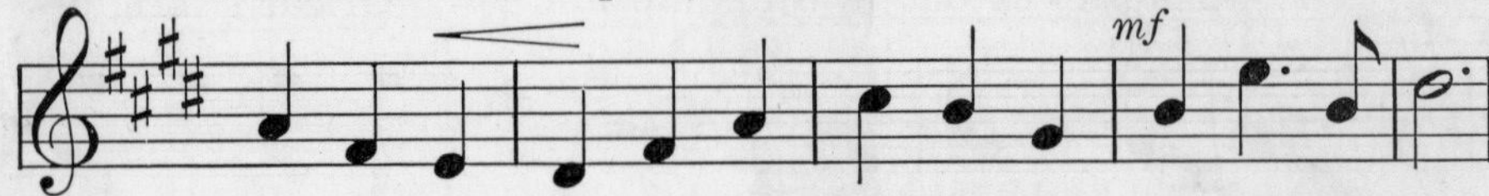

flow-ing where lil - ies are grow-ing; As   si-lent the stream
maid - en with   lil - y buds lad - en; A - ris - es a song

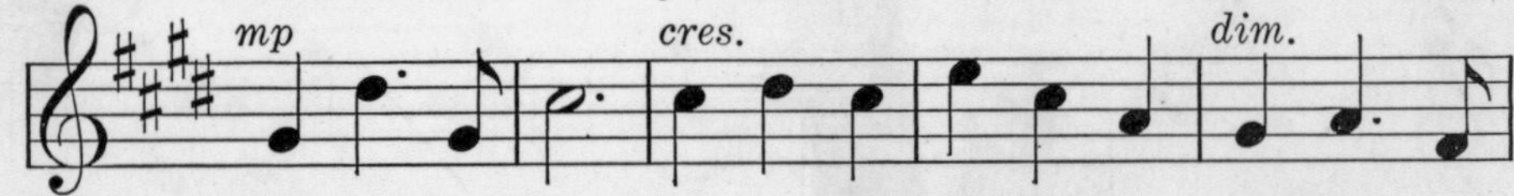

drifts like   a dream, Lil - y buds star-ring its dark-ness with
ten - der and strong, Sea-ward, with sing-ing, still pass-es   the

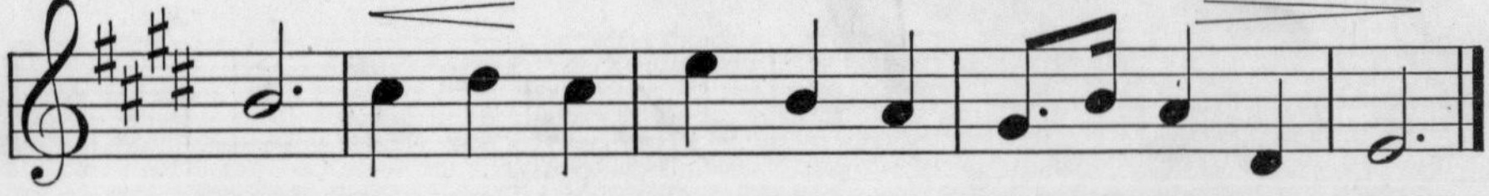

white, Slow - ly   a swan floats a - long through the night.
swan; Crowned with her   lil - ies the   maid - en   is   gone.

ROBERT BRIGHAM

MABEL OSBORNE

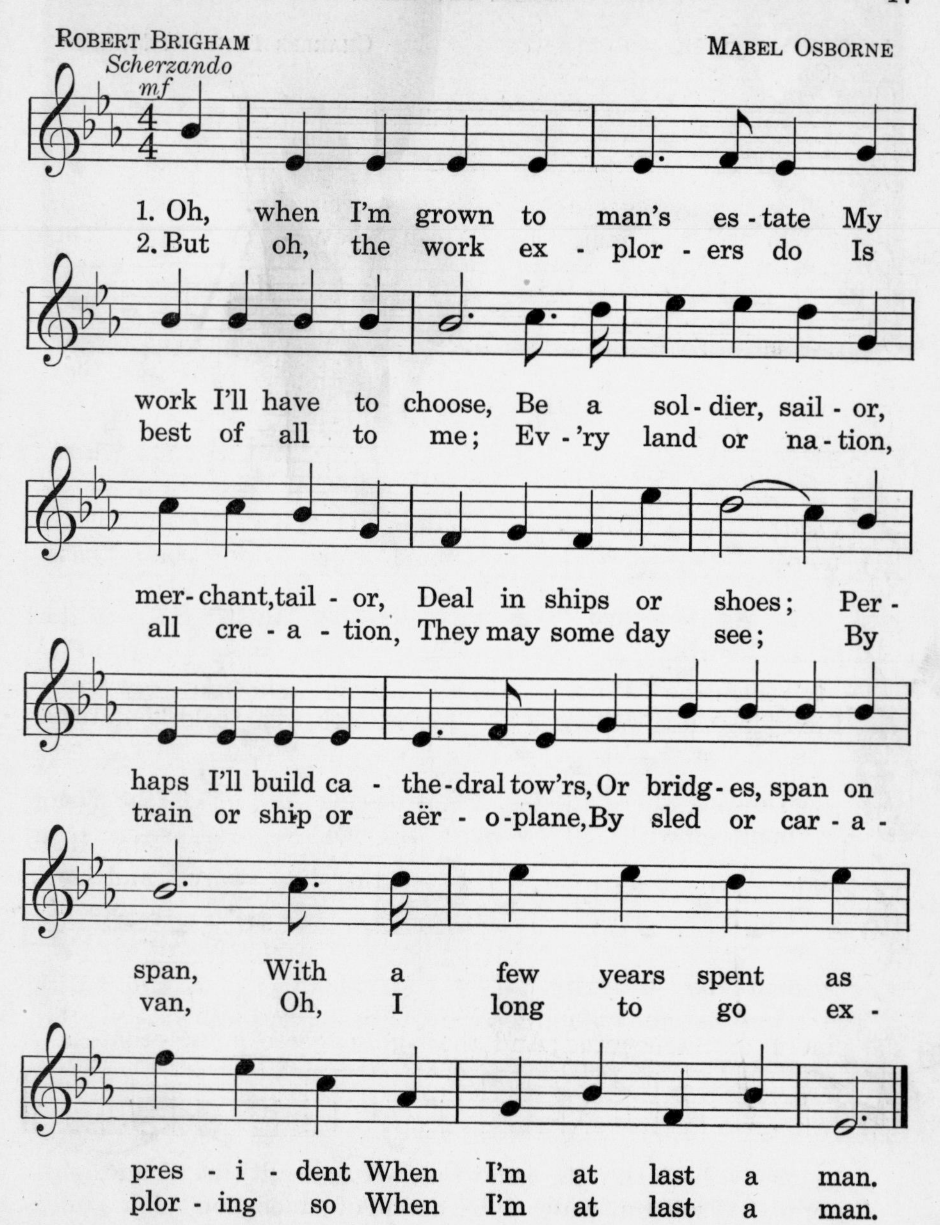

Scherzando
mf

1. Oh, when I'm grown to man's es-tate My
2. But oh, the work ex-plor-ers do Is

work I'll have to choose, Be a sol-dier, sail-or,
best of all to me; Ev-'ry land or na-tion,

mer-chant, tail-or, Deal in ships or shoes; Per-
all cre-a-tion, They may some day see; By

haps I'll build ca-the-dral tow'rs, Or bridg-es, span on
train or ship or aër-o-plane, By sled or car-a-

span, With a few years spent as
van, Oh, I long to go ex-

pres-i-dent When I'm at last a man.
plor-ing so When I'm at last a man.

WILD GEESE IN THE FALL

ABBIE FARWELL BROWN

CHARLES FONTEYN MANNEY

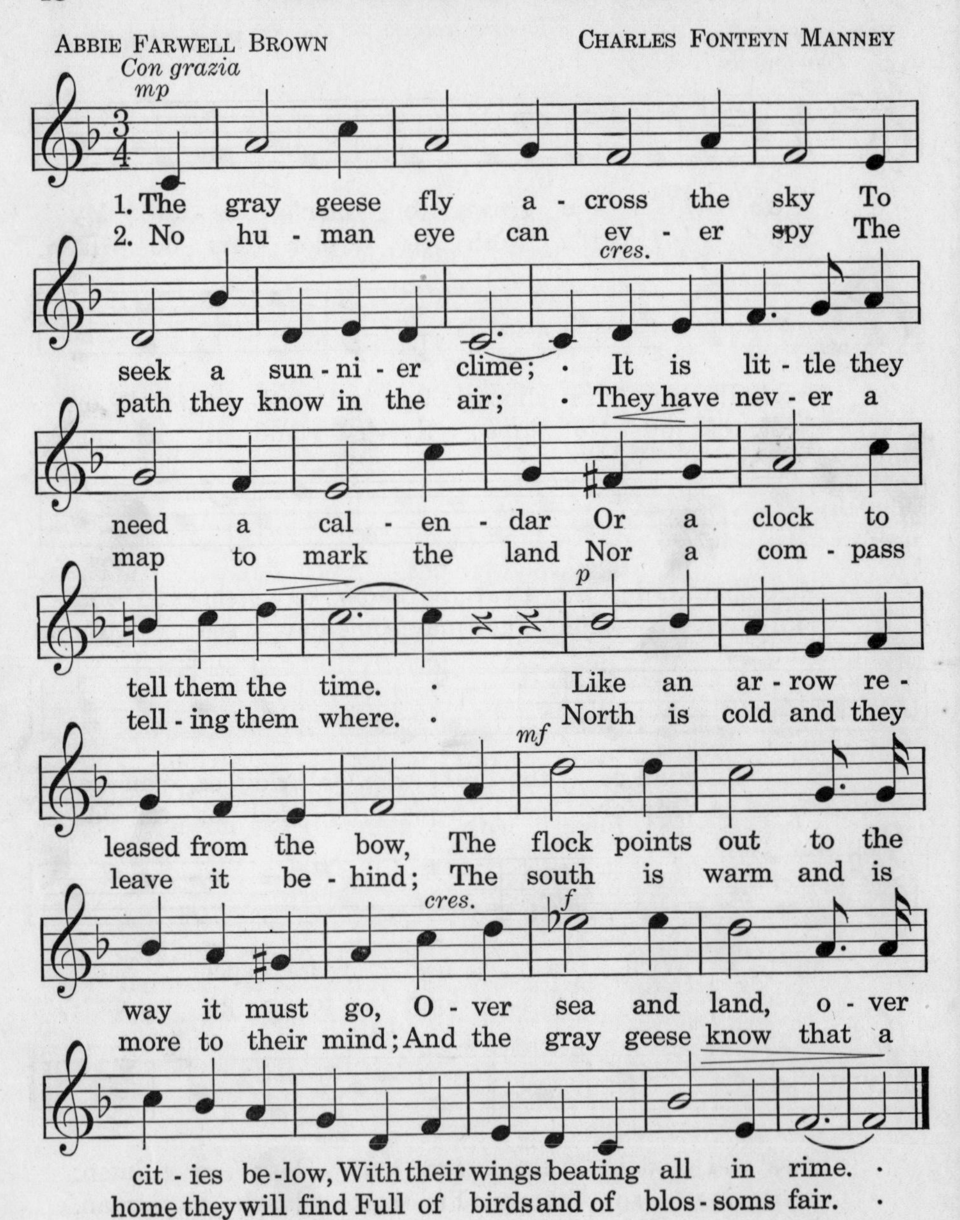

1. The gray geese fly a-cross the sky To
2. No hu-man eye can ev-er spy The

seek a sun-ni-er clime; · It is lit-tle they
path they know in the air; · They have nev-er a

need a cal-en-dar Or a clock to
map to mark the land Nor a com-pass

tell them the time. · Like an ar-row re-
tell-ing them where. · North is cold and they

leased from the bow, The flock points out to the
leave it be-hind; The south is warm and is

way it must go, O-ver sea and land, o-ver
more to their mind; And the gray geese know that a

cit-ies be-low, With their wings beating all in rime. ·
home they will find Full of birds and of blos-soms fair. ·

MARY STANHOPE   SCOUT SONG   WELSH FOLK TUNE

Con spirito

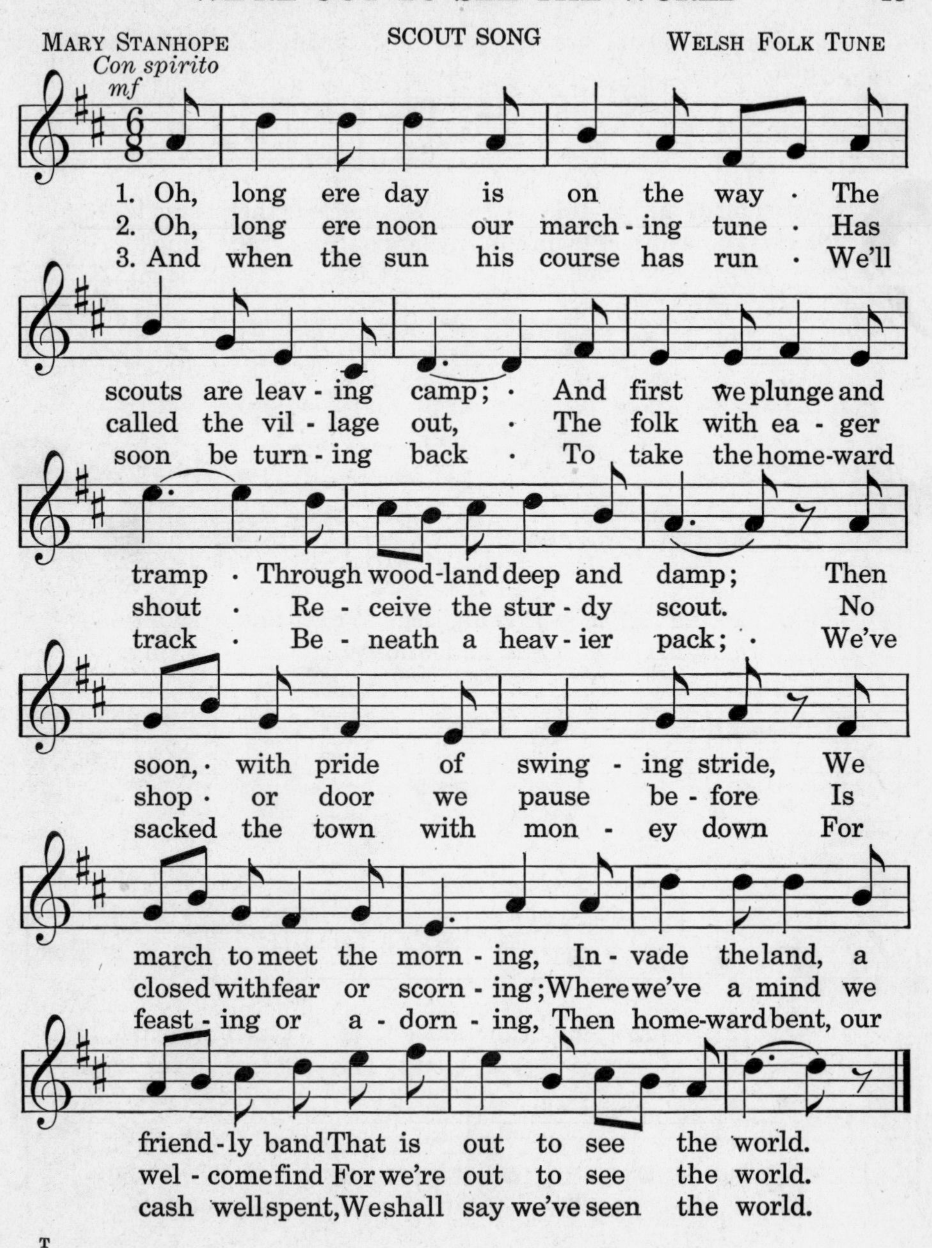

1. Oh, long ere day is on the way · The scouts are leav-ing camp; · And first we plunge and tramp · Through wood-land deep and damp; Then soon, · with pride of swing-ing stride, We march to meet the morn-ing, In-vade the land, a friend-ly band That is out to see the world.

2. Oh, long ere noon our march-ing tune · Has called the vil-lage out, · The folk with ea-ger shout · Re-ceive the stur-dy scout. No shop · or door we pause be-fore Is closed with fear or scorn-ing; Where we've a mind we wel-come find For we're out to see the world.

3. And when the sun his course has run · We'll soon be turn-ing back · To take the home-ward track · Be-neath a heav-ier pack; · We've sacked the town with mon-ey down For feast-ing or a-dorn-ing, Then home-ward bent, our cash well spent, We shall say we've seen the world.

T

A MORN IN SPRING

Denis McCarthy

Harts-Leavitt

Cantabile

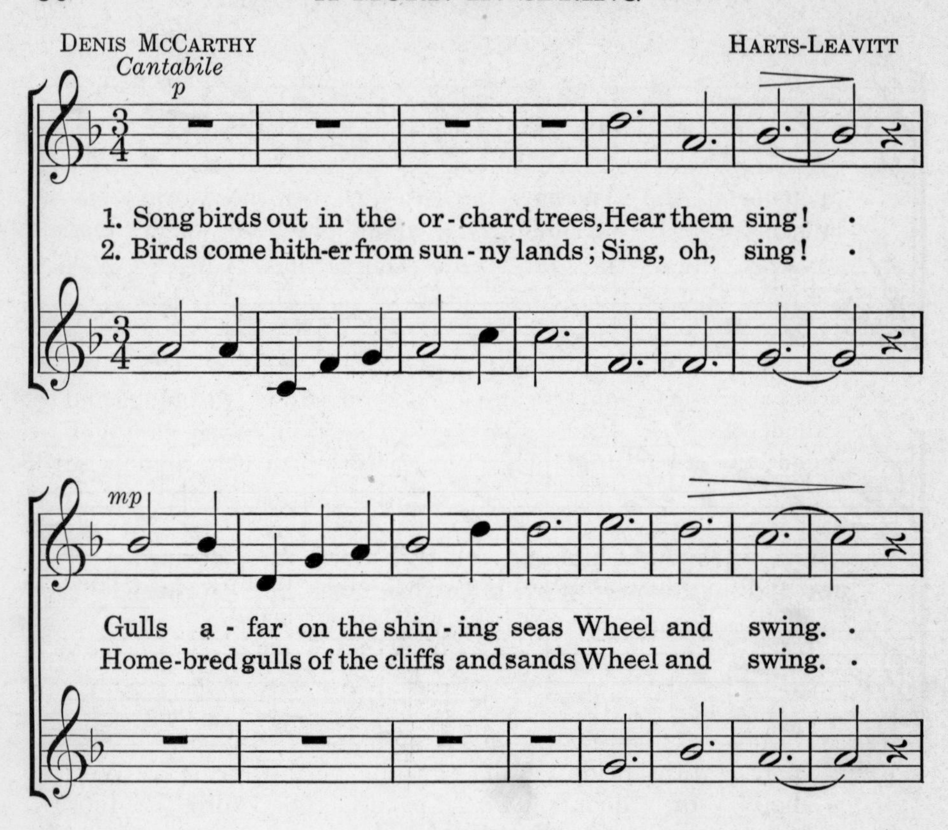

1. Song birds out in the or - chard trees, Hear them sing ! •
2. Birds come hith-er from sun - ny lands ; Sing, oh,   sing ! •

Gulls   a - far on the shin - ing seas Wheel and   swing. •
Home-bred gulls of the cliffs and sands Wheel and   swing. •

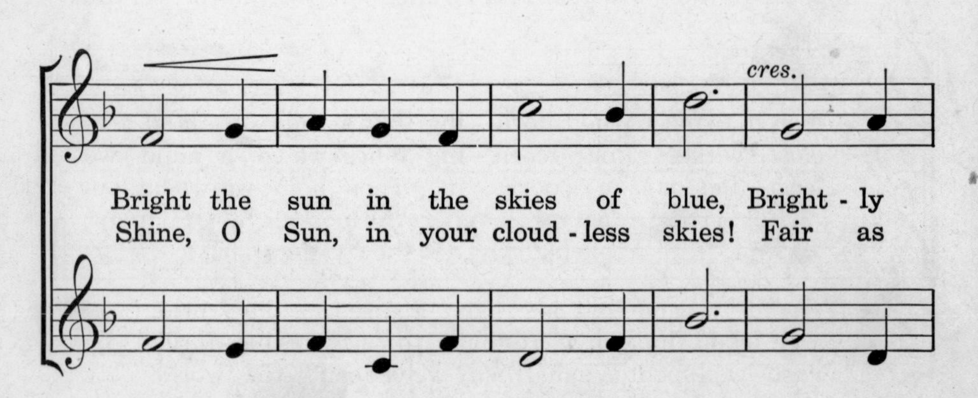

Bright the   sun   in   the skies   of   blue, Bright - ly
Shine, O Sun, in your cloud - less skies! Fair as

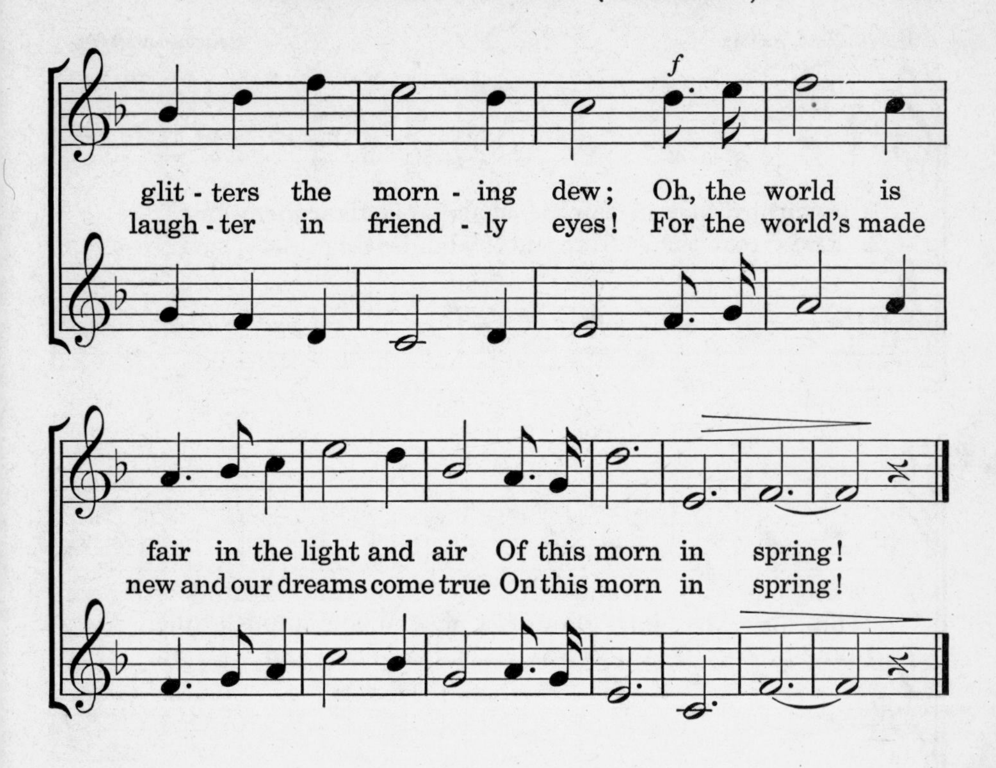

glit - ters the morn - ing dew; Oh, the world is
laugh - ter in friend - ly eyes! For the world's made

fair in the light and air Of this morn in spring!
new and our dreams come true On this morn in spring!

FOOTBALL

Louise Stickney

Laura Streeter

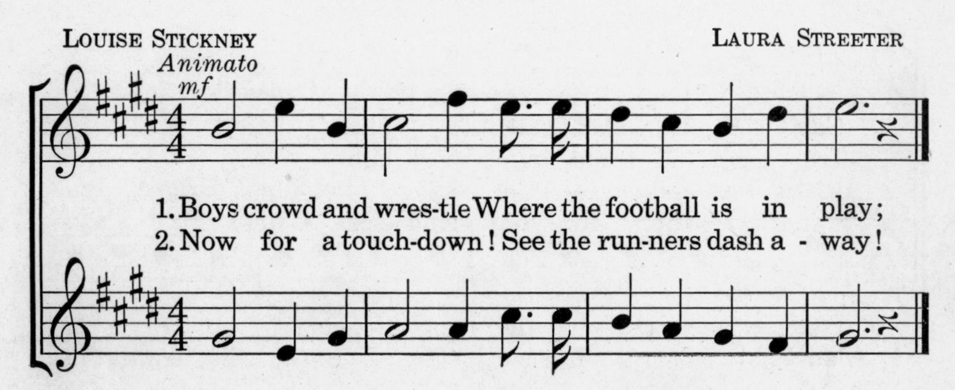

1. Boys crowd and wres-tle Where the football is in play;
2. Now for a touch-down! See the run-ners dash a - way!

GYPSY DANCERS

M. LOUISE BAUM

MARTHA WHITE

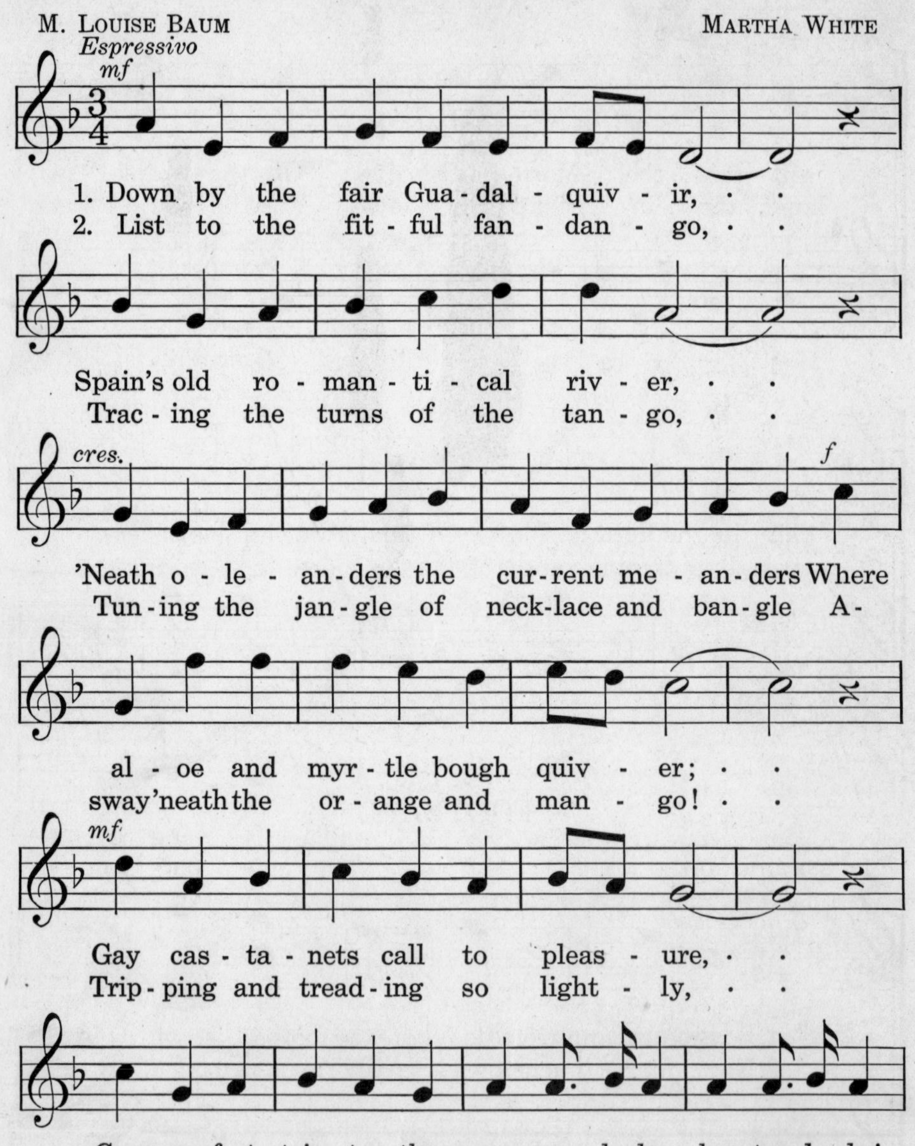

1. Down by the fair Gua - dal - quiv - ir, · ·
2. List to the fit - ful fan - dan - go, · ·

Spain's old ro - man - ti - cal riv - er, · ·
Trac - ing the turns of the tan - go, · ·

'Neath o - le - an - ders the cur - rent me - an - ders Where
Tun - ing the jan - gle of neck - lace and ban - gle A-

al - oe and myr - tle bough quiv - er; · ·
sway 'neath the or - ange and man - go! · · ·

Gay cas - ta - nets call to pleas - ure, · ·
Trip - ping and tread - ing so light - ly, · ·

Gyp - sy feet trip to the meas - ure, la la, ho, tra la la!
Glance like a riv - u - let bright - ly, la la, ho, tra la la!

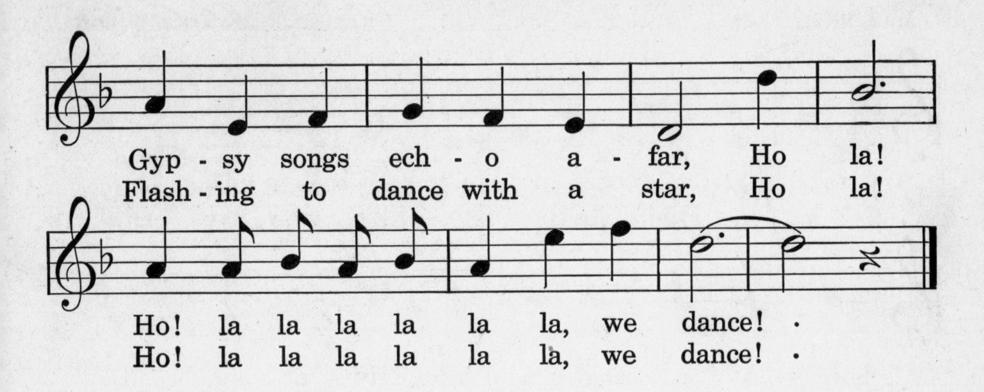

Gyp - sy songs ech - o a - far, Ho la!
Flash - ing to dance with a star, Ho la!

Ho! la la la la la la, we dance! ·
Ho! la la la la la la, we dance! ·

THE LOST HOUR

MARY STANHOPE
Misterioso
mp

ALFRED M. TUFTS

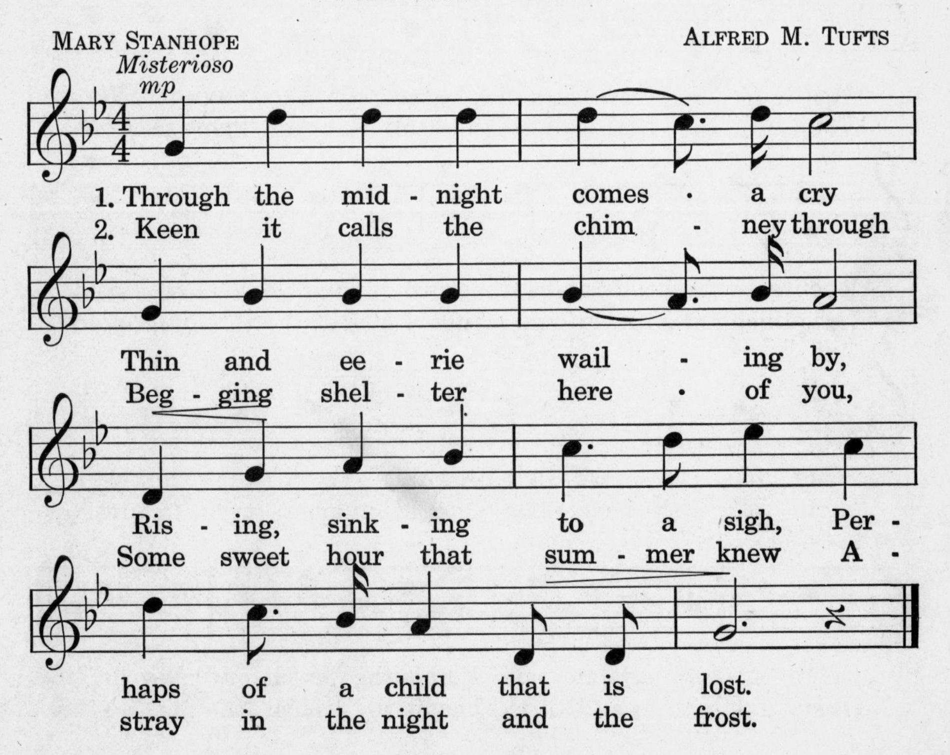

1. Through the mid - night comes · a cry
2. Keen it calls the chim - ney through

Thin and ee - rie wail - ing by,
Beg - ging shel - ter here · of you,

Ris - ing, sink - ing to a sigh, Per -
Some sweet hour that sum - mer knew A -

haps of a child that is lost.
stray in the night and the frost.

John Reed
Animato
mp

Charles François Gounod

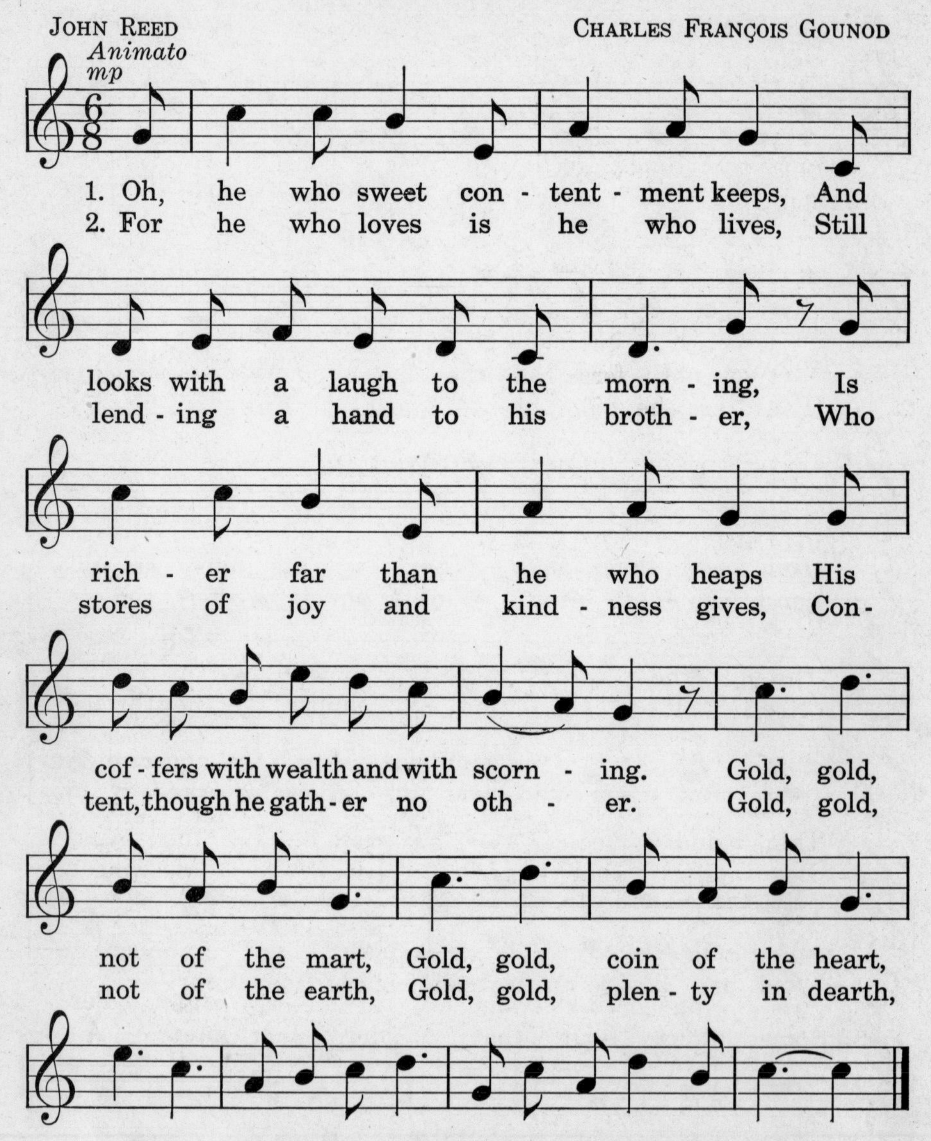

1. Oh, he who sweet con - tent - ment keeps, And
2. For he who loves is he who lives, Still

looks with a laugh to the morn - ing, Is
lend - ing a hand to his broth - er, Who

rich - er far than he who heaps His
stores of joy and kind - ness gives, Con -

cof - fers with wealth and with scorn - ing. Gold, gold,
tent, though he gath - er no oth - er. Gold, gold,

not of the mart, Gold, gold, coin of the heart,
not of the earth, Gold, gold, plen - ty in dearth,

Gold, yet all may have part! That is the wealth for me. · ·
Gold, of kind-ness and mirth! That is the wealth for me. · ·

M. LOUISE BAUM

LOUIS MEYER

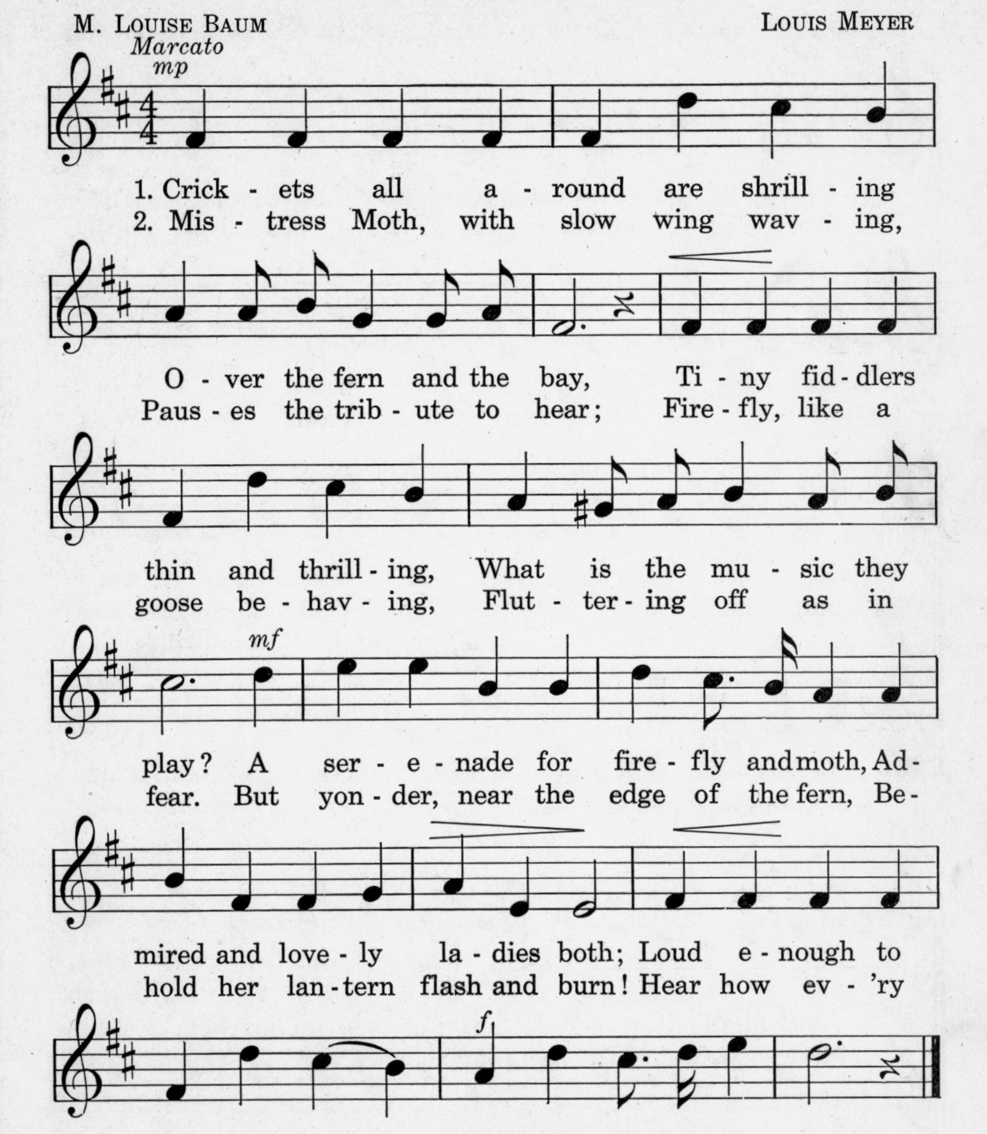

1. Crick - ets all a - round are shrill - ing
2. Mis - tress Moth, with slow wing wav - ing,

O - ver the fern and the bay, Ti - ny fid - dlers
Paus - es the trib - ute to hear; Fire - fly, like a

thin and thrill - ing, What is the mu - sic they
goose be - hav - ing, Flut - ter - ing off as in

play? A ser - e - nade for fire - fly and moth, Ad -
fear. But yon - der, near the edge of the fern, Be -

mired and love - ly la - dies both; Loud e - nough to
hold her lan - tern flash and burn! Hear how ev - 'ry

reach the moon · Sounds the rol - lick - ing tune.
fid - dler lad · · Saws a - way as if mad.

SUMMER TIME

HERBERT RANDALL   FANNY SNOW KNOWLTON

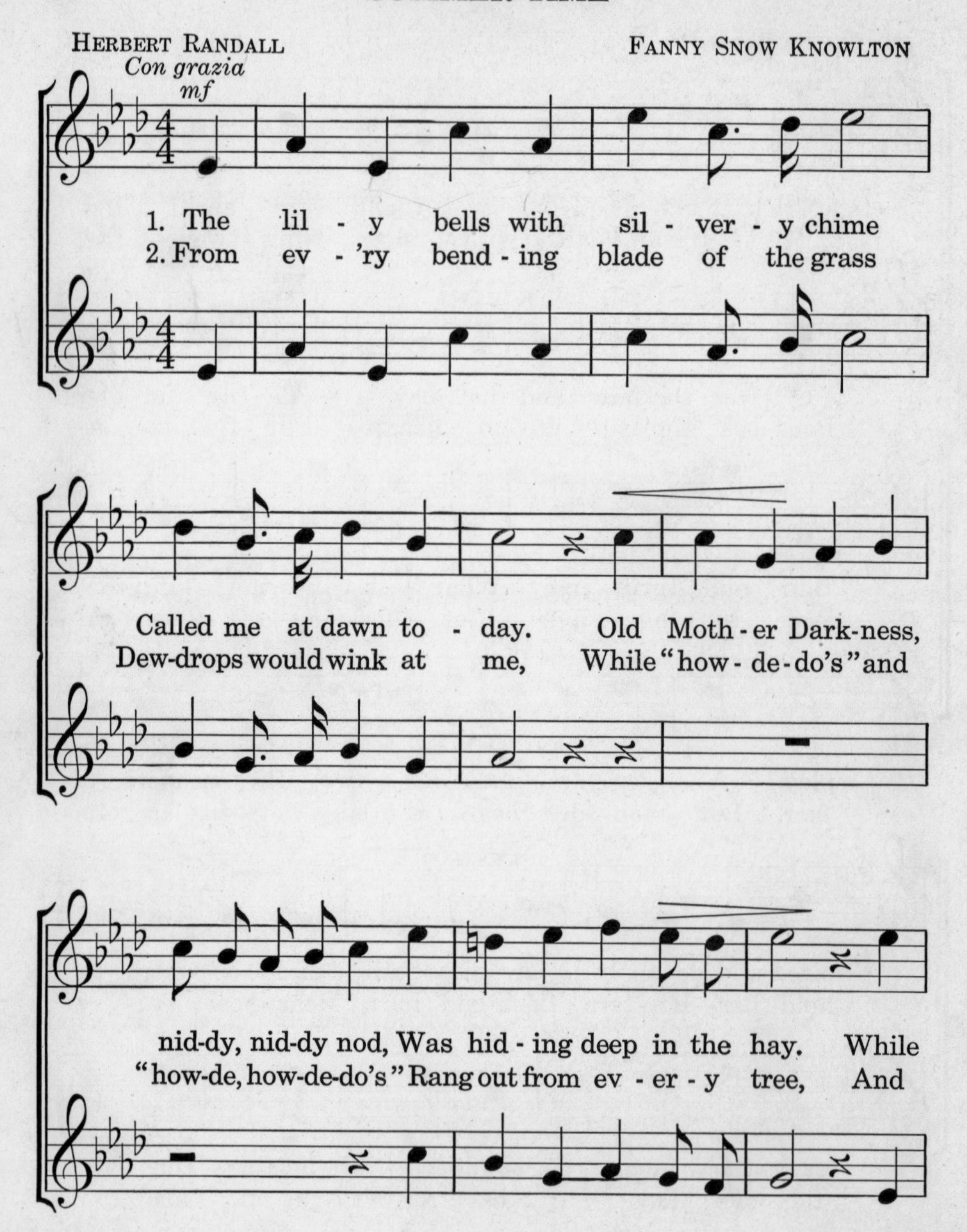

1. The lil - y bells with sil - ver - y chime
2. From ev - 'ry bend - ing blade of the grass

Called me at dawn to - day. Old Moth - er Dark-ness,
Dew-drops would wink at me, While "how - de - do's" and

nid-dy, nid-dy nod, Was hid - ing deep in the hay. While
"how-de, how-de-do's" Rang out from ev - er - y tree, And

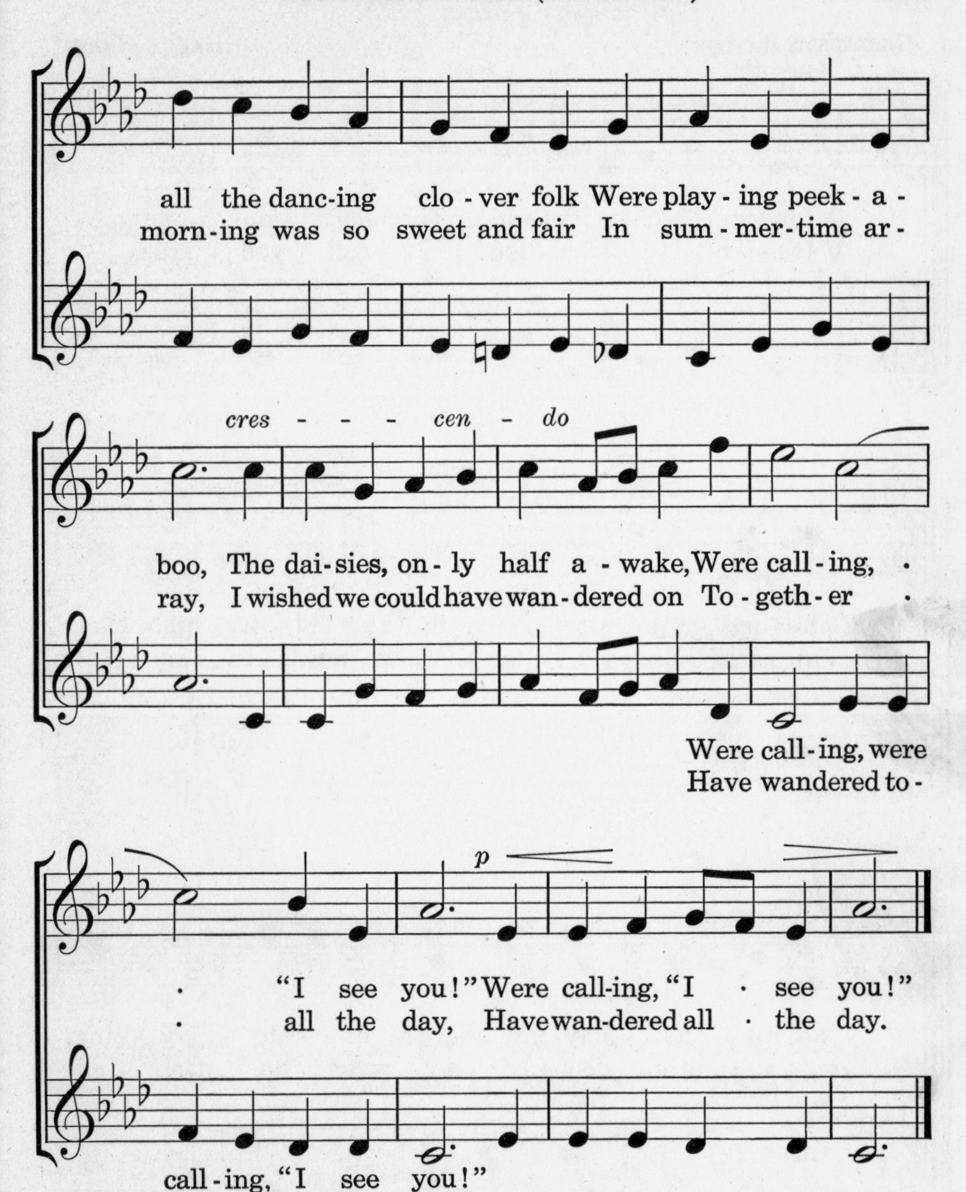

all the danc-ing clo-ver folk Were play-ing peek - a -
morn-ing was so sweet and fair In sum - mer-time ar-

cres - - - cen - do

boo, The dai-sies, on - ly half a - wake, Were call - ing, ·
ray, I wished we could have wan - dered on To - geth - er ·

Were call-ing, were
Have wandered to -

p

"I see you!" Were call-ing, "I · see you!"
all the day, Have wan-dered all · the day.

call - ing, "I see you!"
geth - er all the day,

Elizabeth Taylor

Harry Harts

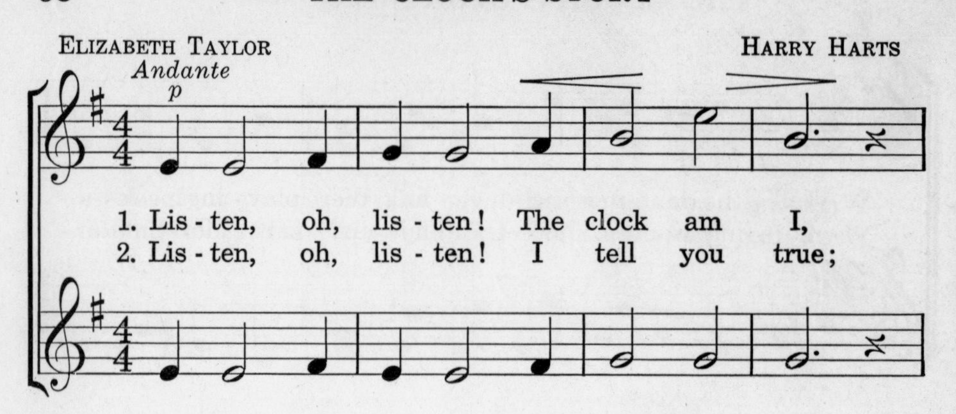

1. Lis - ten, oh, lis - ten! The clock am I,
2. Lis - ten, oh, lis - ten! I tell you true;

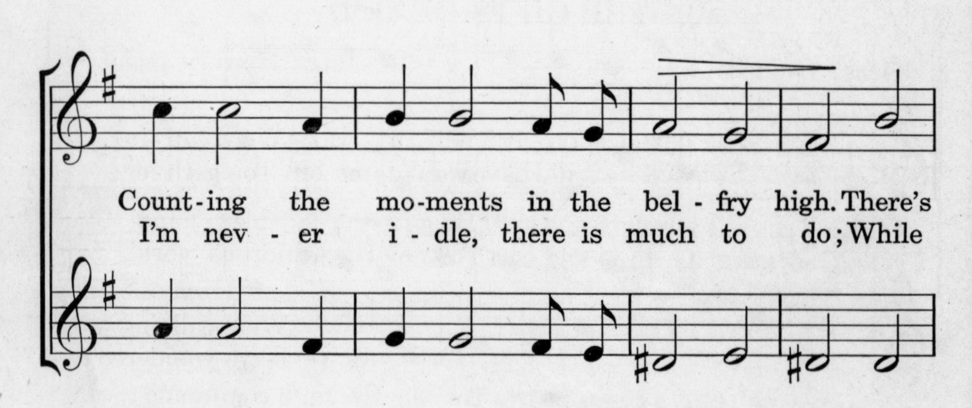

Count - ing the mo - ments in the bel - fry high. There's
I'm nev - er i - dle, there is much to do; While

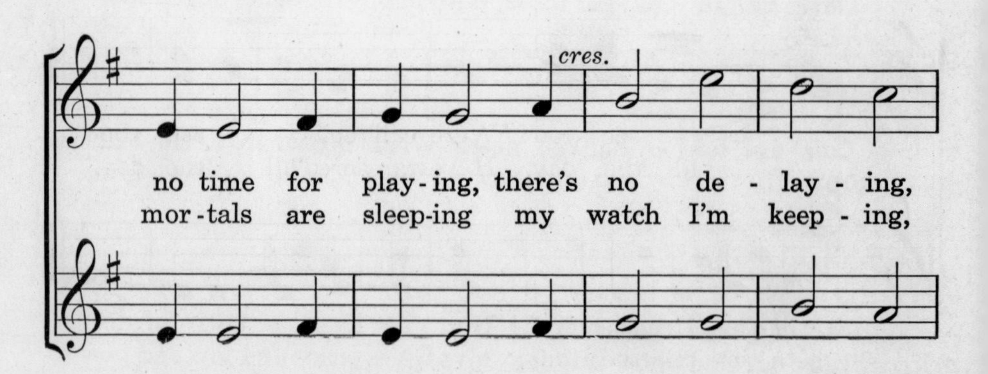

no time for play - ing, there's no de - lay - ing,
mor - tals are sleep - ing my watch I'm keep - ing,

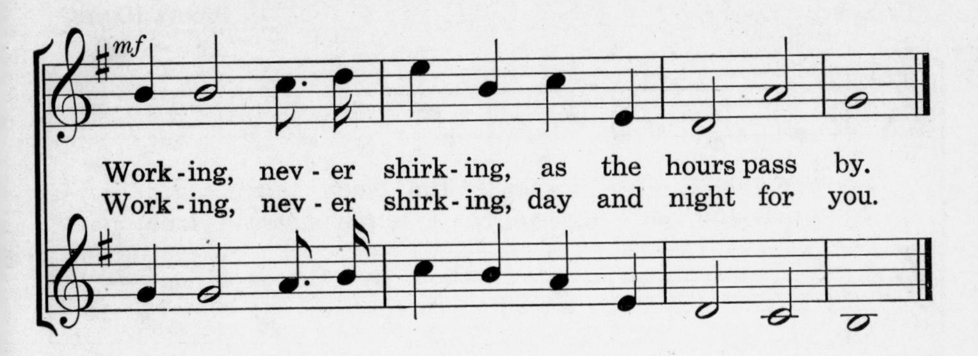

Work-ing, nev-er shirk-ing, as the hours pass by.
Work-ing, nev-er shirk-ing, day and night for you.

THE GIFTS OF GOD

ROBERT BRIGHAM

CHARLES FONTEYN MANNEY

Largo

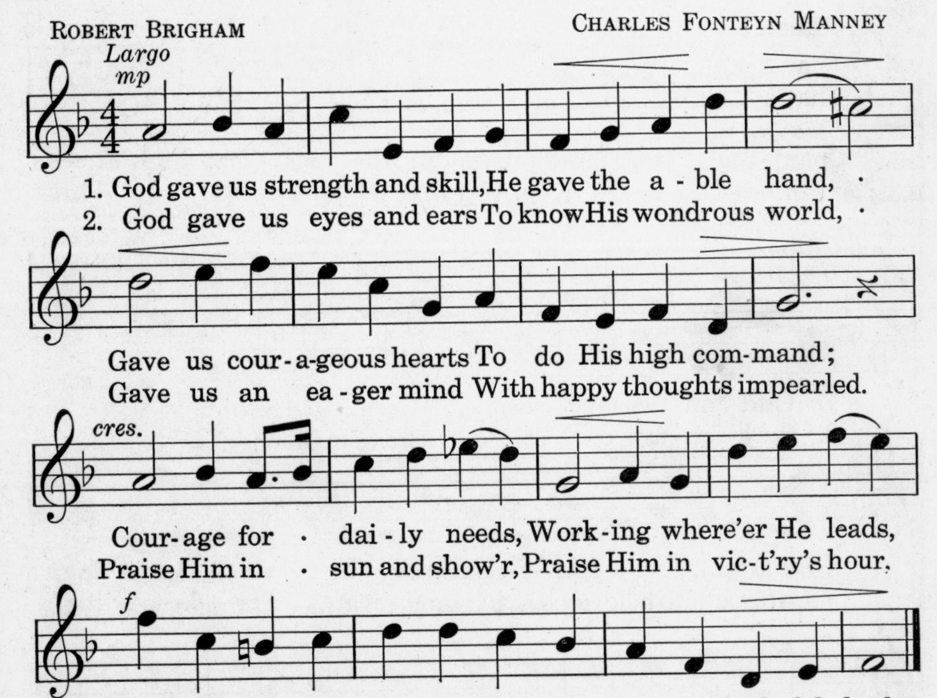

1. God gave us strength and skill, He gave the a - ble hand, ·
2. God gave us eyes and ears To know His wondrous world, ·

Gave us cour-a-geous hearts To do His high com-mand;
Gave us an ea-ger mind With happy thoughts impearled.

Cour-age for · dai-ly needs, Work-ing where'er He leads,
Praise Him in · sun and show'r, Praise Him in vic-t'ry's hour.

Heart and hand that hon-or Him In man-y faith-ful deeds.
Praise our God whose might-y love Gives peace and joy and pow'r.

2

THE BOAT RACE

T. H. MacCrady

W. F. Severns

Con anima

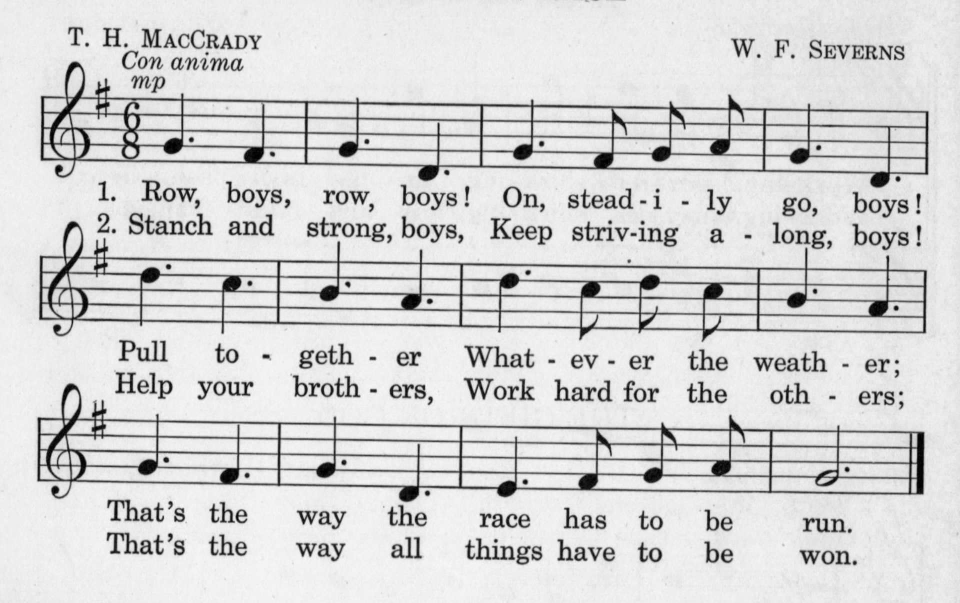

1. Row, boys, row, boys! On, stead-i-ly go, boys!
2. Stanch and strong, boys, Keep striv-ing a-long, boys!

Pull to-geth-er What-ev-er the weath-er;
Help your broth-ers, Work hard for the oth-ers;

That's the way the race has to be run.
That's the way all things have to be won.

FOR HALLOWEEN

John Reed

Nora Evans

Con grazia

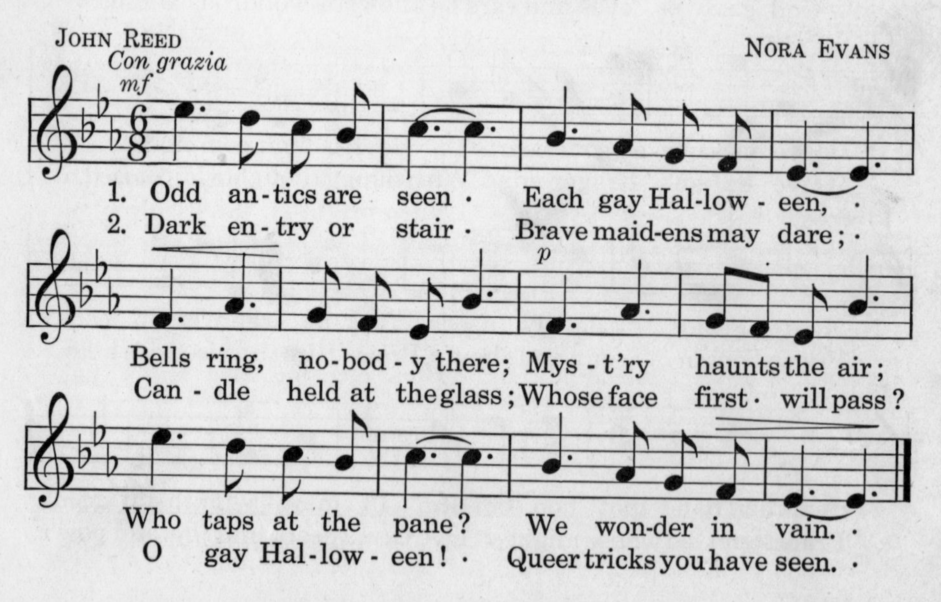

1. Odd an-tics are seen · Each gay Hal-low-een, ·
2. Dark en-try or stair · Brave maid-ens may dare; ·

Bells ring, no-bod-y there; Mys-t'ry haunts the air;
Can-dle held at the glass; Whose face first · will pass?

Who taps at the pane? We won-der in vain. ·
O gay Hal-low-een! · Queer tricks you have seen. ·

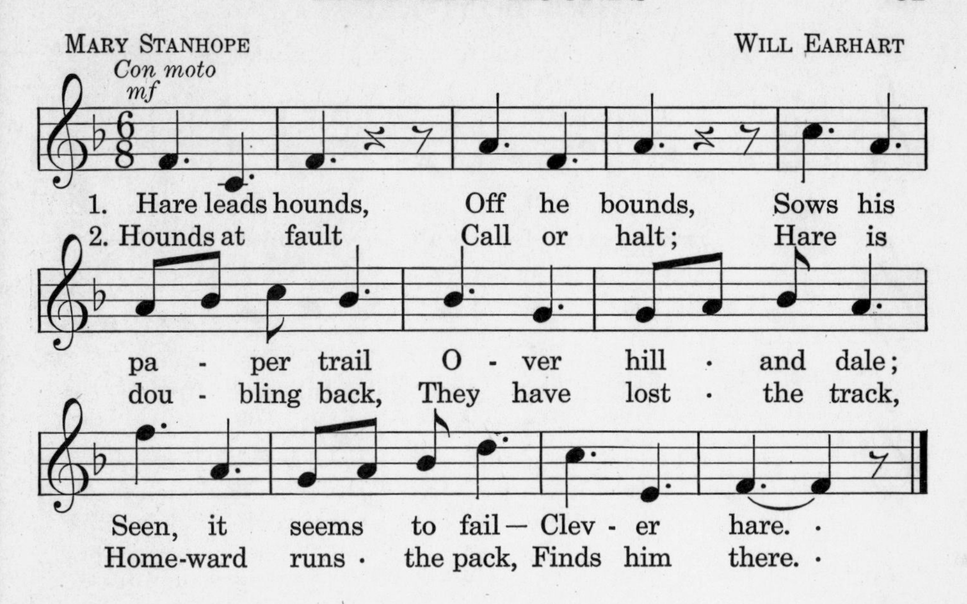

MARY STANHOPE   WILL EARHART
Con moto

1. Hare leads hounds, Off he bounds, Sows his
2. Hounds at fault Call or halt; Hare is

pa - per trail O - ver hill and dale;
dou - bling back, They have lost the track,

Seen, it seems to fail — Clev - er hare.
Home-ward runs the pack, Finds him there.

THE EVENING WINDS

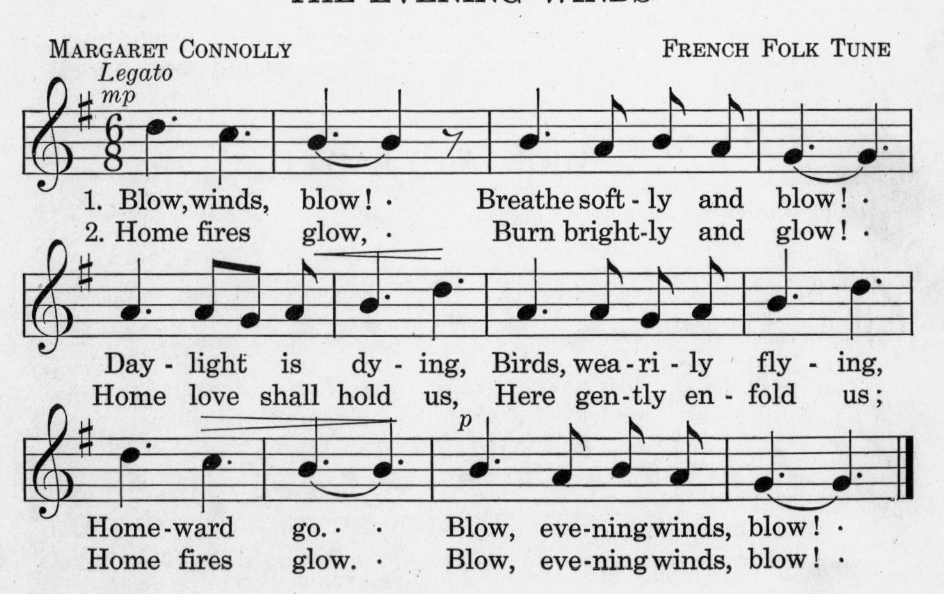

MARGARET CONNOLLY   FRENCH FOLK TUNE
Legato

1. Blow, winds, blow! Breathe soft - ly and blow!
2. Home fires glow, Burn bright-ly and glow!

Day - light is dy - ing, Birds, wea - ri - ly fly - ing,
Home love shall hold us, Here gen-tly en - fold us;

Home-ward go. Blow, eve-ning winds, blow!
Home fires glow. Blow, eve-ning winds, blow!

M. LOUISE BAUM   HELEN S. LEAVITT

Andantino
mf

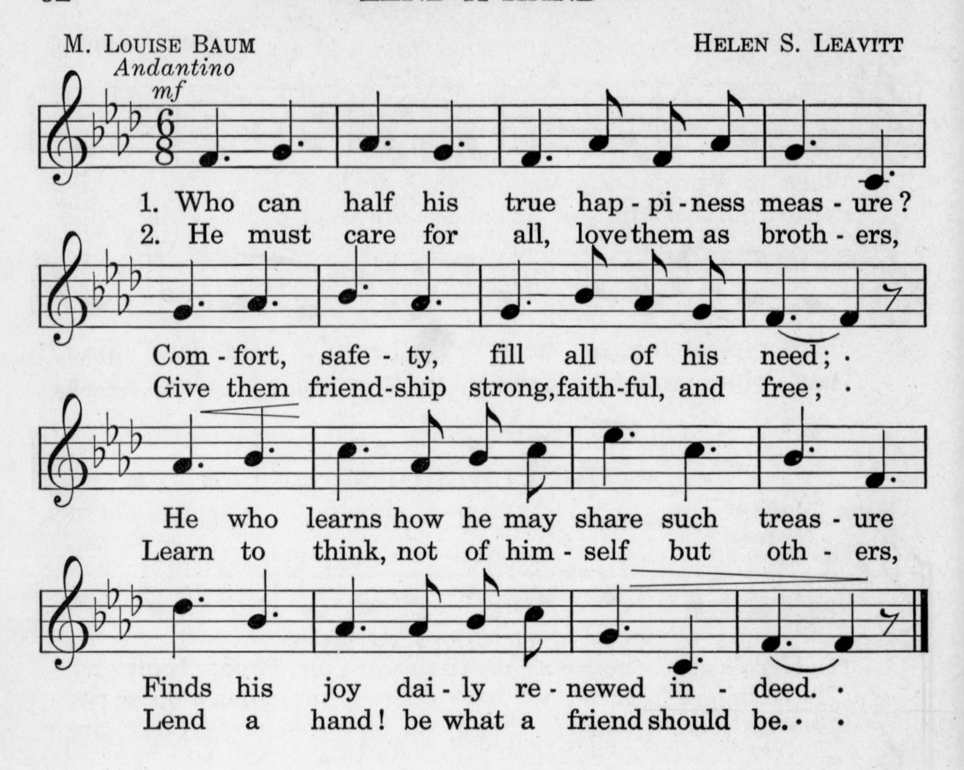

1. Who can   half his   true hap - pi - ness meas - ure?
2. He must   care for   all, love them as   broth - ers,

Com - fort,   safe - ty,   fill   all   of his   need; ·
Give them friend-ship strong, faith-ful, and   free; ·

He   who   learns how he may share such   treas - ure
Learn to   think, not of him - self but   oth - ers,

Finds his   joy dai - ly re - newed in - deed. ·
Lend   a   hand! be what a   friend should be. · ·

HIGHLAND LAD

DENIS MCCARTHY   SCOTCH FOLK TUNE

Con spirito
mf

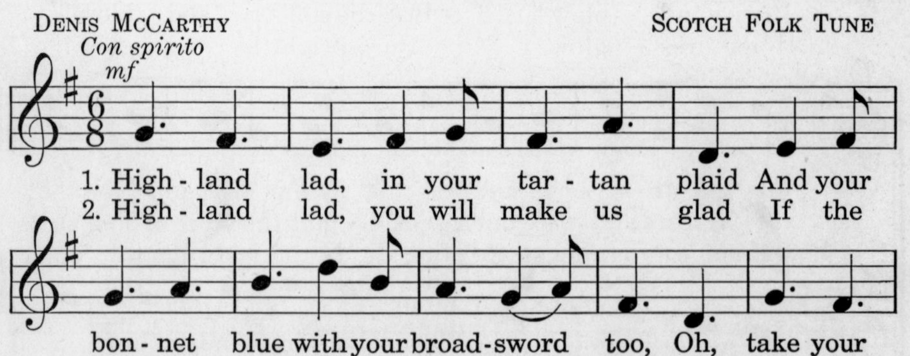

1. High - land   lad, in your   tar - tan   plaid And your
2. High - land   lad, you will make us   glad If the

bon - net   blue with your broad-sword too, Oh, take your
sword dance too you go nim - bly ·through.; Oh, there's no

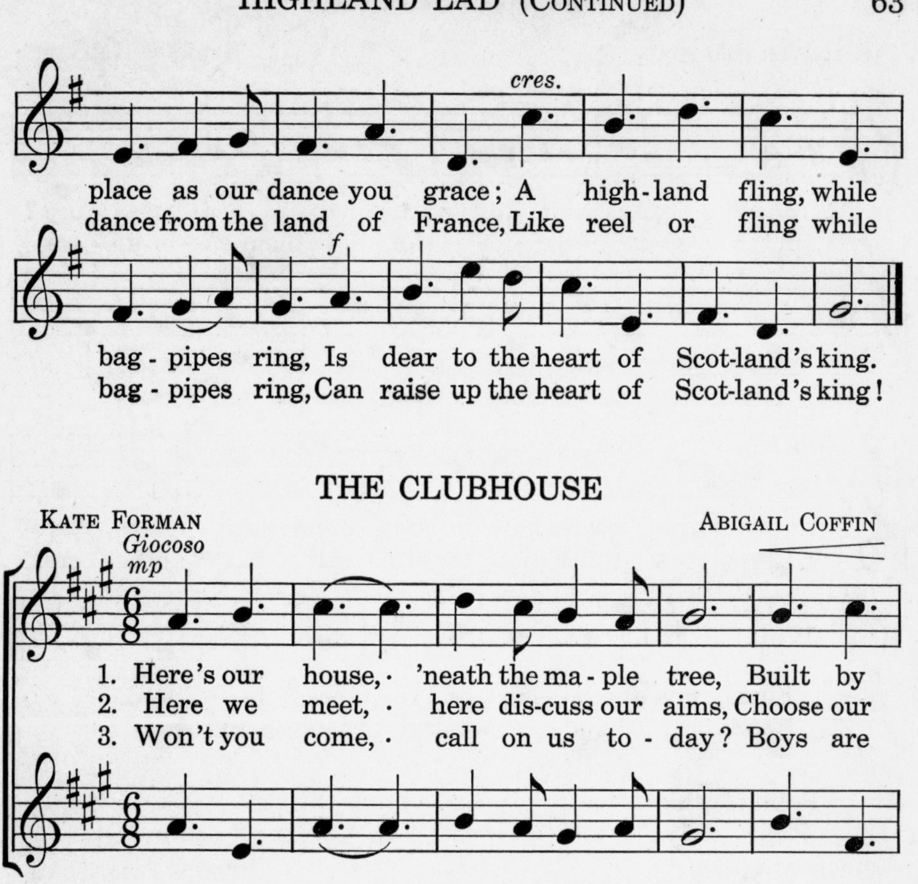

place as our dance you grace; A high-land fling, while
dance from the land of France, Like reel or fling while

bag - pipes ring, Is dear to the heart of Scot-land's king.
bag - pipes ring, Can raise up the heart of Scot-land's king!

THE CLUBHOUSE

Kate Forman

Abigail Coffin

Giocoso

1. Here's our house, · 'neath the ma - ple tree, Built by
2. Here we meet, · here dis-cuss our aims, Choose our
3. Won't you come, · call on us to - day? Boys are

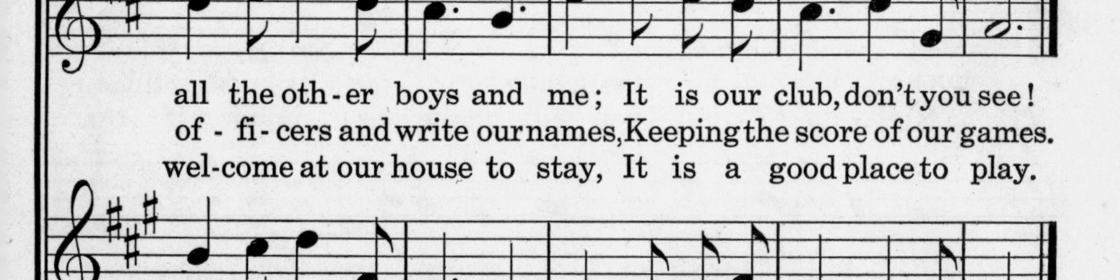

all the oth - er boys and me; It is our club, don't you see!
of - fi - cers and write our names, Keeping the score of our games.
wel-come at our house to stay, It is a good place to play.

PINS

M. LOUISE BAUM

WILL EARHART

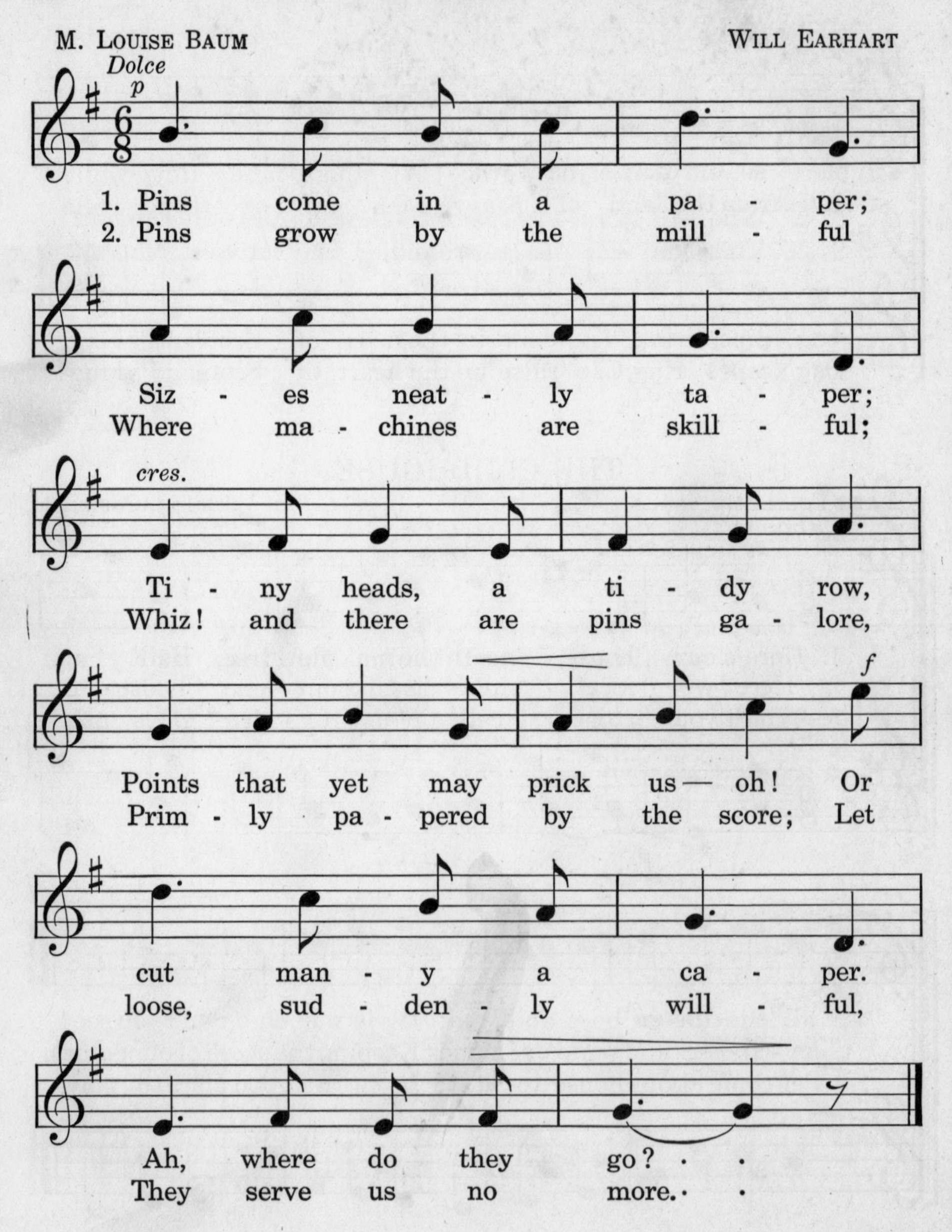

Dolce

1. Pins come in a pa - per;
2. Pins grow by the mill - ful

Siz - es neat - ly ta - per;
Where ma - chines are skill - ful;

Ti - ny heads, a ti - dy row,
Whiz! and there are pins ga - lore,

Points that yet may prick us — oh! Or
Prim - ly pa - pered by the score; Let

cut man - y a ca - per.
loose, sud - den - ly will - ful,

Ah, where do they go? · ·
They serve us no more. · ·

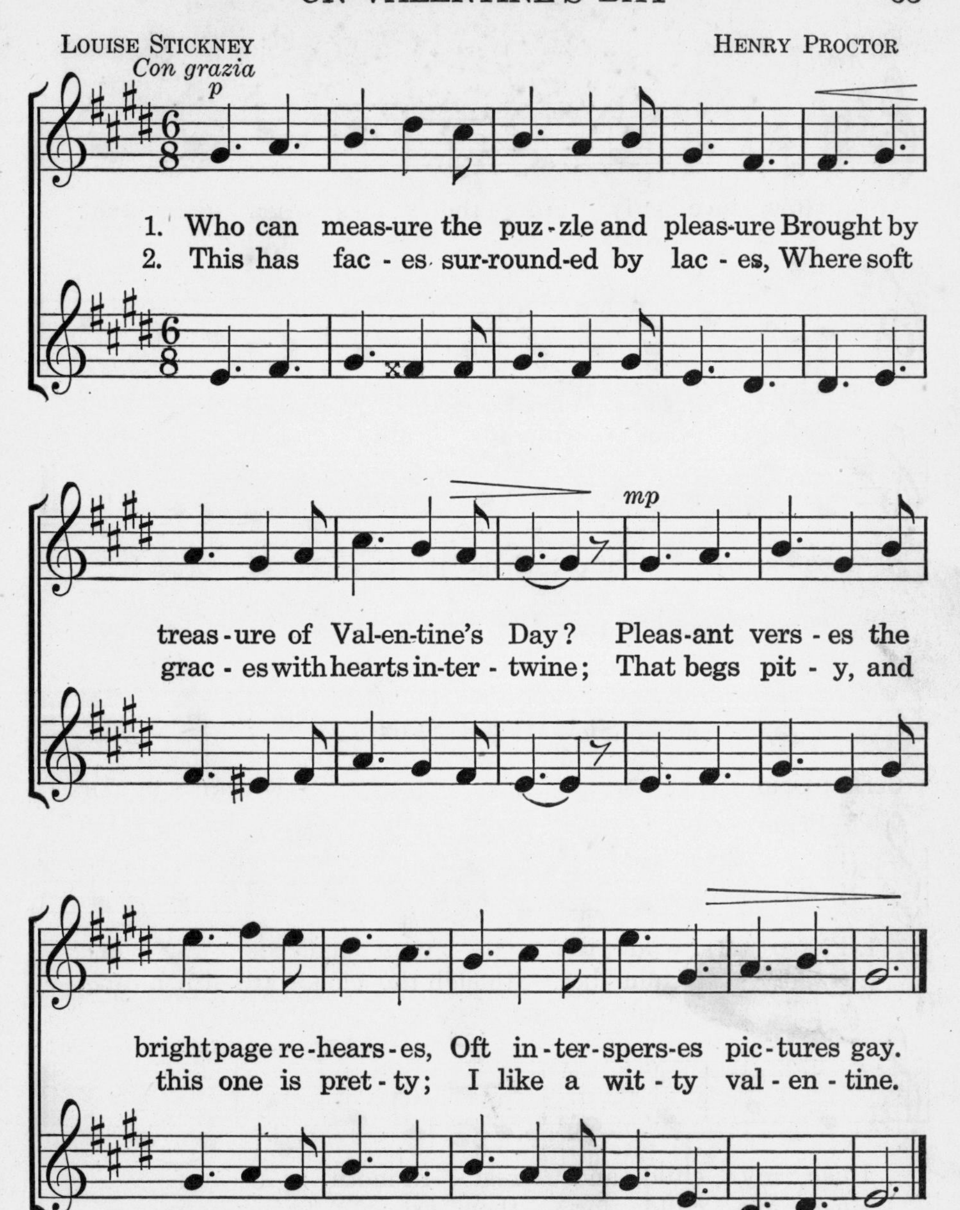

Louise Stickney
Con grazia
p

Henry Proctor

1. Who can meas-ure the puz-zle and pleas-ure Brought by
2. This has fac-es sur-round-ed by lac-es, Where soft

treas-ure of Val-en-tine's Day? Pleas-ant vers-es the
grac-es with hearts in-ter-twine; That begs pit-y, and

bright page re-hears-es, Oft in-ter-spers-es pic-tures gay.
this one is pret-ty; I like a wit-ty val-en-tine.

T

HOW LOVELY ARE THE MESSENGERS

FROM THE BIBLE

Andante con moto

FELIX MENDELSSOHN

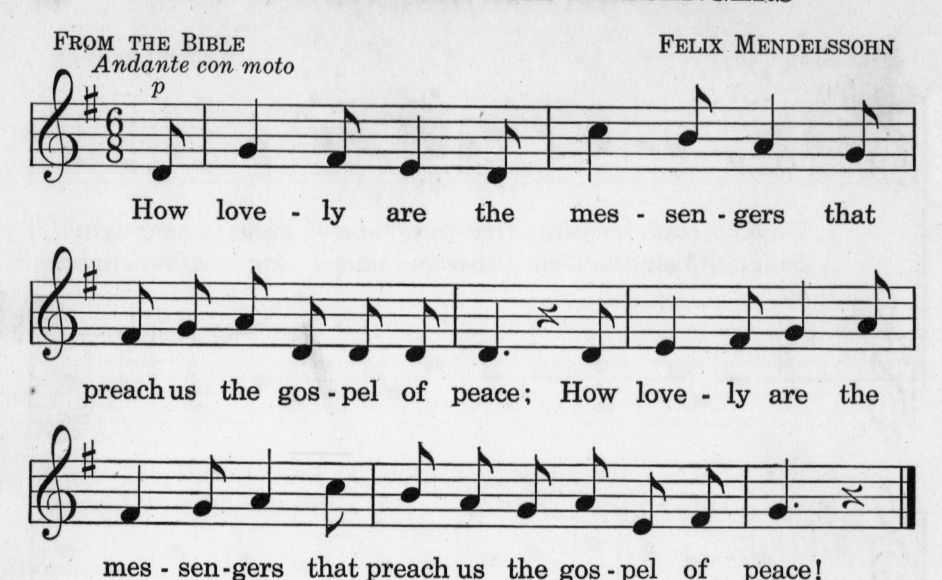

How love - ly are the mes - sen - gers that preach us the gos - pel of peace; How love - ly are the mes - sen - gers that preach us the gos - pel of peace!

SLUMBER SONG

CELIA STANDISH

Andante

ROBERT SCHUMANN

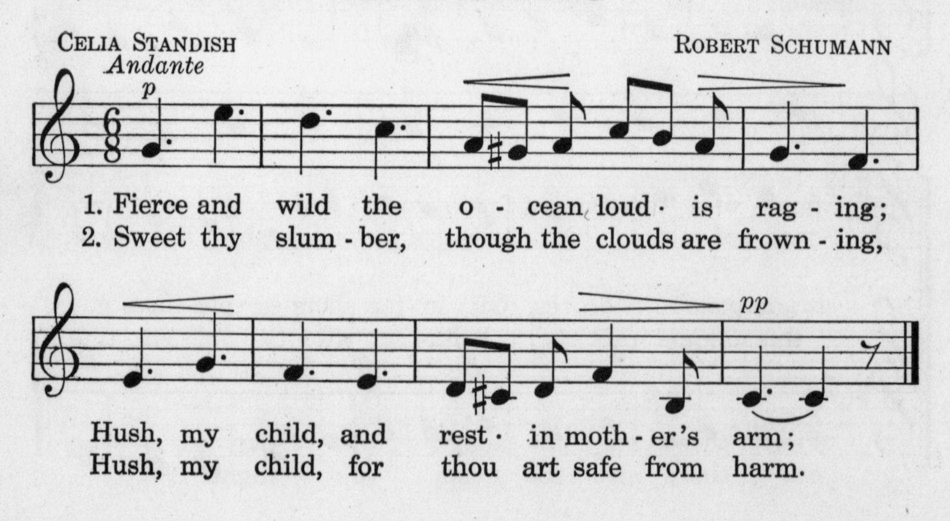

1. Fierce and wild the o - cean loud · is rag - ing;
2. Sweet thy slum - ber, though the clouds are frown - ing,

Hush, my child, and rest · in moth - er's arm;
Hush, my child, for thou art safe from harm.

DAY AND NIGHT

DENIS McCARTHY   MABEL OSBORNE

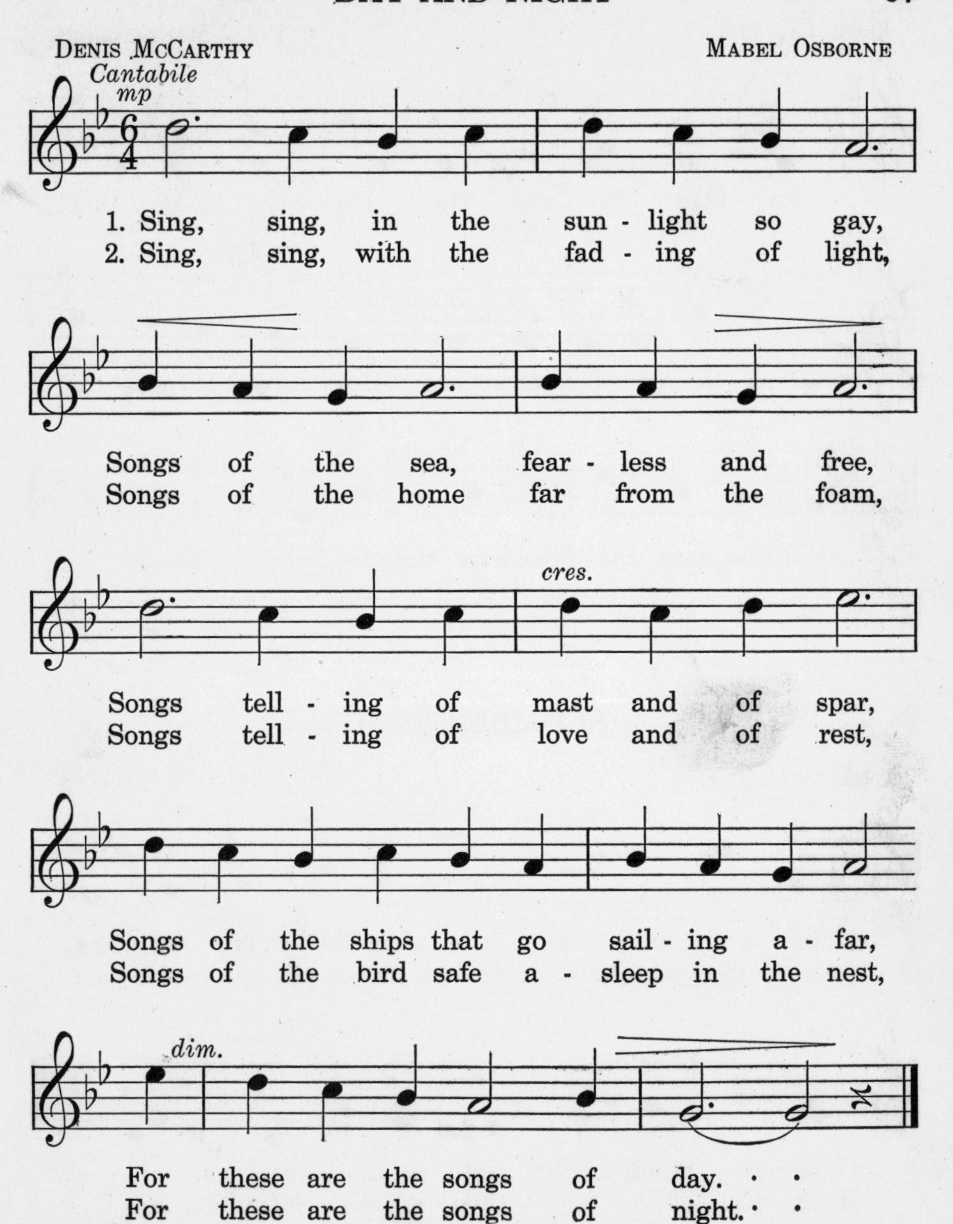

1. Sing, sing, in the sun - light so gay,
2. Sing, sing, with the fad - ing of light,

Songs of the sea, fear - less and free,
Songs of the home far from the foam,

Songs tell - ing of mast and of spar,
Songs tell - ing of love and of rest,

Songs of the ships that go sail - ing a - far,
Songs of the bird safe a - sleep in the nest,

For these are the songs of day.
For these are the songs of night.

THE FOOT RACE

MARY STANHOPE

FRENCH FOLK TUNE

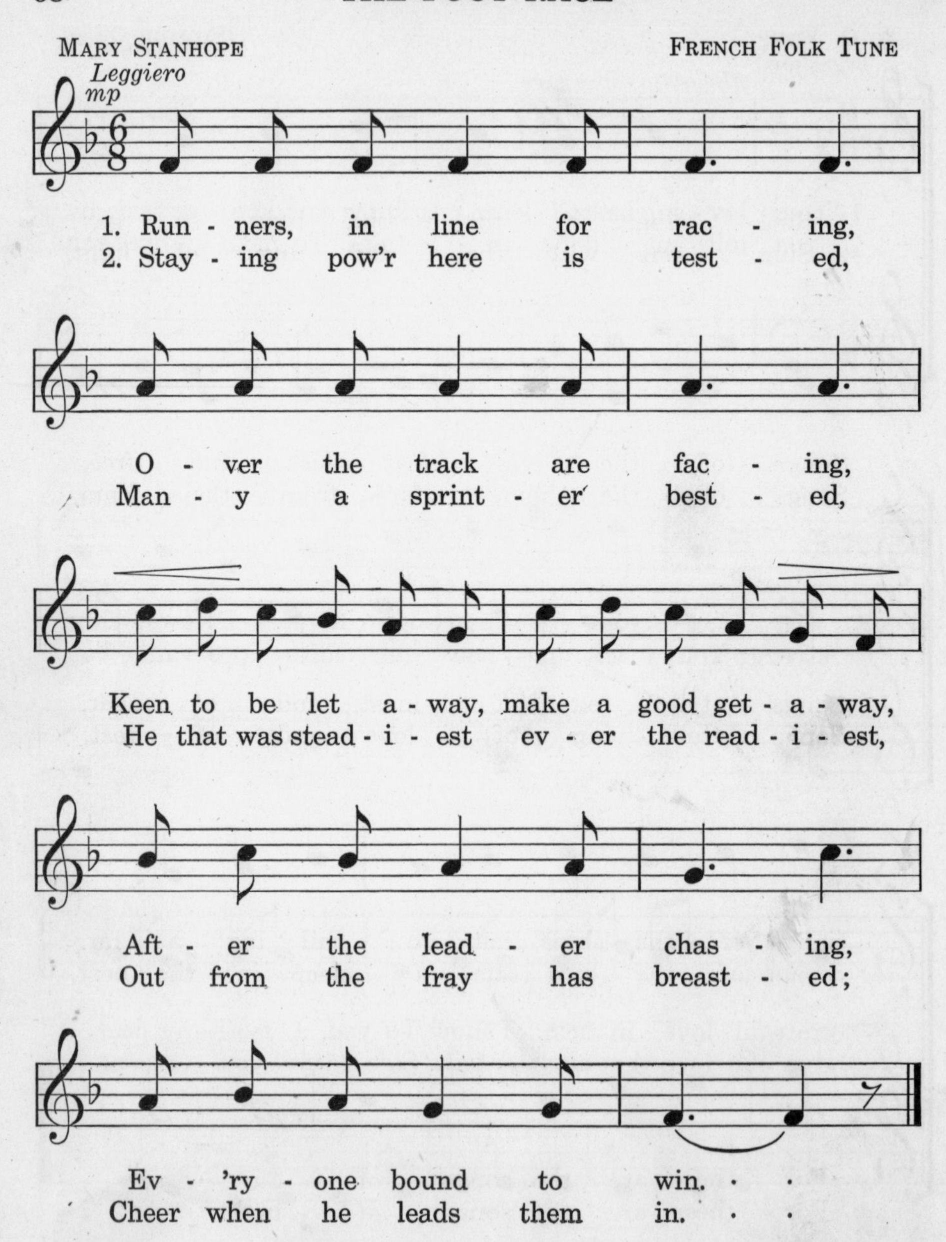

Leggiero
mp

1. Run - ners, in line for rac - ing,
2. Stay - ing pow'r here is test - ed,

O - ver the track are fac - ing,
Man - y a sprint - er best - ed,

Keen to be let a - way, make a good get - a - way,
He that was stead - i - est ev - er the read - i - est,

Aft - er the lead - er chas - ing,
Out from the fray has breast - ed;

Ev - 'ry - one bound to win. · ·
Cheer when he leads them in. · ·

A. O. VINJE
Translated

EDVARD GRIEG

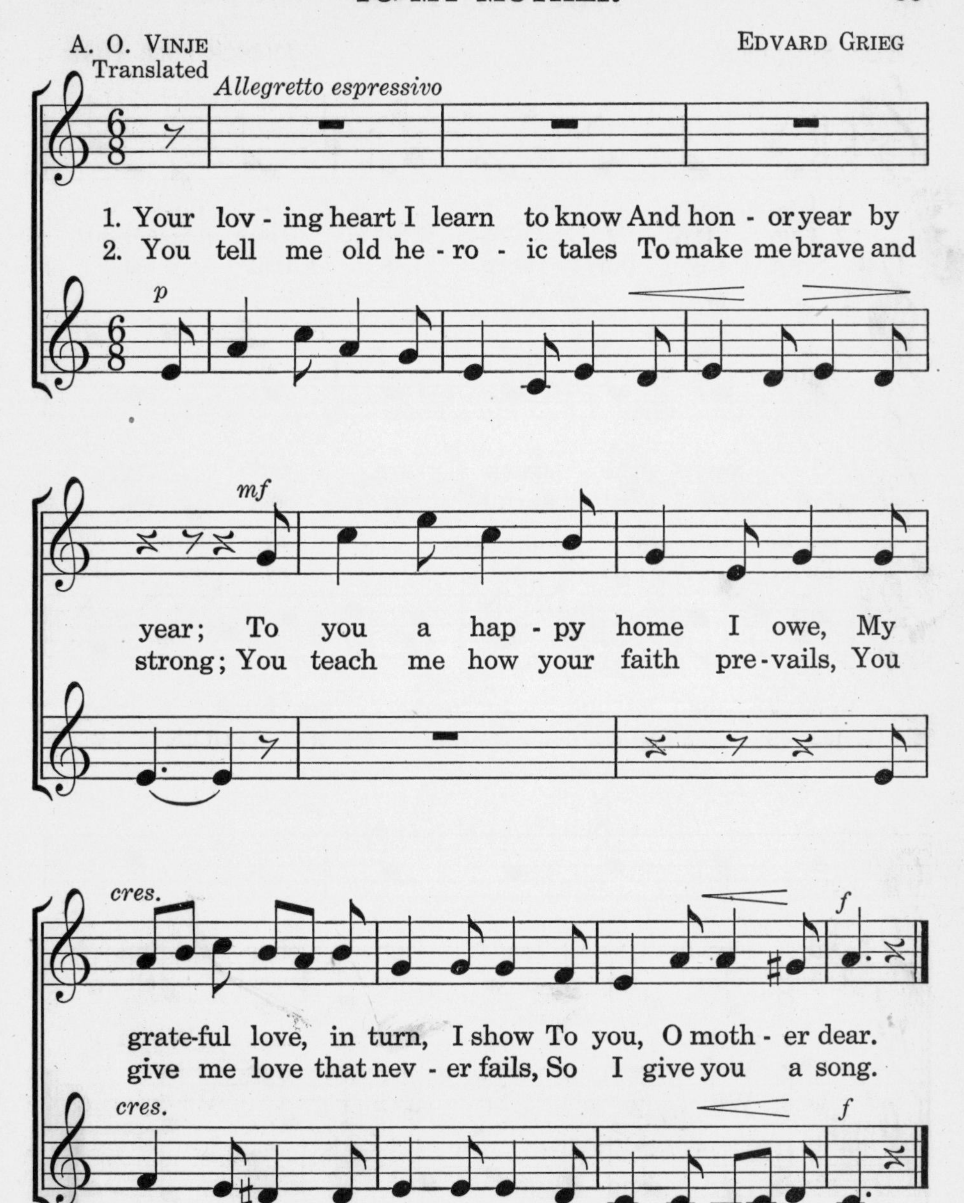

1. Your lov - ing heart I learn   to know And hon - or year by
2. You tell me old he - ro - ic tales To make me brave and

year; To you a hap - py home I owe, My
strong; You teach me how your faith pre - vails, You

grate-ful love, in turn, I show To you, O moth - er dear.
give me love that nev - er fails, So I give you   a song.

COME, DANCE, YE MAIDENS

T. H. MacCrady

Welsh Folk Tune

Dolce

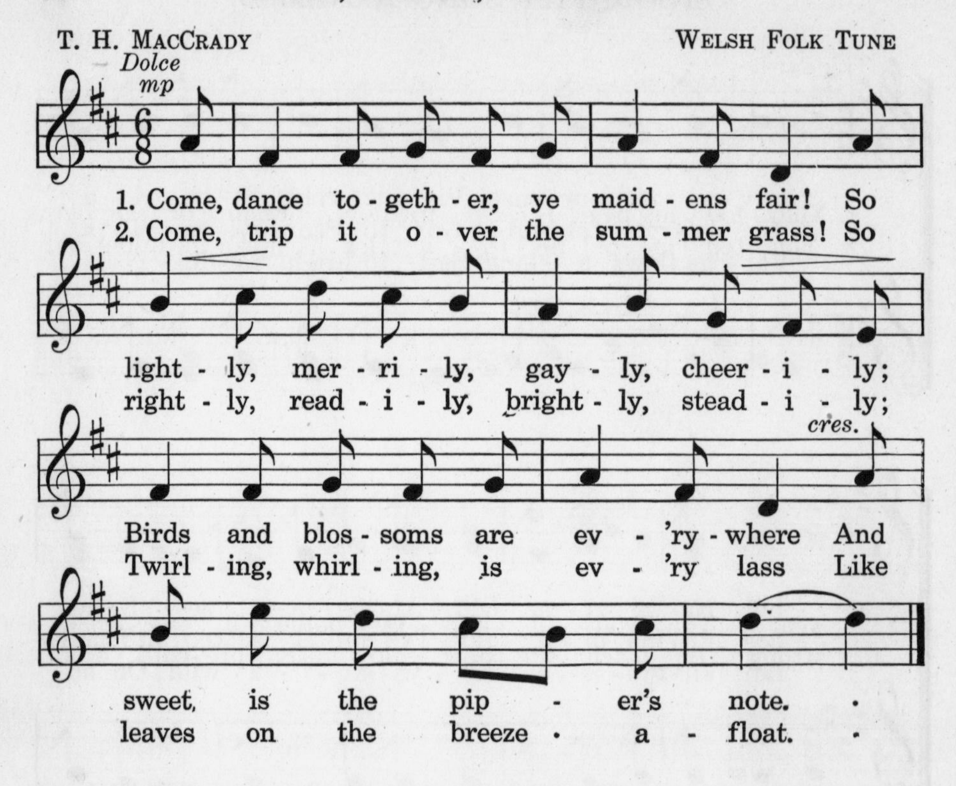

1. Come, dance to-geth-er, ye maid-ens fair! So
2. Come, trip it o-ver the sum-mer grass! So

light-ly, mer-ri-ly, gay-ly, cheer-i-ly;
right-ly, read-i-ly, bright-ly, stead-i-ly;

Birds and blos-soms are ev-'ry-where And
Twirl-ing, whirl-ing, is ev-'ry lass Like

sweet, is the pip - er's note.
leaves on the breeze - a - float.

GEOGRAPHY SONG

M. Louise Baum

French Folk Tune

Con moto

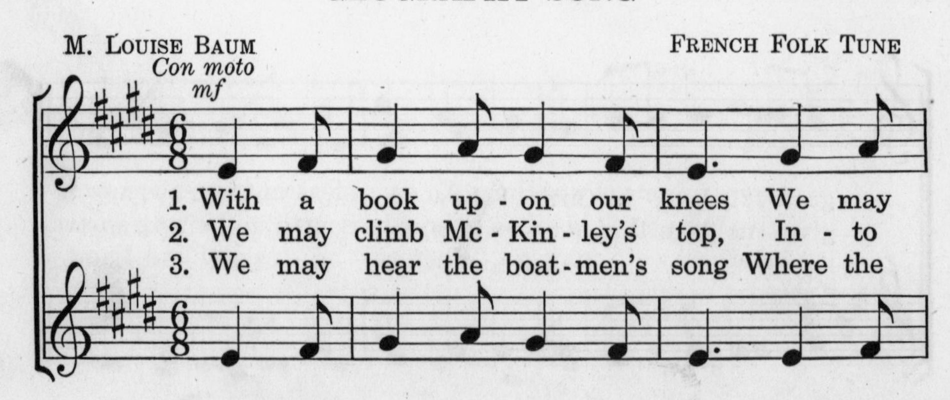

1. With a book up-on our knees We may
2. We may climb Mc-Kin-ley's top, In-to
3. We may hear the boat-men's song Where the

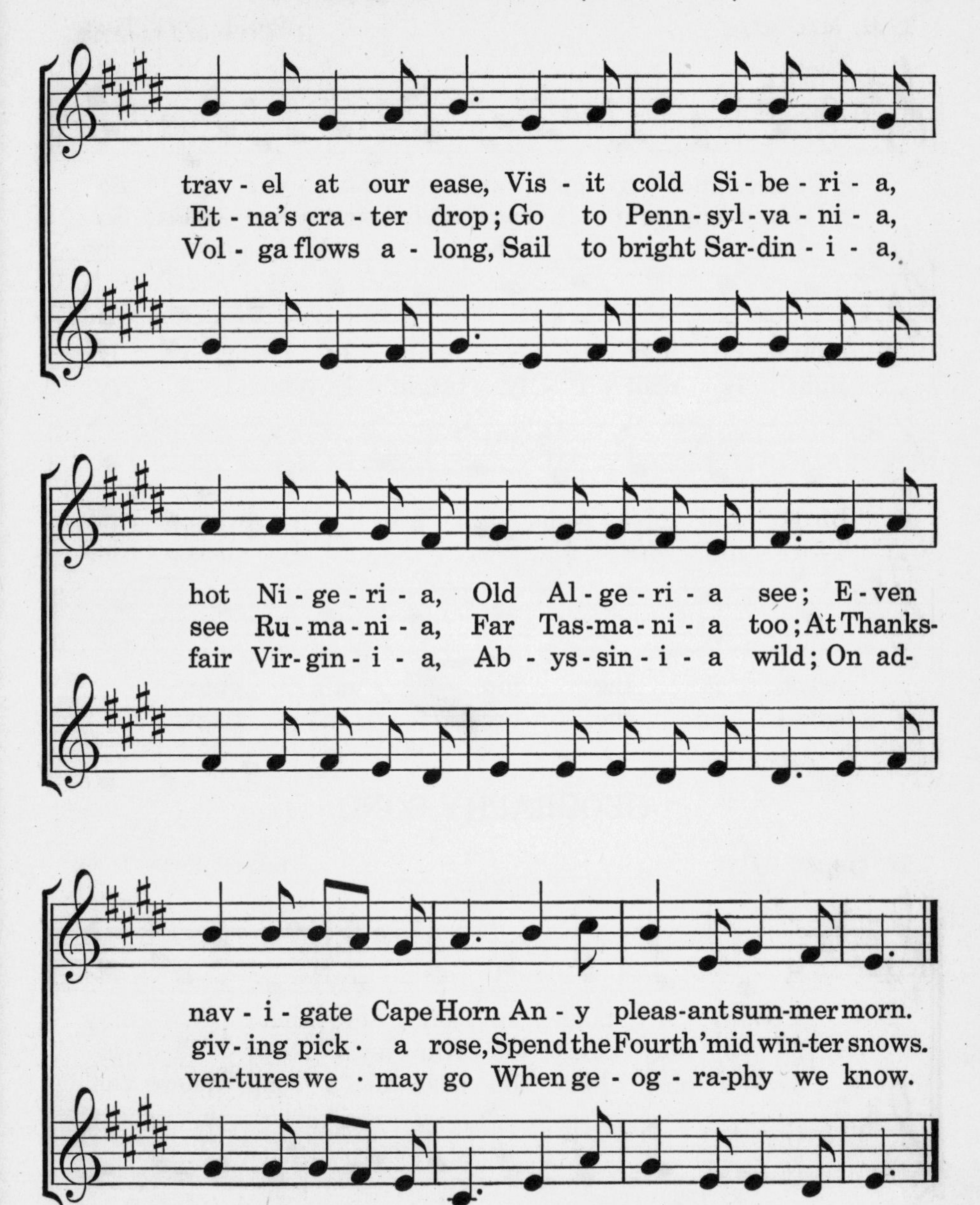
trav - el at our ease, Vis - it cold Si - be - ri - a,
Et - na's cra - ter drop; Go to Penn - syl - va - ni - a,
Vol - ga flows a - long, Sail to bright Sar-din - i - a,
hot Ni - ge - ri - a, Old Al - ge - ri - a see; E - ven
see Ru - ma - ni - a, Far Tas-ma - ni - a too; At Thanks-
fair Vir - gin - i - a, Ab - ys - sin - i - a wild; On ad-
nav - i - gate Cape Horn An - y pleas-ant sum-mer morn.
giv - ing pick - a rose, Spend the Fourth 'mid win-ter snows.
ven-tures we - may go When ge - og - ra-phy we know.

THE MAY PROCESSION

MARGARET CONNOLLY

H. CLOUGH-LEIGHTER

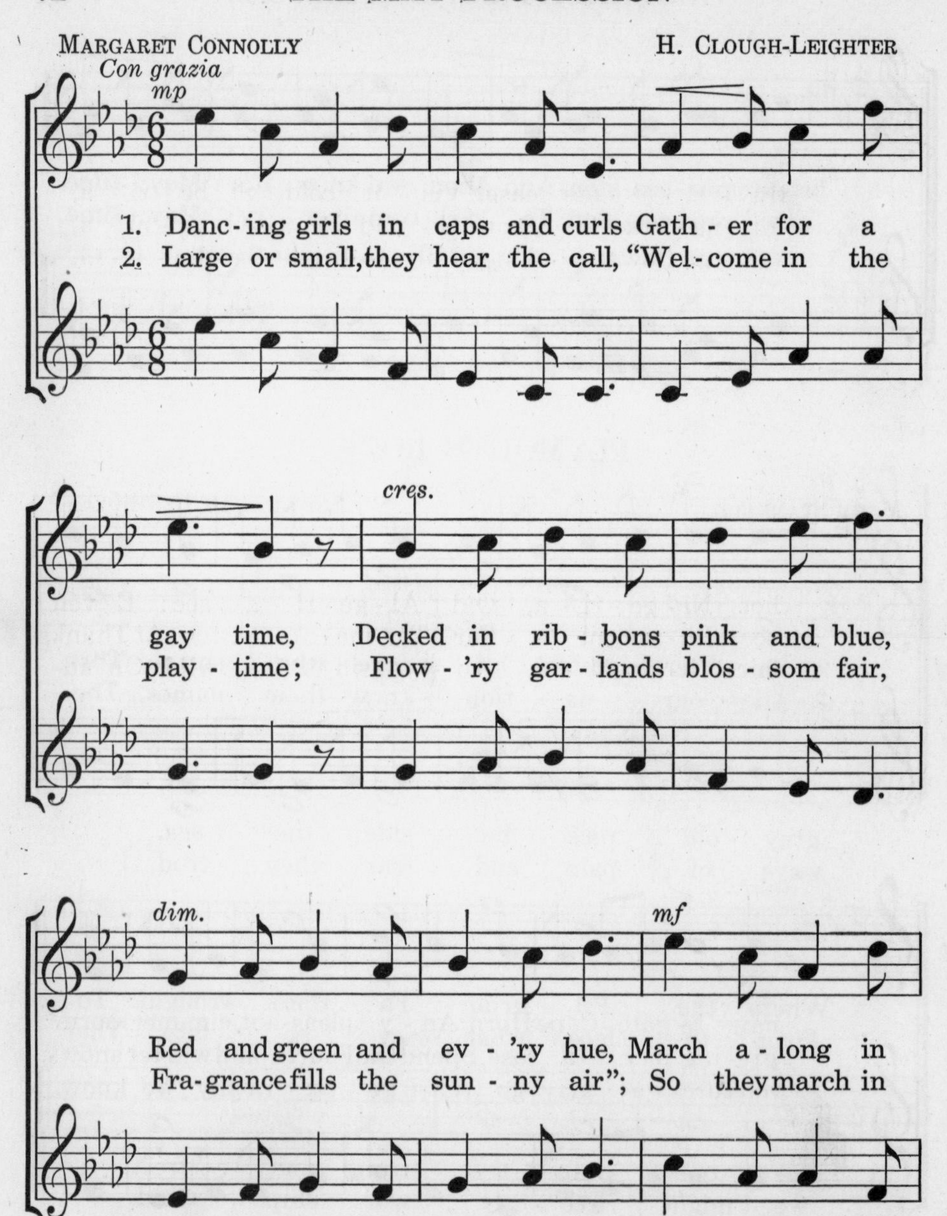

1. Danc-ing girls in caps and curls Gath - er for a
2. Large or small, they hear the call, "Wel - come in the

gay time, Decked in rib - bons pink and blue,
play - time; Flow - 'ry gar - lands blos - som fair,

Red and green and ev - 'ry hue, March a - long in
Fra-grance fills the sun - ny air"; So they march in

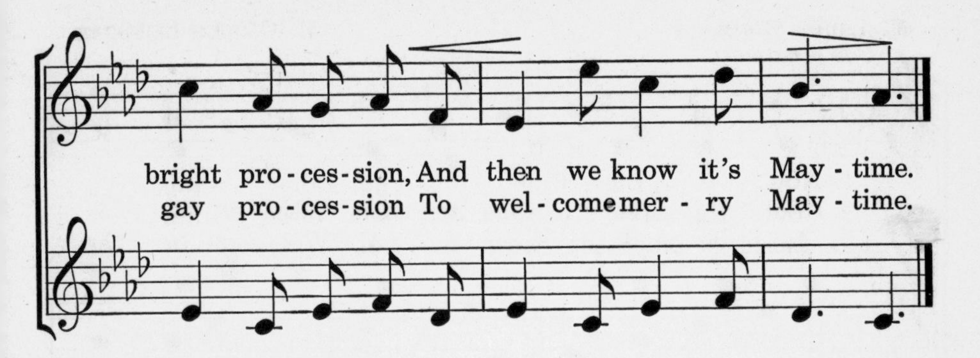

bright pro - ces - sion, And then we know it's May - time.
gay pro - ces - sion To wel - come mer - ry May - time.

PLYMOUTH ROCK

MARY STANHOPE

LUDWIG VAN BEETHOVEN

Maestoso
mf

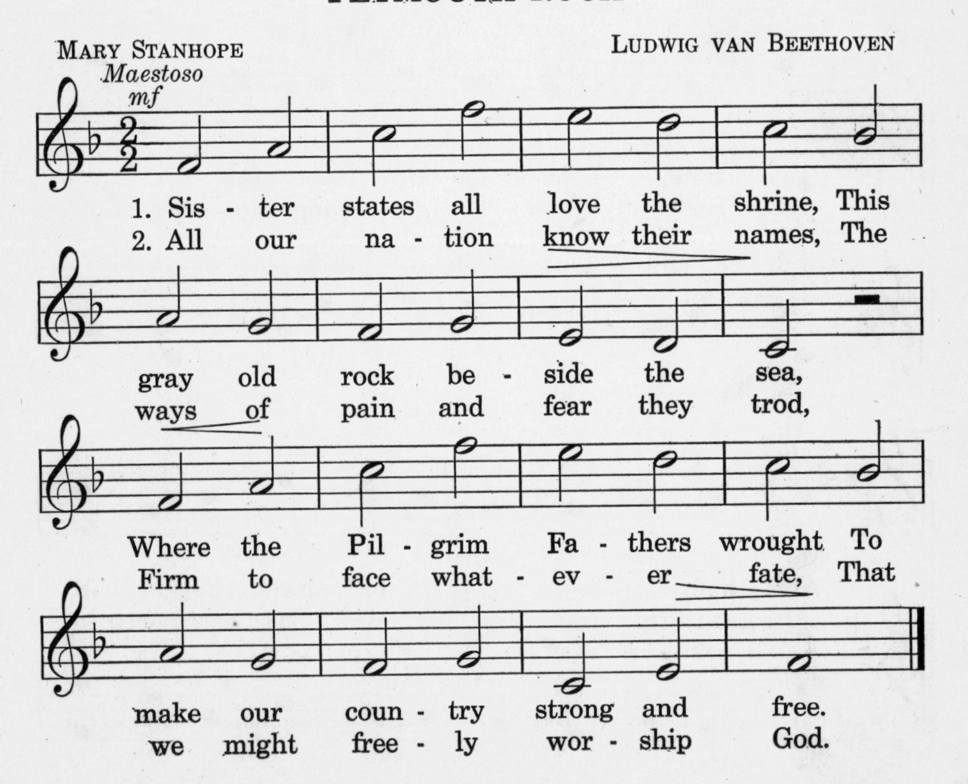

1. Sis - ter states all love the shrine, This
2. All our na - tion know their names, The

gray old rock be - side the sea,
ways of pain and fear they trod,

Where the Pil - grim Fa - thers wrought To
Firm to face what - ev - er fate, That

make our coun - try strong and free.
we might free - ly wor - ship God.

MOTORING

M. Louise Baum

Louis Meyer

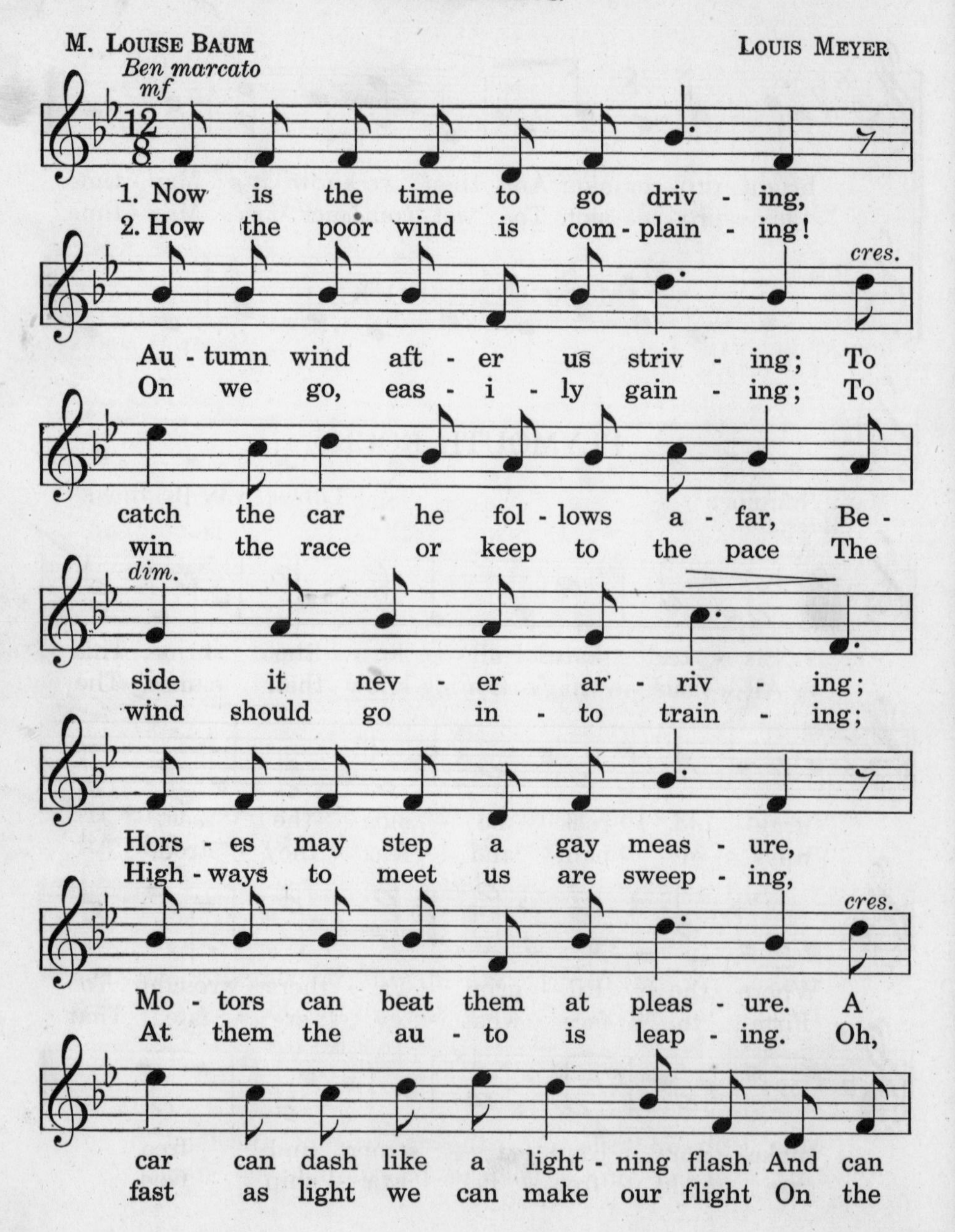

Ben marcato
mf

1. Now is the time to go driv - ing,
2. How the poor wind is com - plain - ing!

cres.

Au - tumn wind aft - er us striv - ing; To
On we go, eas - i - ly gain - ing; To

catch the car he fol - lows a - far, Be -
win the race or keep to the pace The

dim.

side it nev - er ar - riv - ing;
wind should go in - to train - ing;

Hors - es may step a gay meas - ure,
High - ways to meet us are sweep - ing,

cres.

Mo - tors can beat them at pleas - ure. A
At them the au - to is leap - ing. Oh,

car can dash like a light - ning flash And can
fast as light we can make our flight On the

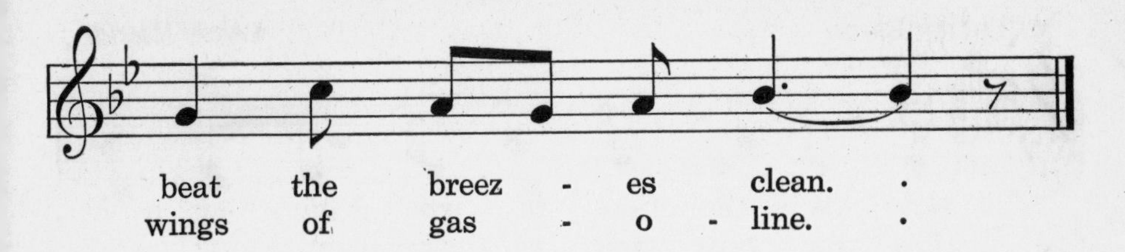

beat   the   breez - es   clean. ·

wings   of   gas - o - line. ·

MARCHING SONG

Robert Brigham   Mabel Osborne

Con brio

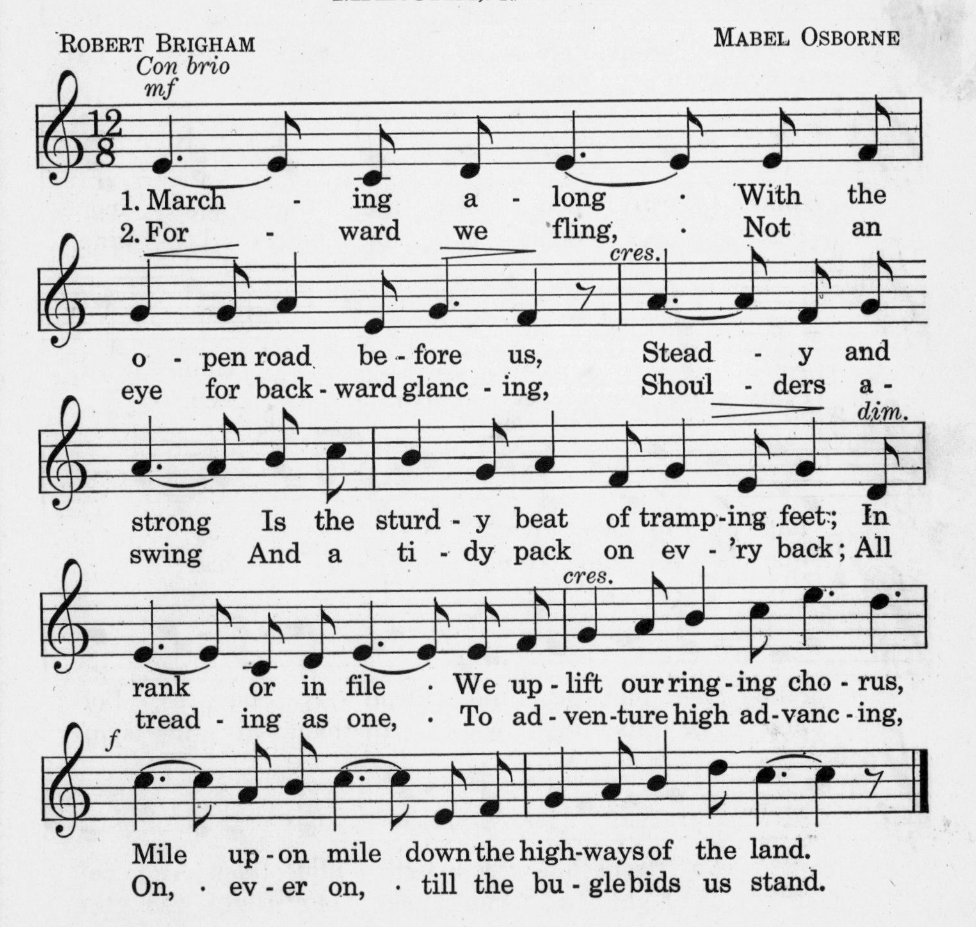

1. March - ing a - long · With the
2. For - ward we fling, · Not an

o - pen road be - fore us, Stead - y and

eye for back - ward glanc - ing, Shoul - ders a -

strong Is the sturd - y beat of tramp-ing feet; In

swing And a ti - dy pack on ev - 'ry back; All

rank or in file · We up - lift our ring-ing cho - rus,

tread - ing as one, · To ad - ven-ture high ad-vanc - ing,

Mile up - on mile down the high-ways of the land.

On, · ev - er on, · till the bu - gle bids us stand.

ON THANKSGIVING DAY

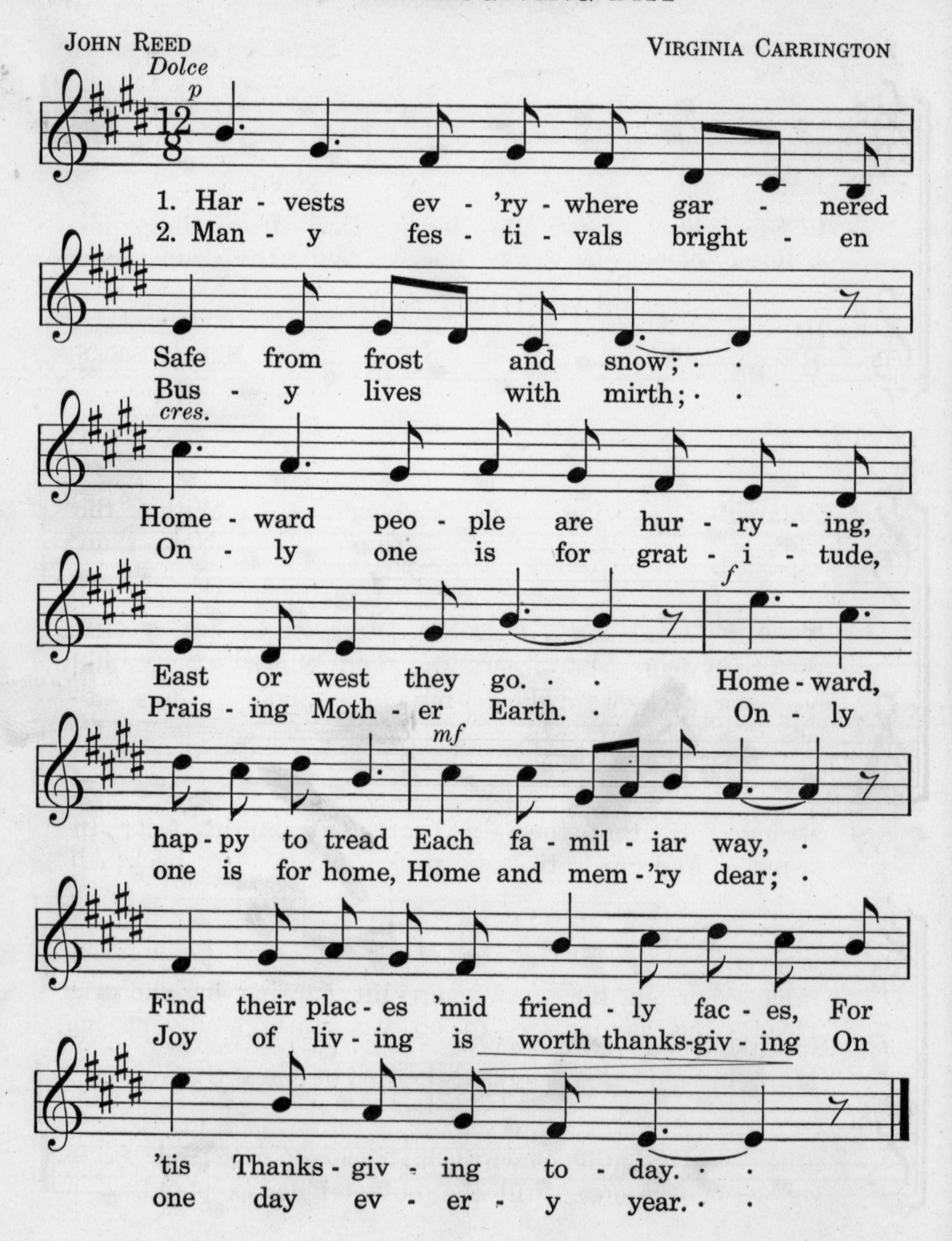

JOHN REED

VIRGINIA CARRINGTON

Dolce

1. Har - vests ev - 'ry - where gar - nered
2. Man - y fes - ti - vals bright - en

Safe from frost and snow; · ·
Bus - y lives with mirth; · ·

Home - ward peo - ple are hur - ry - ing,
On - ly one is for grat - i - tude,

East or west they go. · · Home - ward,
Prais - ing Moth - er Earth. · On - ly

hap - py to tread Each fa - mil - iar way, ·
one is for home, Home and mem - 'ry dear; ·

Find their plac - es 'mid friend - ly fac - es, For
Joy of liv - ing is worth thanks - giv - ing On

'tis Thanks - giv - ing to - day. · ·
one day ev - er - y year. · ·

EARLY RISERS

STICKNEY-CONNOLLY

RUTH McCONN SPENCER

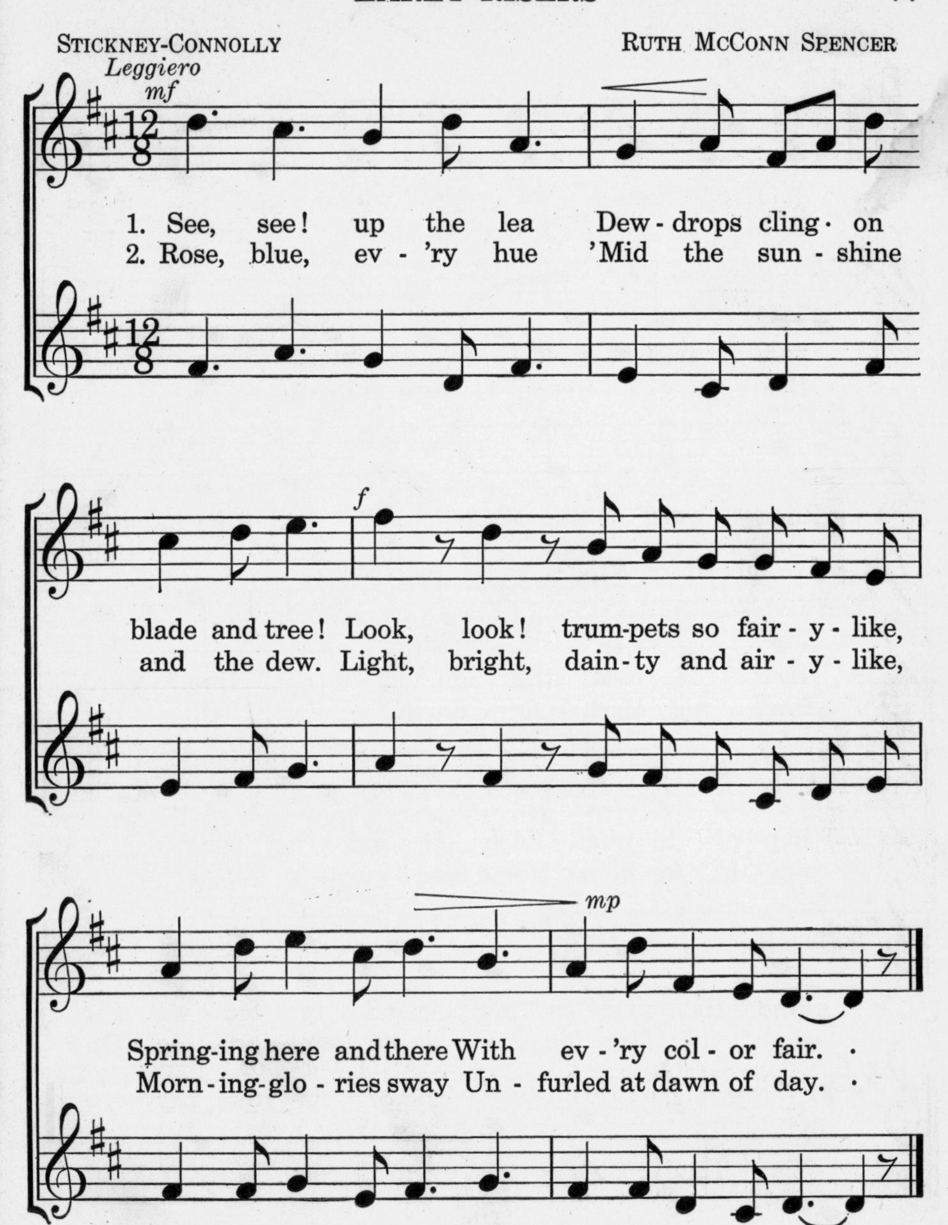

1. See, see! up the lea Dew-drops cling· on
2. Rose, blue, ev-'ry hue 'Mid the sun-shine

blade and tree! Look, look! trum-pets so fair-y-like,
and the dew. Light, bright, dain-ty and air-y-like,

Spring-ing here and there With ev-'ry col-or fair. ·
Morn-ing-glo-ries sway Un-furled at dawn of day. ·

RALLY

STANHOPE-MacCRADY

E. W. NEWTON

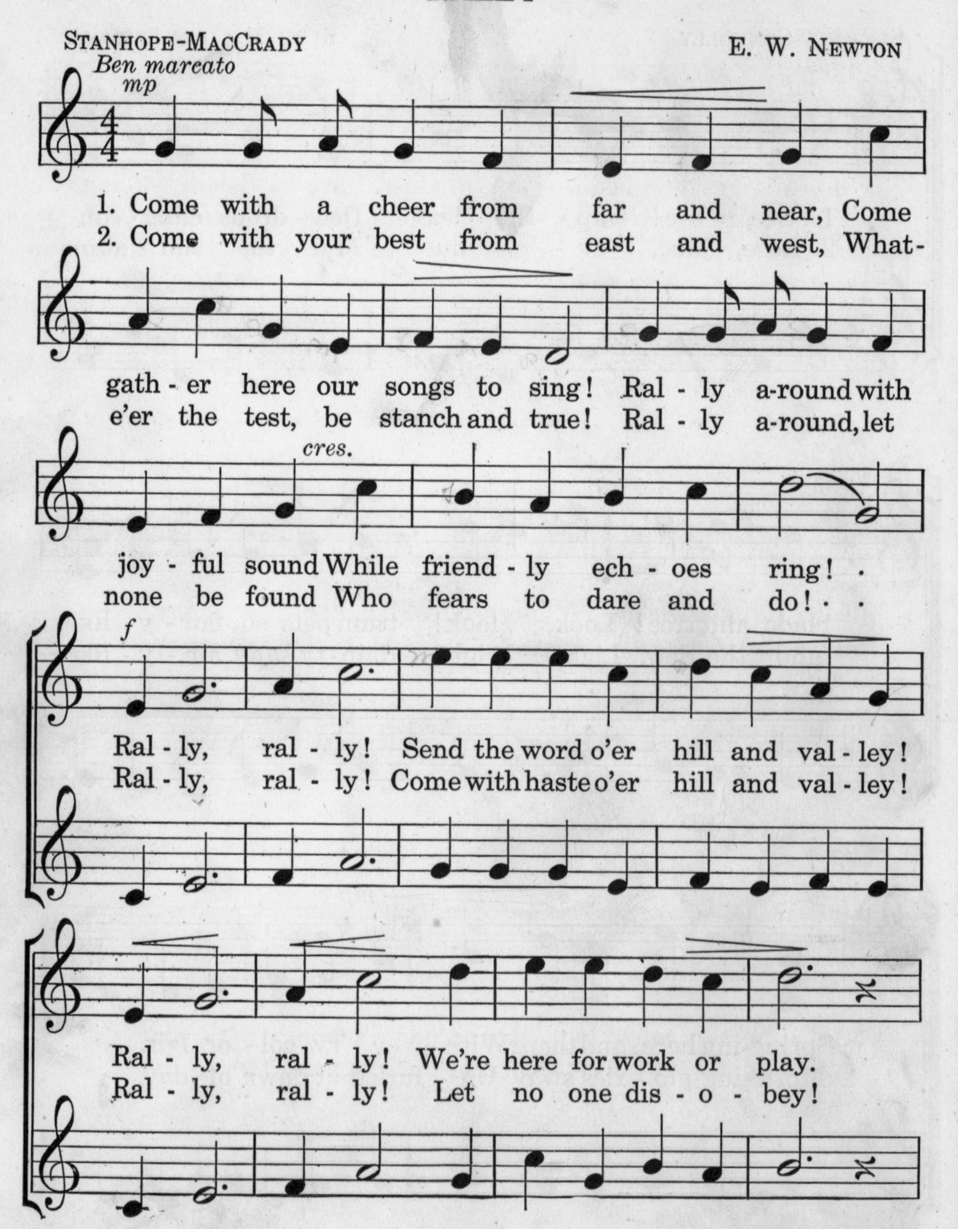

Ben mareato

1. Come with a cheer from far and near, Come
2. Come with your best from east and west, What-

gath-er here our songs to sing! Ral-ly a-round with
e'er the test, be stanch and true! Ral-ly a-round, let

cres.

joy-ful sound While friend-ly ech-oes ring! .
none be found Who fears to dare and do! . .

Ral-ly, ral-ly! Send the word o'er hill and val-ley!
Ral-ly, ral-ly! Come with haste o'er hill and val-ley!

Ral-ly, ral-ly! We're here for work or play.
Ral-ly, ral-ly! Let no one dis-o-bey!

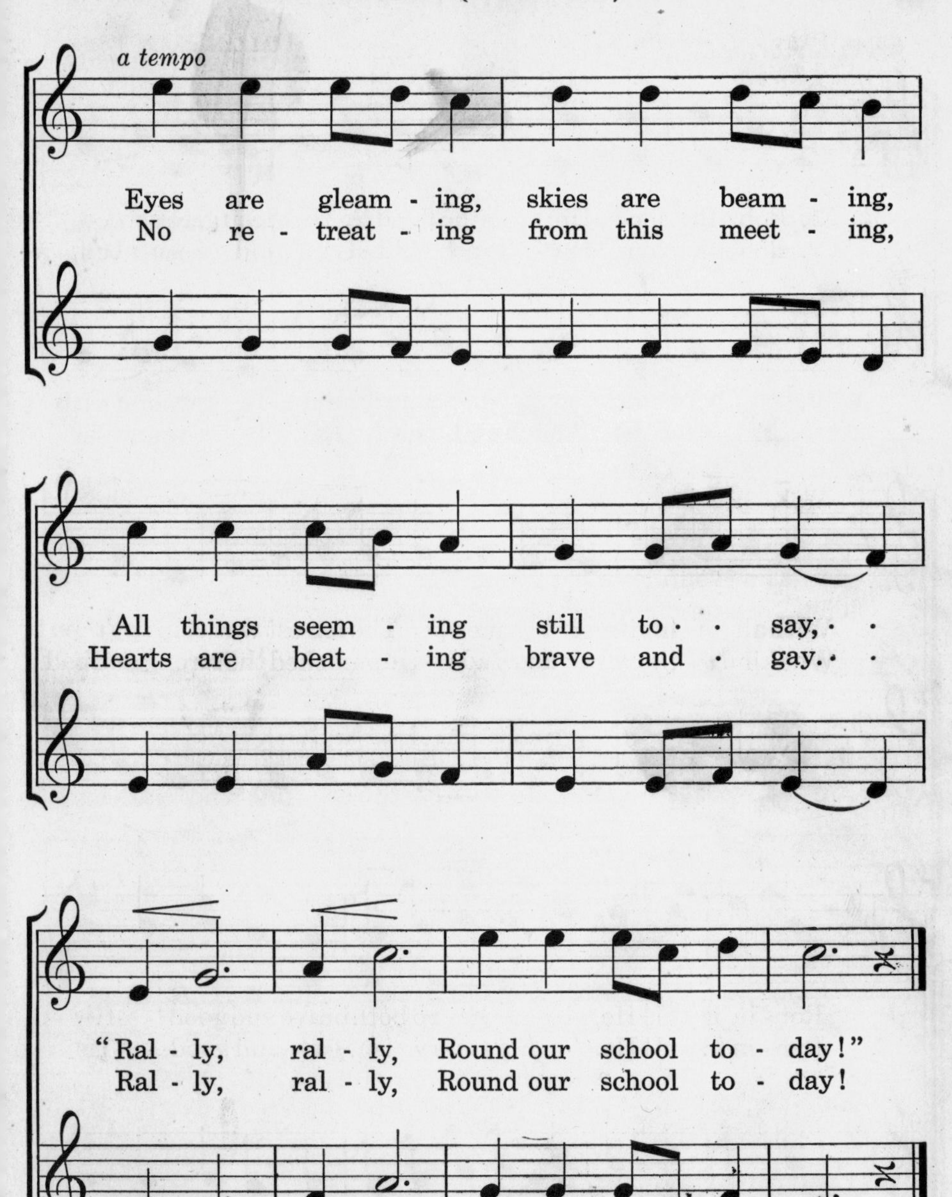

a tempo

Eyes   are   gleam - ing,   skies   are   beam - ing,
No   re - treat - ing   from   this   meet - ing,

All   things   seem - ing   still   to · · say, · ·
Hearts   are   beat - ing   brave   and · gay. · ·

"Ral - ly,   ral - ly,   Round our   school   to - day!"
Ral - ly,   ral - ly,   Round our   school   to - day!

ROBIN HOOD

ABBIE FARWELL BROWN

ITALIAN FOLK TUNE

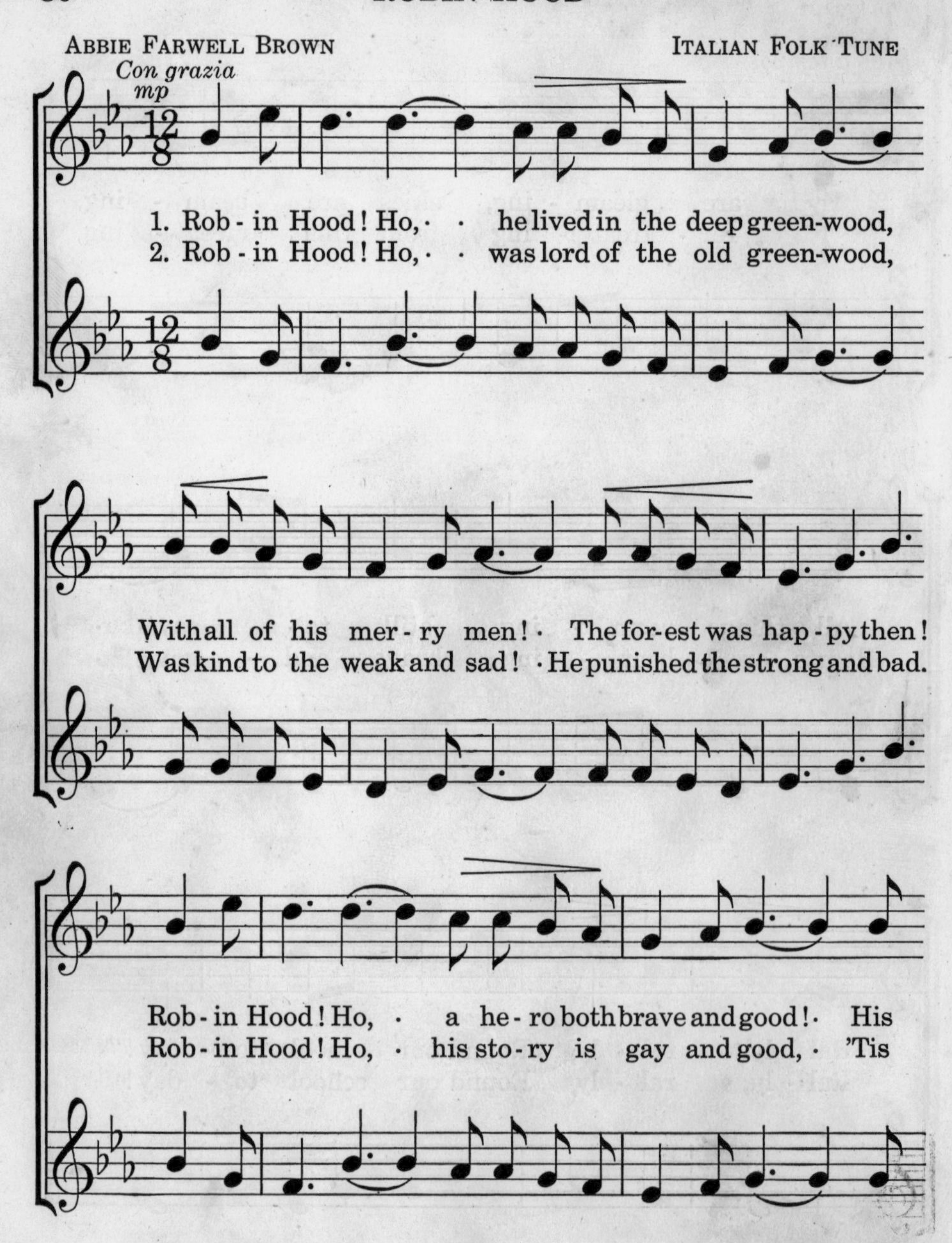

Con grazia
mp

1. Rob - in Hood! Ho, · · he lived in the deep green-wood,
2. Rob - in Hood! Ho, · · was lord of the old green-wood,

With all of his mer - ry men! · The for - est was hap - py then!
Was kind to the weak and sad! · He punished the strong and bad.

Rob - in Hood! Ho, · a he - ro both brave and good! · His
Rob - in Hood! Ho, · his sto - ry is gay and good, · 'Tis

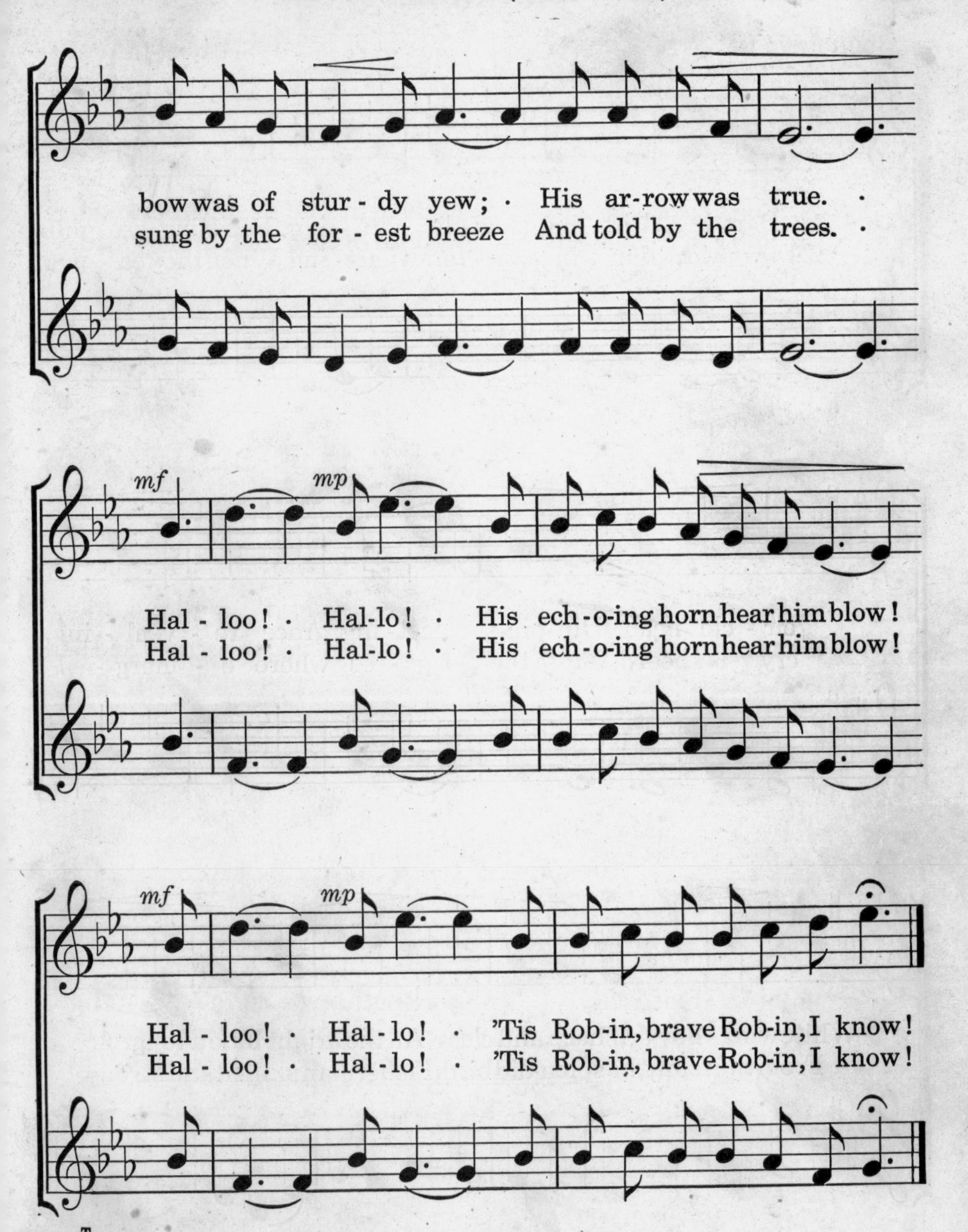

bow was of stur - dy yew; · His ar - row was true. ·
sung by the for - est breeze And told by the trees. ·

Hal - loo! · Hal - lo! · His ech - o - ing horn hear him blow!
Hal - loo! · Hal - lo! · His ech - o - ing horn hear him blow!

Hal - loo! · Hal - lo! · 'Tis Rob - in, brave Rob - in, I know!
Hal - loo! · Hal - lo! · 'Tis Rob - in, brave Rob - in, I know!

SEA GULLS

JOHN REED

SPENCER-LEAVITT

Cantabile

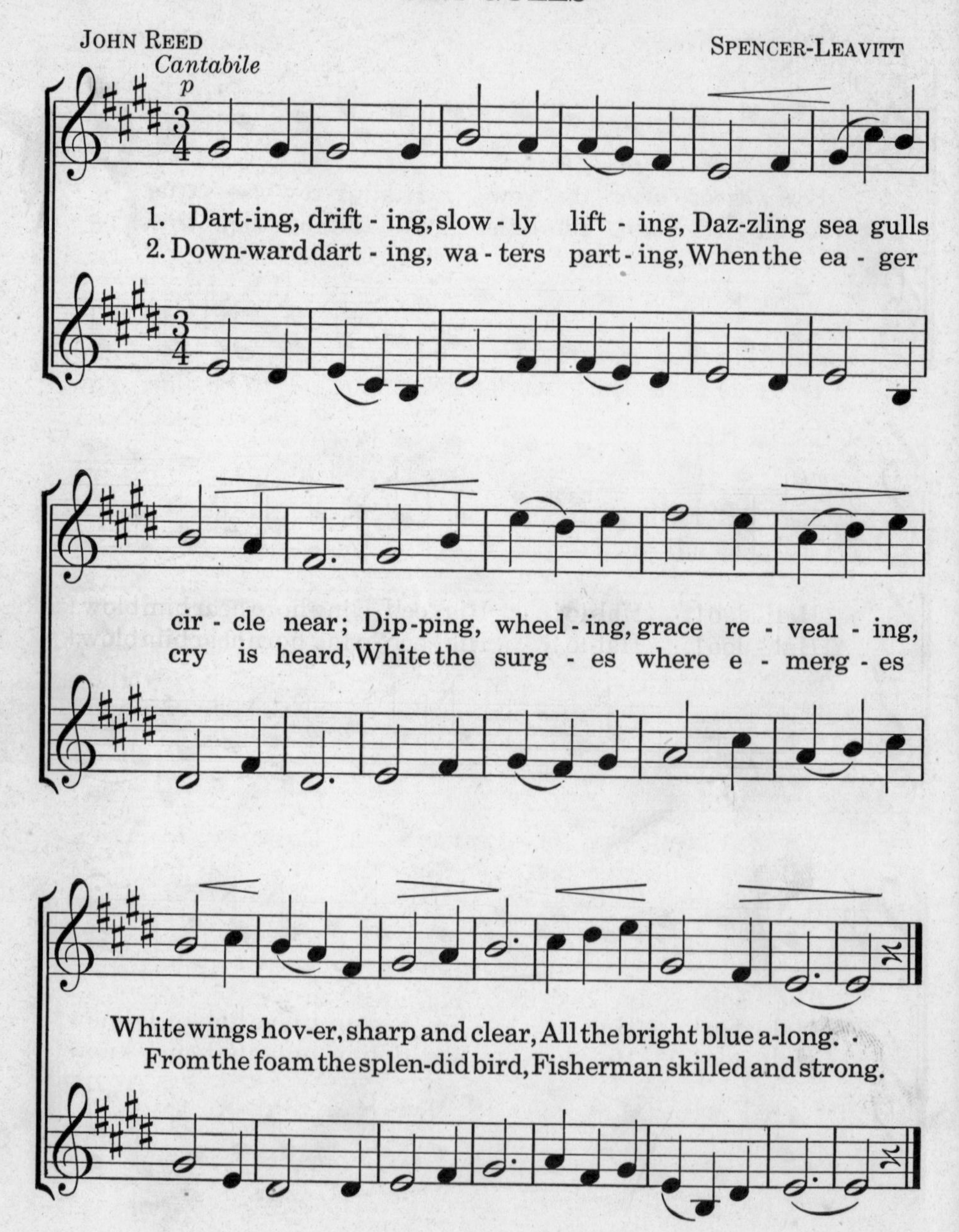

1. Dart-ing, drift - ing, slow - ly   lift - ing, Daz-zling sea gulls
2. Down-ward dart - ing, wa - ters   part - ing, When the ea - ger

cir - cle near; Dip-ping, wheel - ing, grace re - veal - ing,
cry   is heard, White the surg - es where e - merg - es

White wings hov-er, sharp and clear, All the bright blue a-long.
From the foam the splen-did bird, Fisherman skilled and strong.

ABBIE FARWELL BROWN

ITALIAN FOLK TUNE

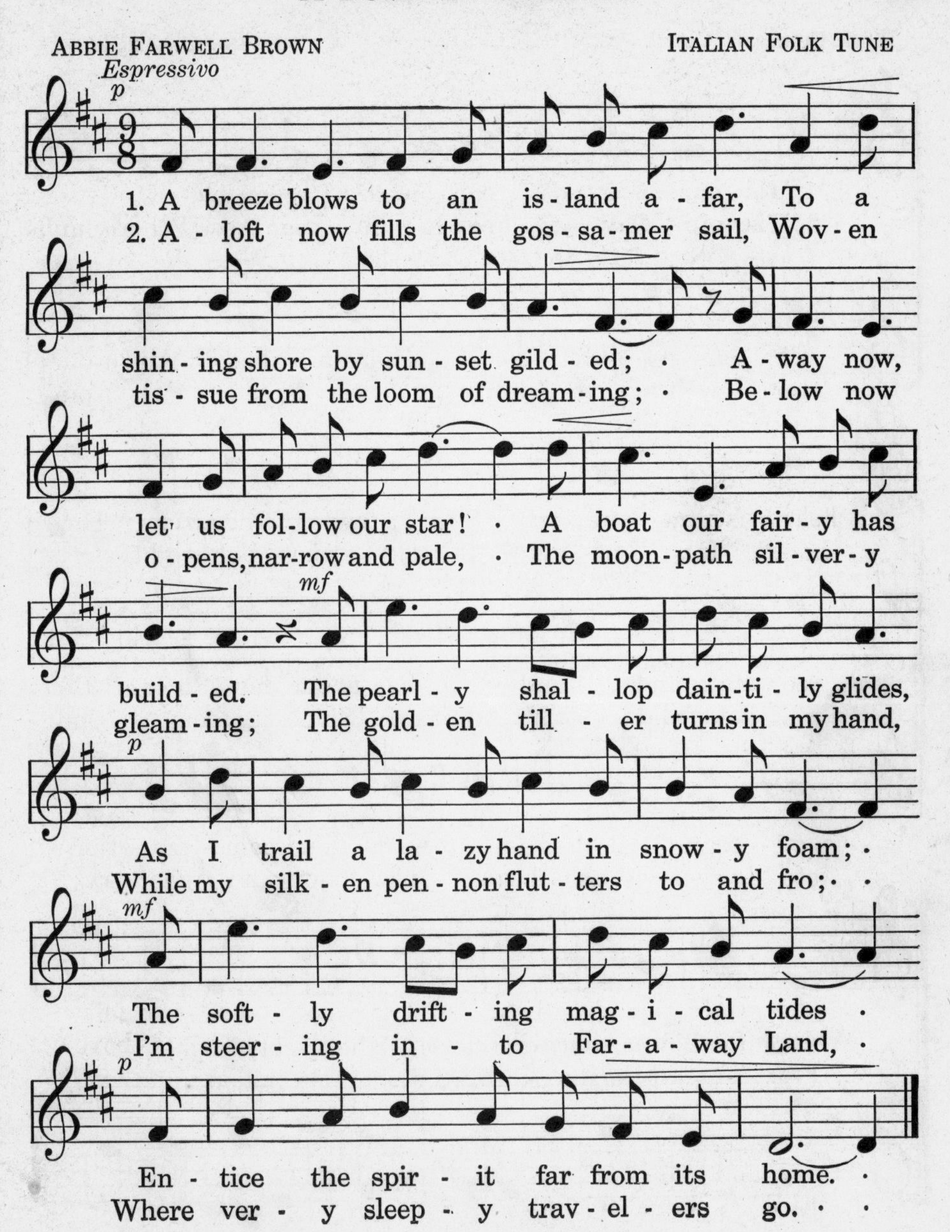

1. A breeze blows to an is-land a-far, To a
2. A-loft now fills the gos-sa-mer sail, Wov-en

shin-ing shore by sun-set gild-ed; · A-way now,
tis-sue from the loom of dream-ing; · Be-low now

let us fol-low our star! · A boat our fair-y has
o-pens, nar-row and pale, · The moon-path sil-ver-y

build-ed. The pearl-y shal-lop dain-ti-ly glides,
gleam-ing; The gold-en till-er turns in my hand,

As I trail a la-zy hand in snow-y foam; ·
While my silk-en pen-non flut-ters to and fro; · ·

The soft-ly drift-ing mag-i-cal tides ·
I'm steer-ing in-to Far-a-way Land, ·

En-tice the spir-it far from its home. · ·
Where ver-y sleep-y trav-el-ers go. · ·

FLAG DAY

Kate Forman

French Folk Tune

Con spirito

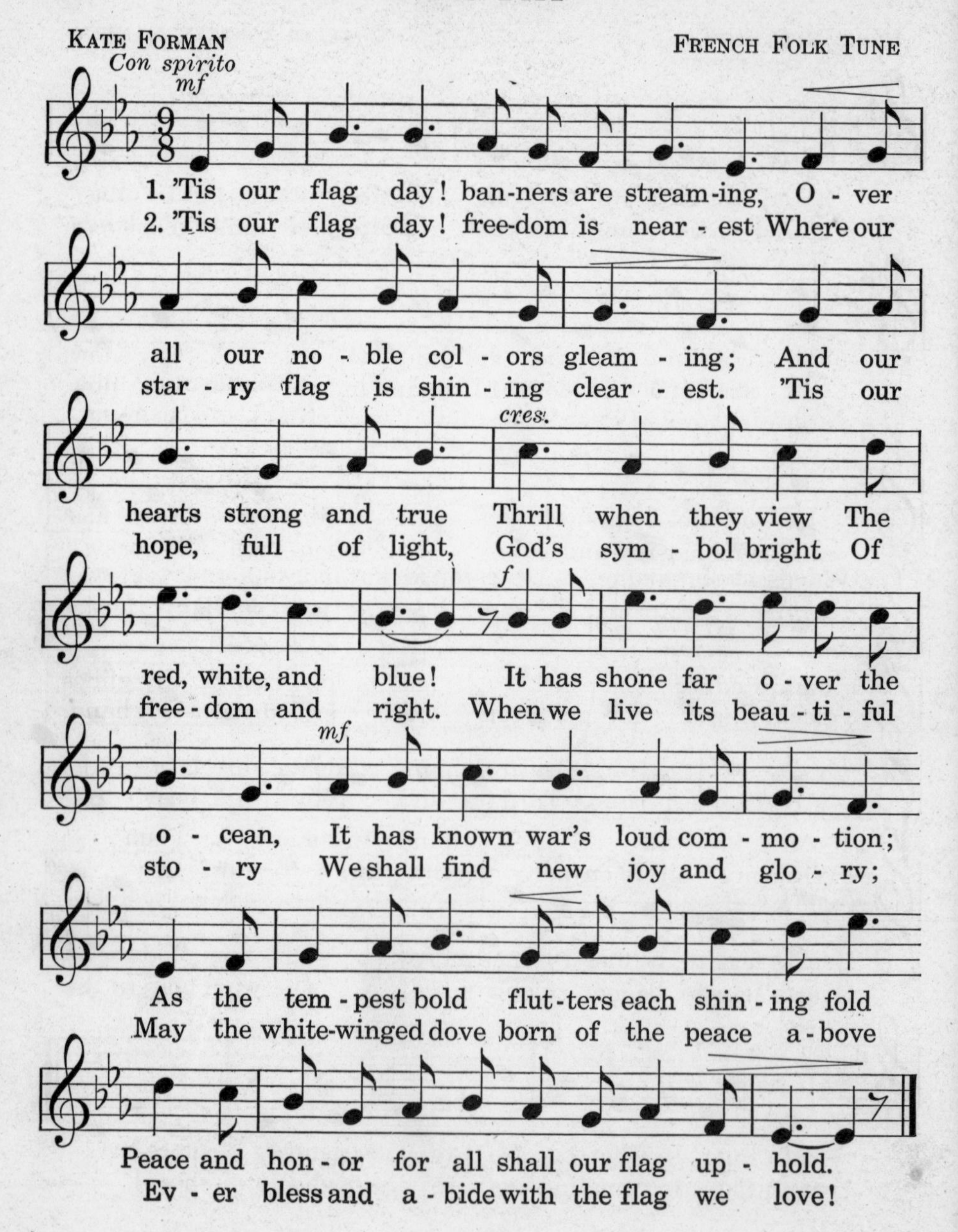

1. 'Tis our flag day! ban-ners are stream-ing, O - ver
2. 'Tis our flag day! free-dom is near - est Where our

all our no - ble col - ors gleam - ing; And our
star - ry flag is shin - ing clear - est. 'Tis our

hearts strong and true Thrill when they view The
hope, full of light, God's sym - bol bright Of

red, white, and blue! It has shone far o - ver the
free - dom and right. When we live its beau - ti - ful

o - cean, It has known war's loud com - mo - tion;
sto - ry We shall find new joy and glo - ry;

As the tem - pest bold flut-ters each shin - ing fold
May the white-winged dove born of the peace a - bove

Peace and hon - or for all shall our flag up - hold.
Ev - er bless and a - bide with the flag we love!

IN FROM THE SEA

DENIS MCCARTHY

CHARLES FONTEYN MANNEY

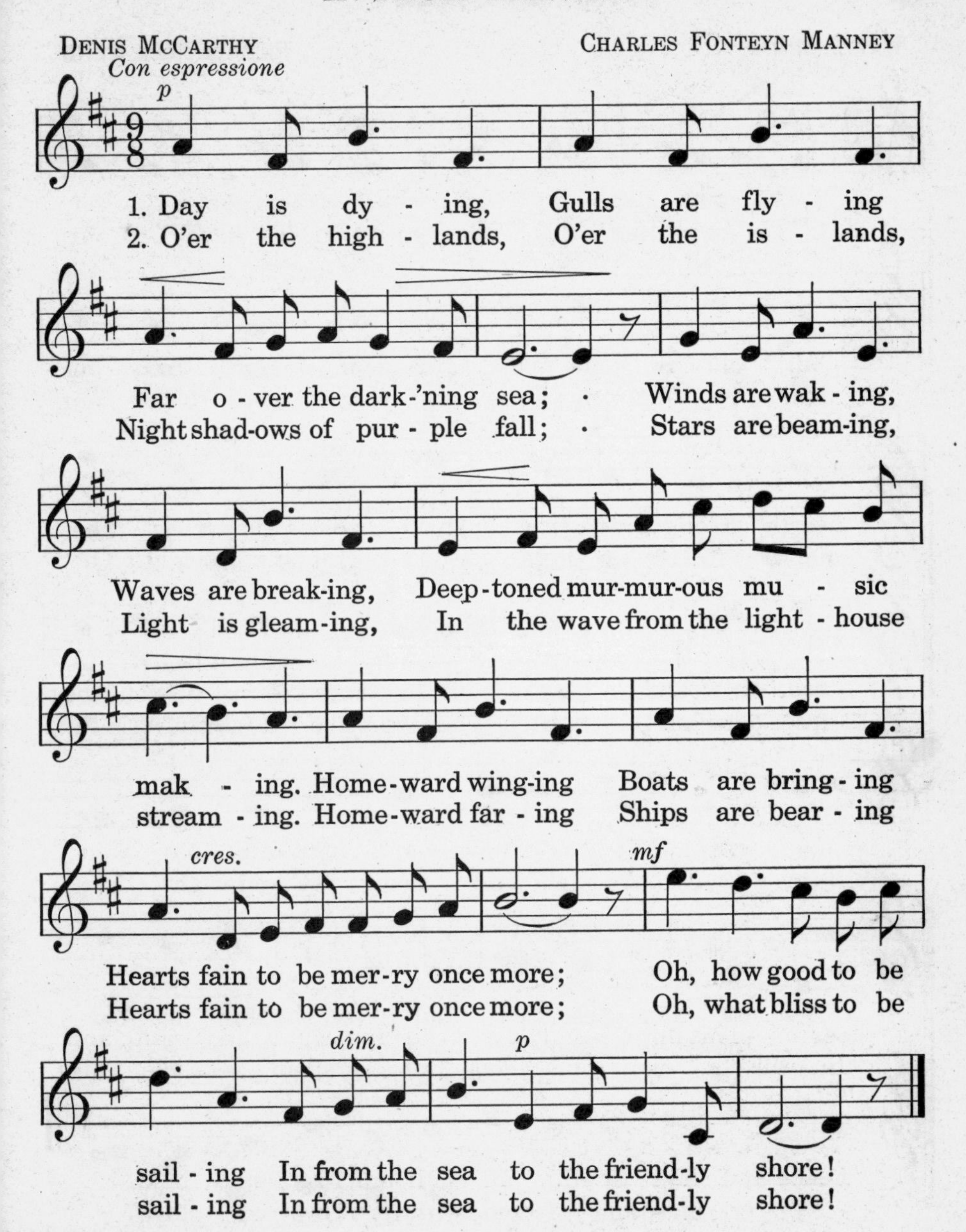

Con espressione

1. Day is dy - ing, Gulls are fly - ing
2. O'er the high - lands, O'er the is - lands,

Far o - ver the dark-'ning sea; · Winds are wak - ing,
Night shad-ows of pur - ple fall; · Stars are beam-ing,

Waves are break-ing, Deep-toned mur-mur-ous mu - sic
Light is gleam-ing, In the wave from the light - house

mak - ing. Home-ward wing-ing Boats are bring - ing
stream - ing. Home-ward far - ing Ships are bear - ing

Hearts fain to be mer-ry once more; Oh, how good to be
Hearts fain to be mer-ry once more; Oh, what bliss to be

sail - ing In from the sea to the friend-ly shore!
sail - ing In from the sea to the friend-ly shore!

COLUMBUS

Abbie Farwell Brown

Miner-Streeter

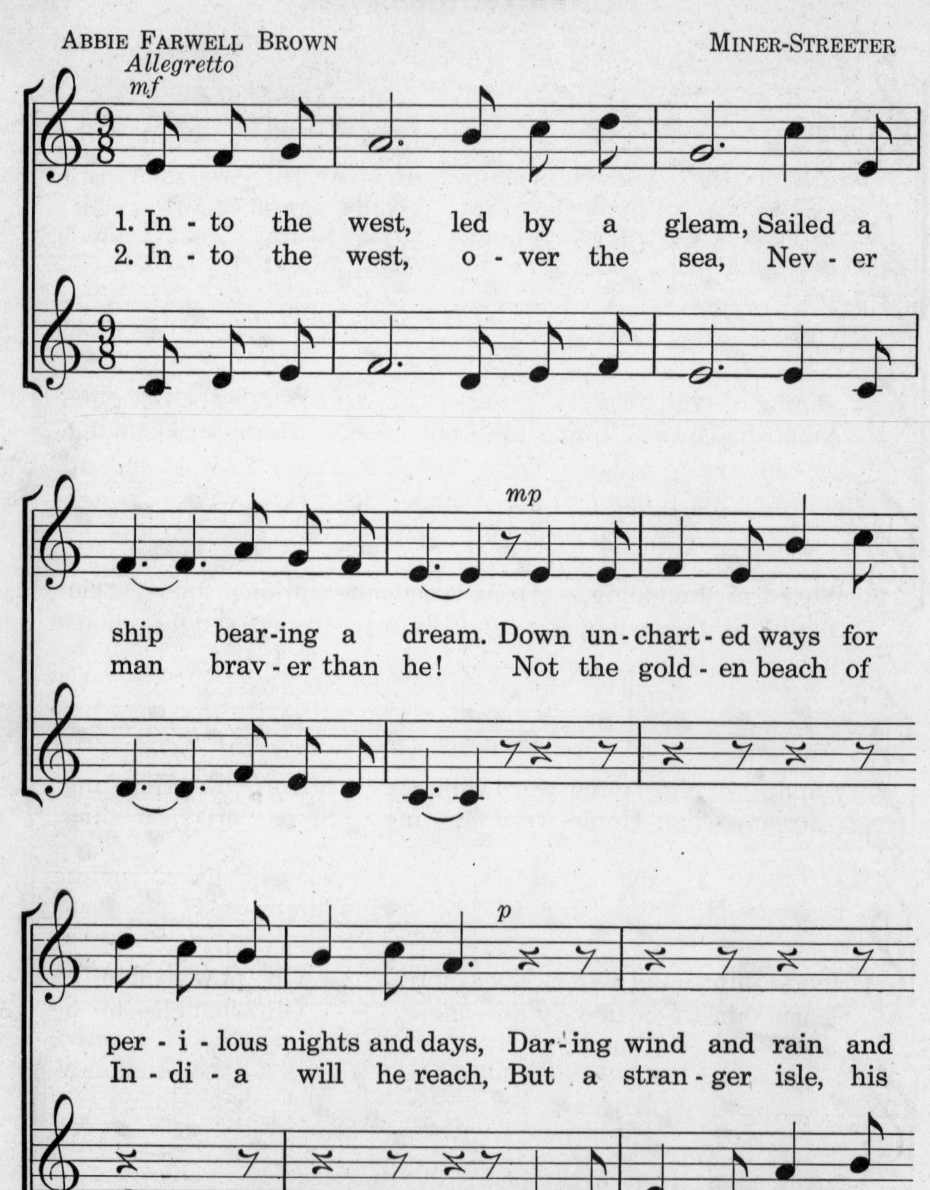

1. In - to the west, led by a gleam, Sailed a
2. In - to the west, o - ver the sea, Nev - er

ship bear-ing a dream. Down un-chart-ed ways for
man brav-er than he! Not the gold-en beach of

per - i - lous nights and days, Dar-ing wind and rain and
In - di - a will he reach, But a stran-ger isle, his

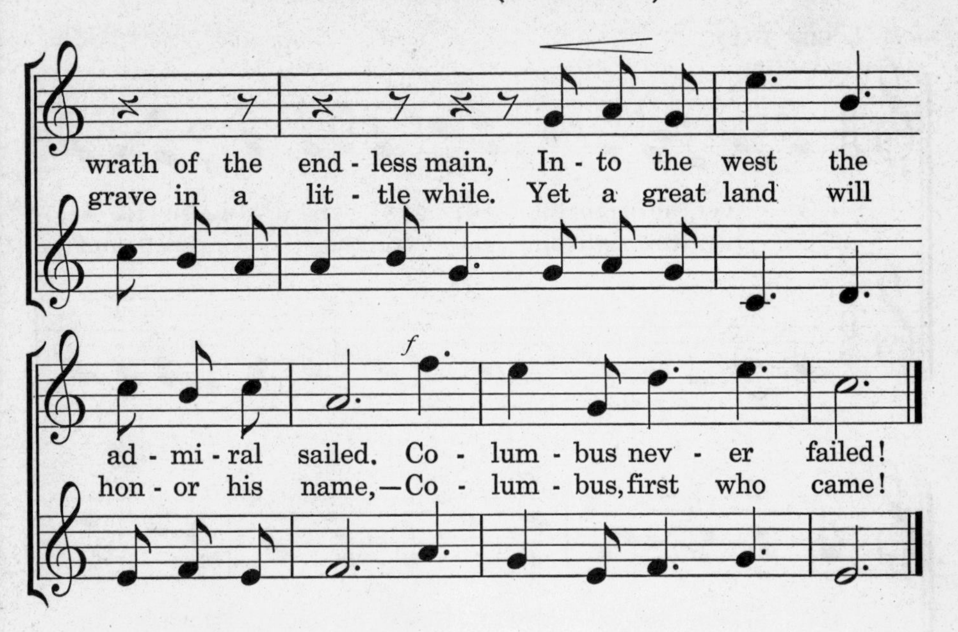

wrath of the end - less main, In - to the west the
grave in a lit - tle while. Yet a great land will

ad - mi - ral sailed. Co - lum - bus nev - er failed!
hon - or his name,—Co - lum - bus, first who came!

FRINGED GENTIANS

MARY STANHOPE

WILL EARHART

Andante
mp

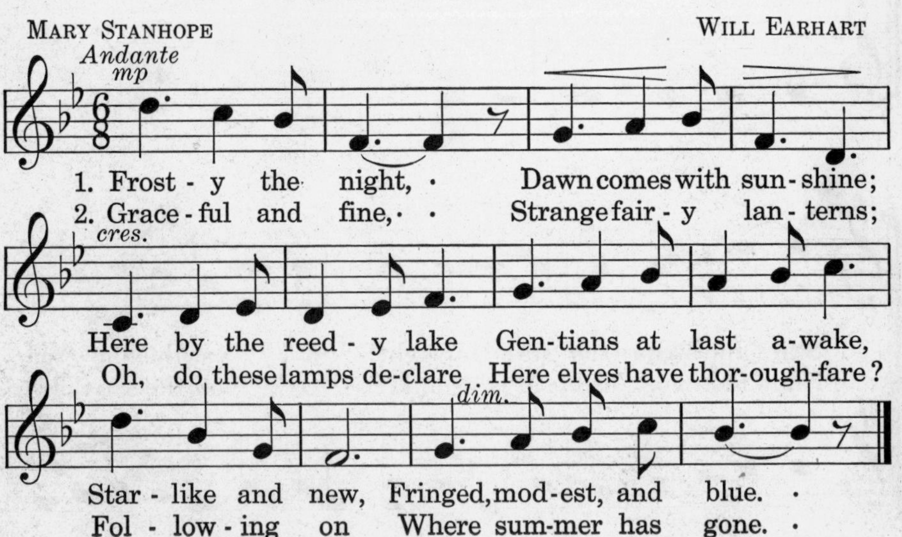

1. Frost - y the night, · Dawn comes with sun - shine;
2. Grace - ful and fine, · Strange fair - y lan - terns;

cres.

Here by the reed - y lake Gen - tians at last a - wake,
Oh, do these lamps de - clare Here elves have thor - ough - fare?

dim.

Star - like and new, Fringed, mod - est, and blue. ·
Fol - low - ing on Where sum - mer has gone. ·

OVER THE BRIGHT BLUE SEA

M. LOUISE BAUM

ARTHUR S. SULLIVAN

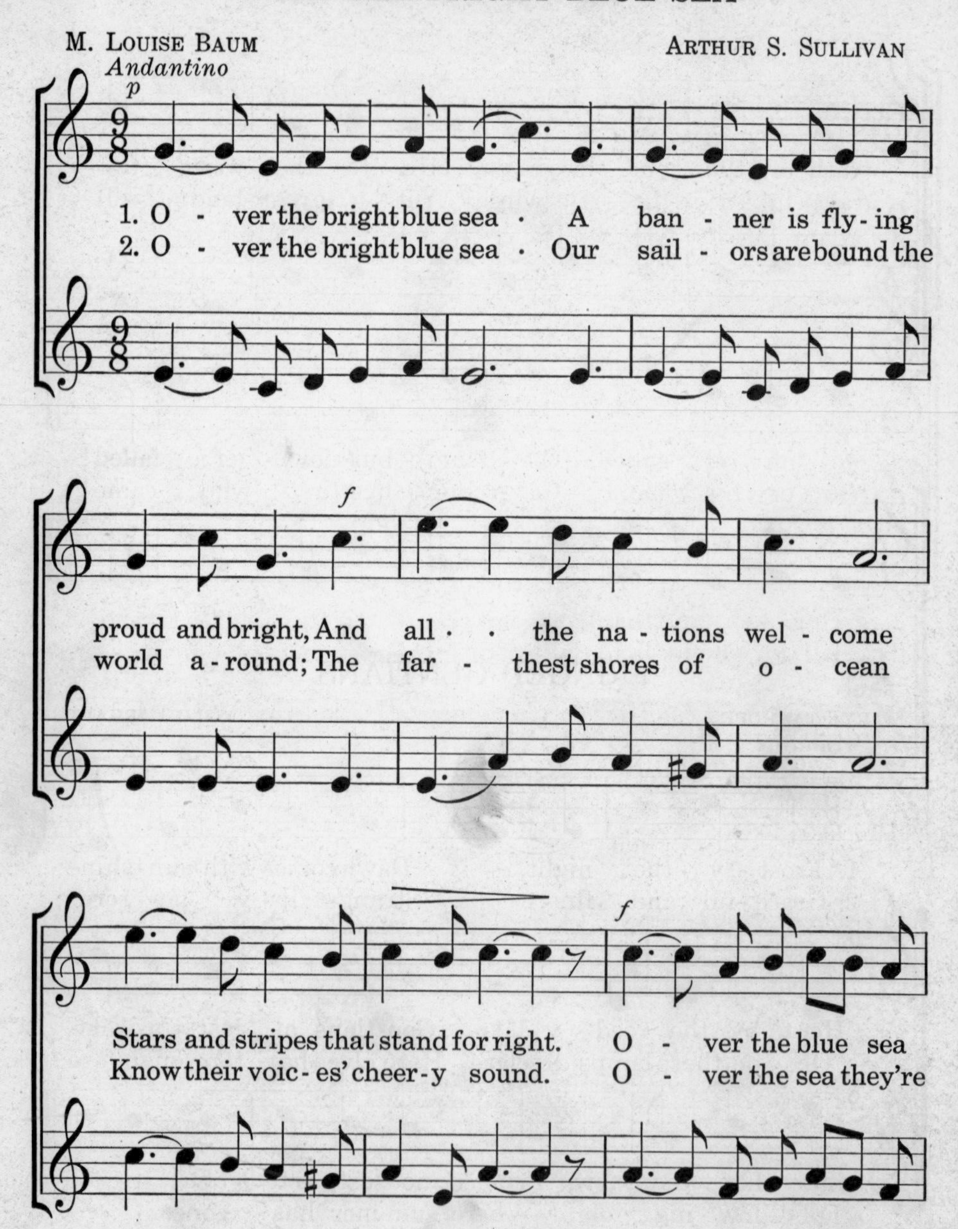

Andantino

1. O - ver the bright blue sea · A ban - ner is fly - ing
2. O - ver the bright blue sea · Our sail - ors are bound the

proud and bright, And all · · the na - tions wel - come
world a - round; The far - thest shores of o - cean

Stars and stripes that stand for right. O - ver the blue sea
Know their voic - es' cheer - y sound. O - ver the sea they're

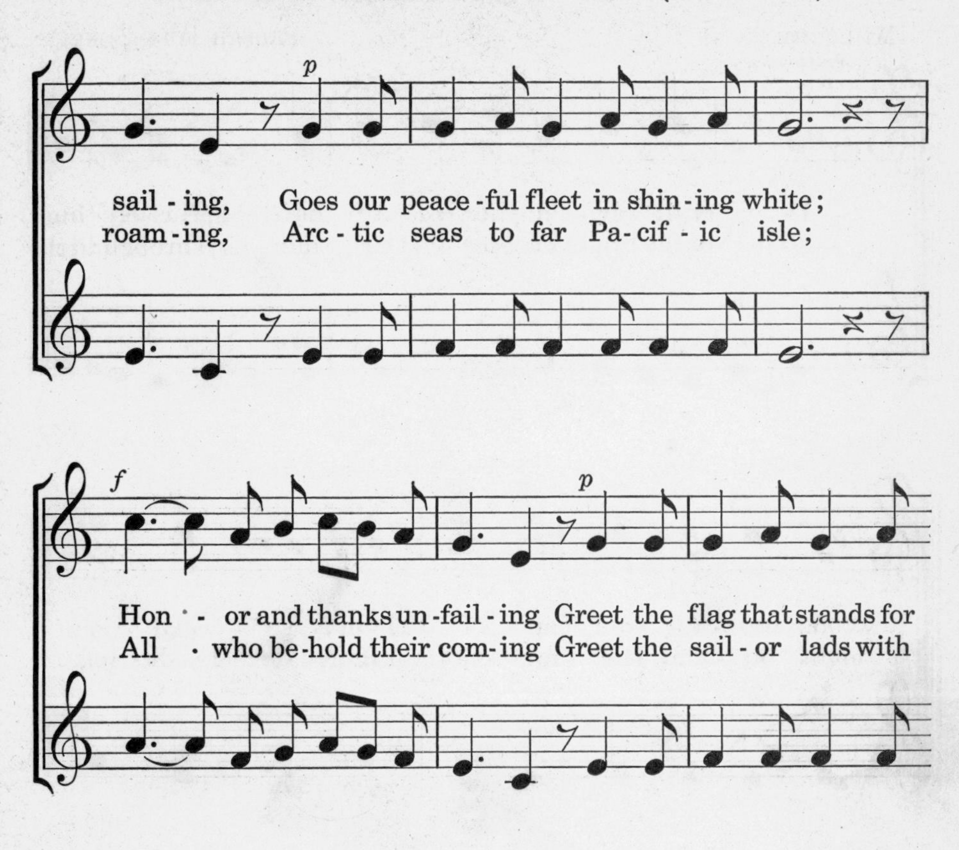

sail - ing, Goes our peace -ful fleet in shin -ing white;
roam -ing, Arc - tic seas to far Pa- cif - ic isle;

Hon · - or and thanks un -fail - ing Greet the flag that stands for
All · who be -hold their com- ing Greet the sail - or lads with

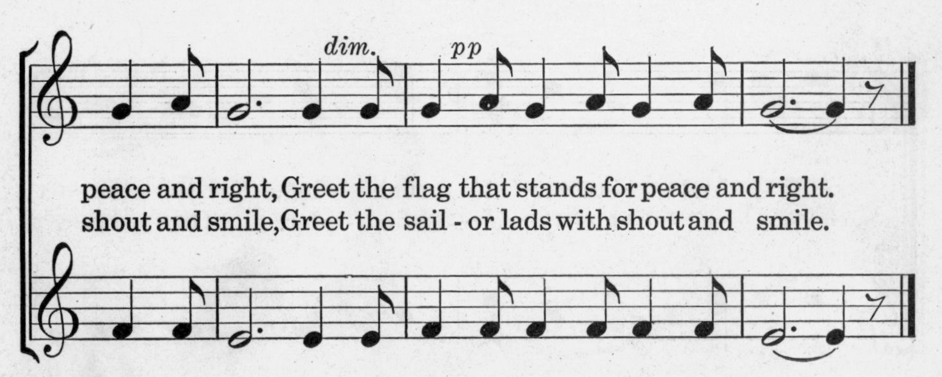

peace and right, Greet the flag that stands for peace and right.
shout and smile, Greet the sail - or lads with shout and smile.

THE STORM KING

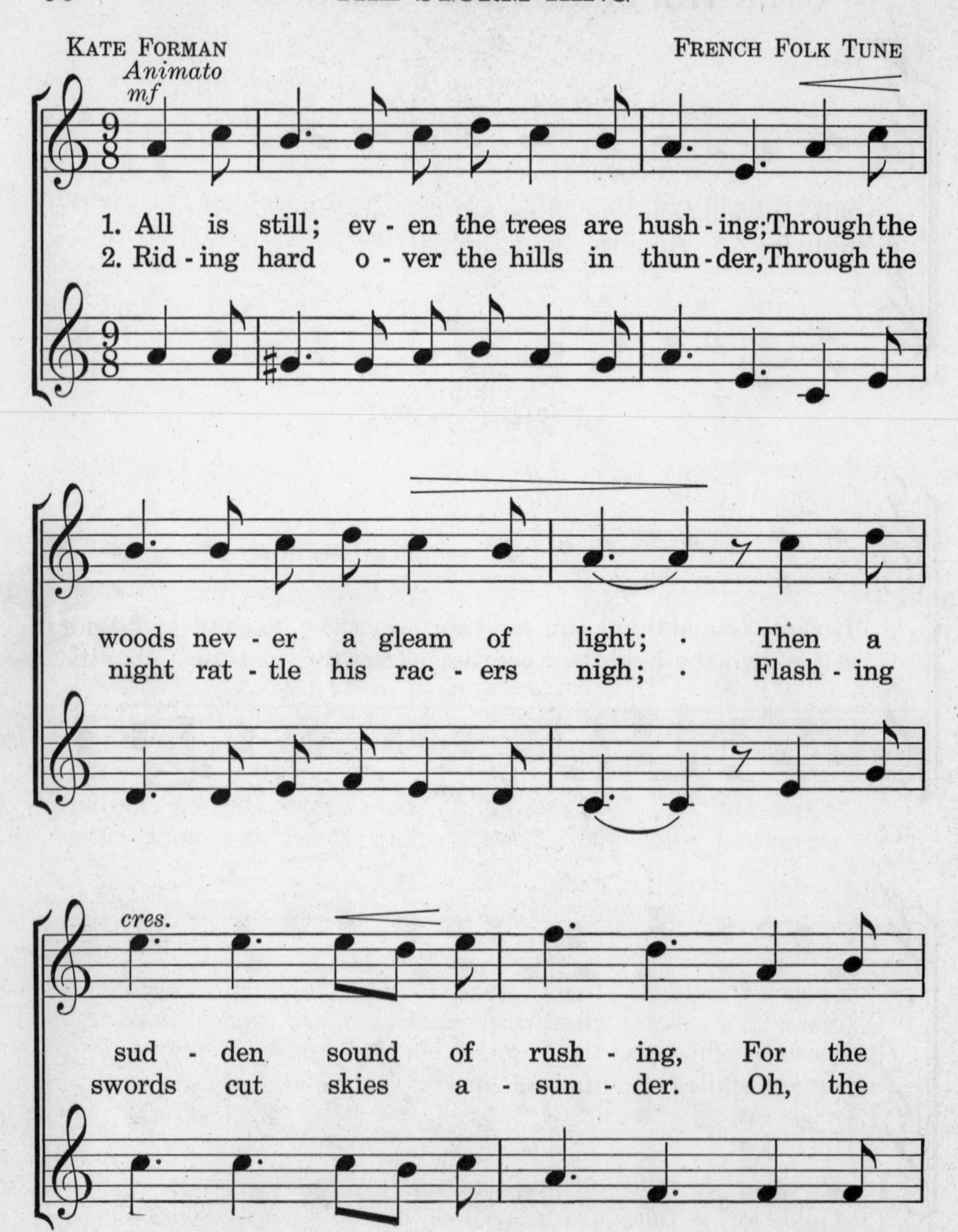

KATE FORMAN

FRENCH FOLK TUNE

Animato
mf

1. All is still; ev - en the trees are hush - ing; Through the
2. Rid - ing hard o - ver the hills in thun - der, Through the

woods nev - er a gleam of light; · Then a
night rat - tle his rac - ers nigh; · Flash - ing

cres.

sud - den sound of rush - ing, For the
swords cut skies a - sun - der. Oh, the

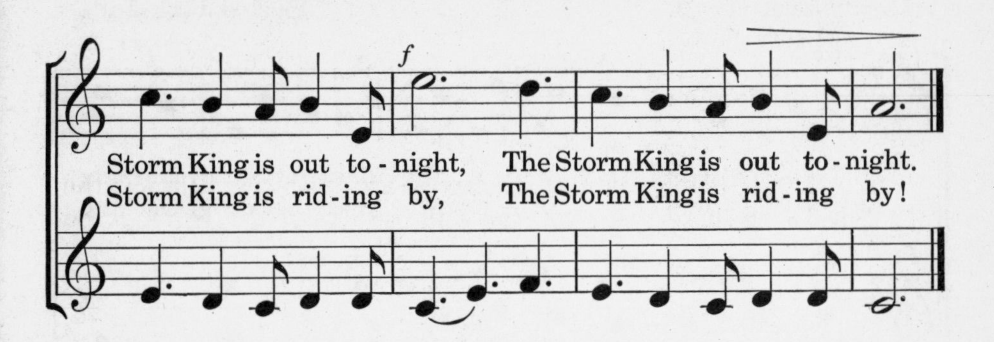

Storm King is out to-night, The Storm King is out to-night.
Storm King is rid-ing by, The Storm King is rid-ing by!

A TREE SONG

AFTER THE FRENCH

BELGIAN FOLK TUNE

Vivace

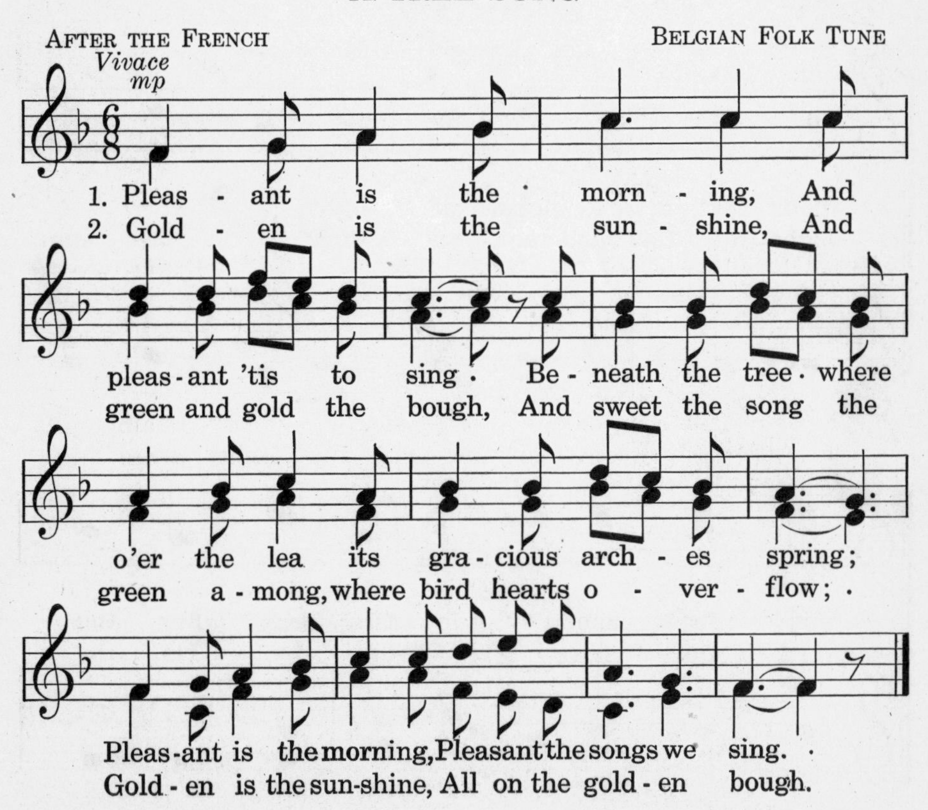

1. Pleas - ant is the morn - ing, And
2. Gold - en is the sun - shine, And

pleas-ant 'tis to sing. Be-neath the tree where
green and gold the bough, And sweet the song the

o'er the lea its gra-cious arch - es spring;
green a-mong, where bird hearts o - ver-flow;

Pleas-ant is the morning, Pleasant the songs we sing.
Gold - en is the sun-shine, All on the gold - en bough.

THE VOICE OF THE BROOK

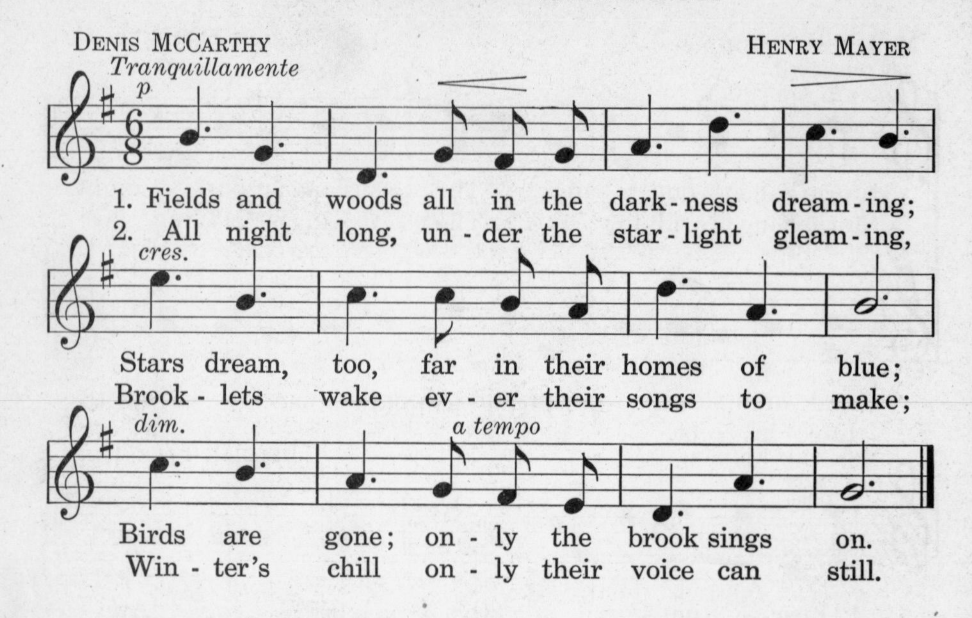

DENIS McCARTHY HENRY MAYER

Tranquillamente

1. Fields and woods all in the dark-ness dream-ing;
2. All night long, un-der the star-light gleam-ing,

Stars dream, too, far in their homes of blue;
Brook-lets wake ev-er their songs to make;

Birds are gone; on-ly the brook sings on.
Win-ter's chill on-ly their voice can still.

THE VOICE OF THE BROOK

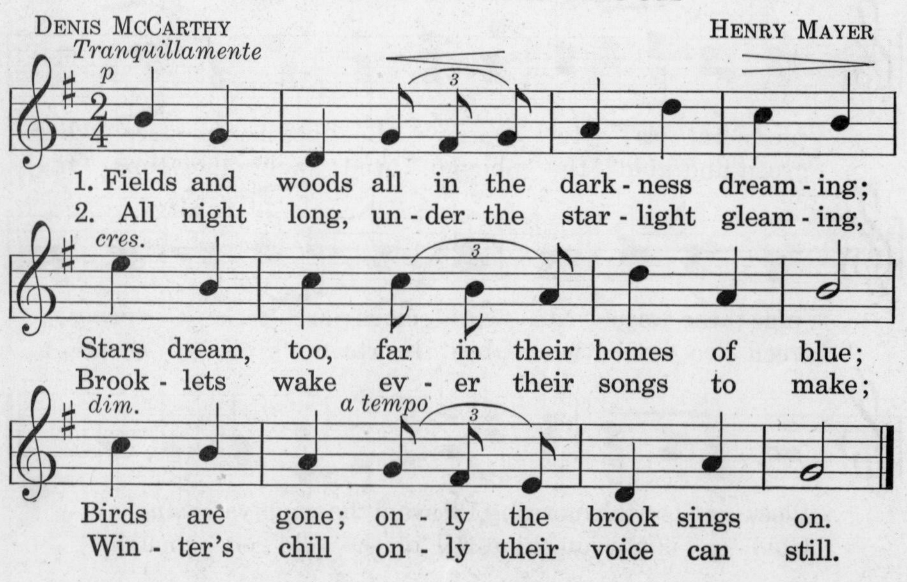

DENIS McCARTHY HENRY MAYER

Tranquillamente

1. Fields and woods all in the dark-ness dream-ing;
2. All night long, un-der the star-light gleam-ing,

Stars dream, too, far in their homes of blue;
Brook-lets wake ev-er their songs to make;

Birds are gone; on-ly the brook sings on.
Win-ter's chill on-ly their voice can still.

M. LOUISE BAUM
Translated

RUSSIAN FOLK SONG

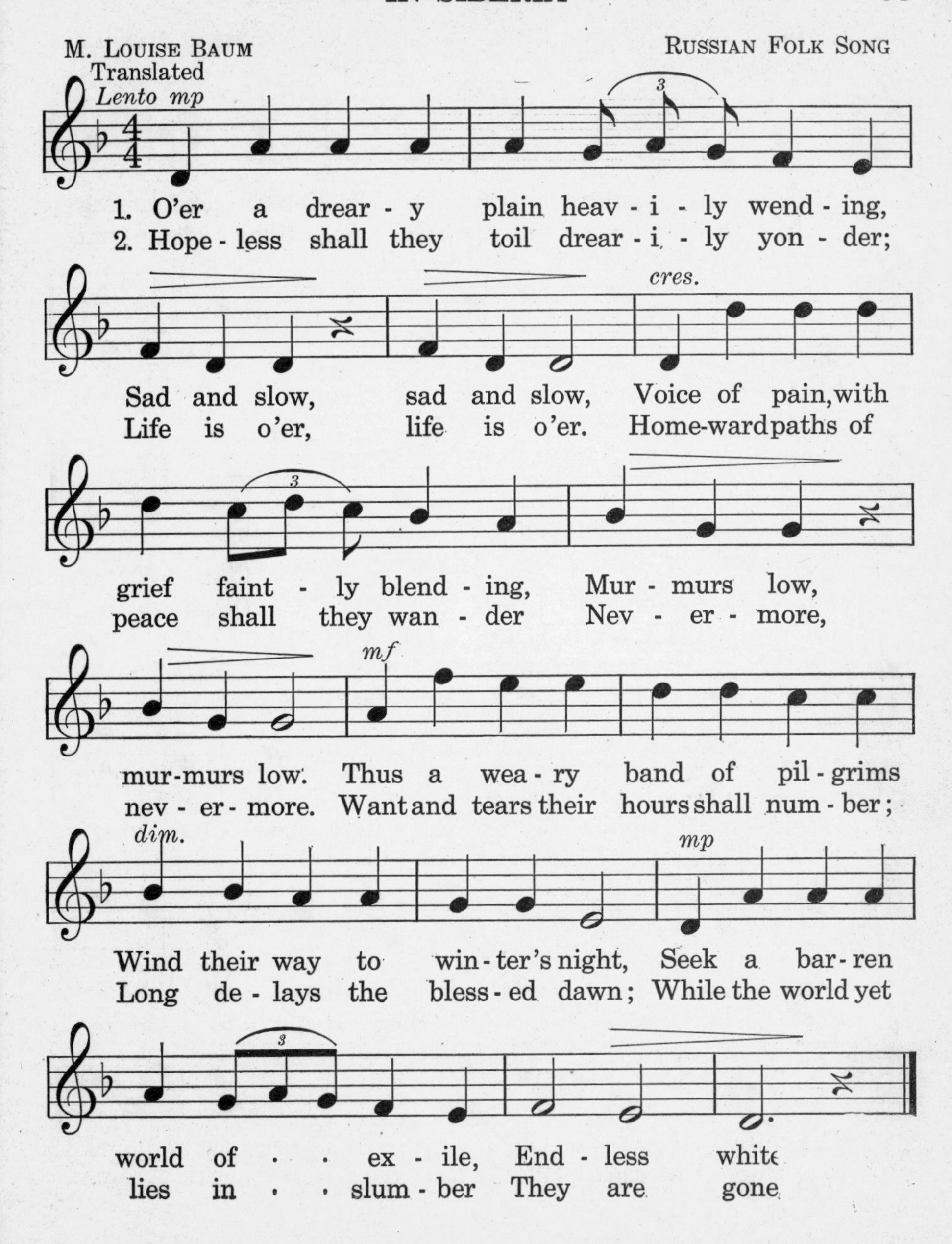

1. O'er a drear-y plain heav-i-ly wend-ing,
2. Hope-less shall they toil drear-i-ly yon-der;

Sad and slow, sad and slow, Voice of pain, with
Life is o'er, life is o'er. Home-ward paths of

grief faint-ly blend-ing, Mur-murs low,
peace shall they wan-der Nev-er-more,

mur-murs low. Thus a wea-ry band of pil-grims
nev-er-more. Want and tears their hours shall num-ber;

Wind their way to win-ter's night, Seek a bar-ren
Long de-lays the bless-ed dawn; While the world yet

world of ex-ile, End-less white
lies in slum-ber They are gone

THE BICYCLER

ROBERT BRIGHAM   CHARLES FONTEYN MANNEY

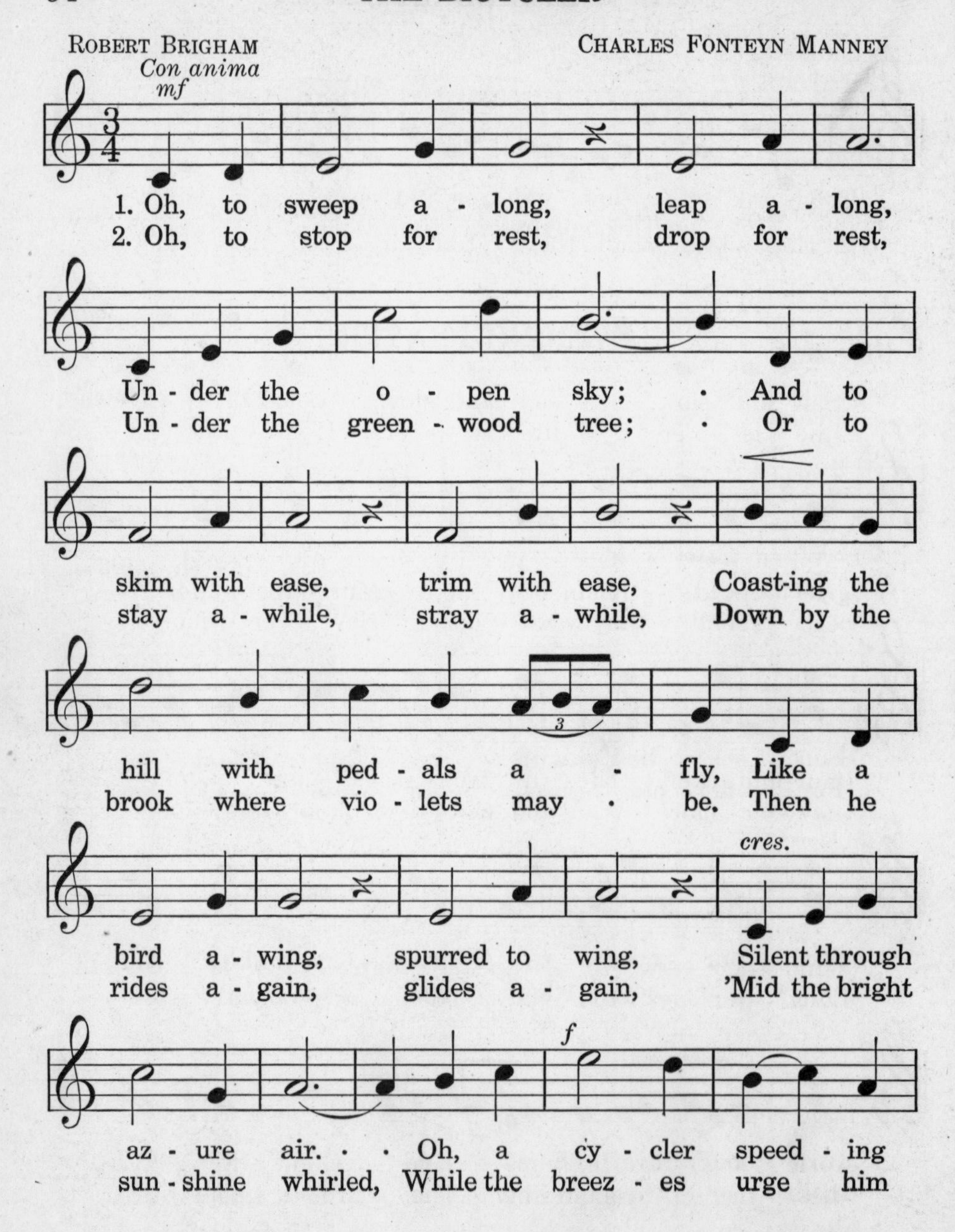

1. Oh, to sweep a - long, leap a - long,
2. Oh, to stop for rest, drop for rest,

Un - der the o - pen sky; · And to
Un - der the green - wood tree; · Or to

skim with ease, trim with ease, Coast-ing the
stay a - while, stray a - while, Down by the

hill with ped - als a - fly, Like a
brook where vio - lets may · be. Then he

bird a - wing, spurred to wing, Silent through
rides a - gain, glides a - gain, 'Mid the bright

az - ure air. · · Oh, a cy - cler speed - ing
sun - shine whirled, While the breez - es urge him

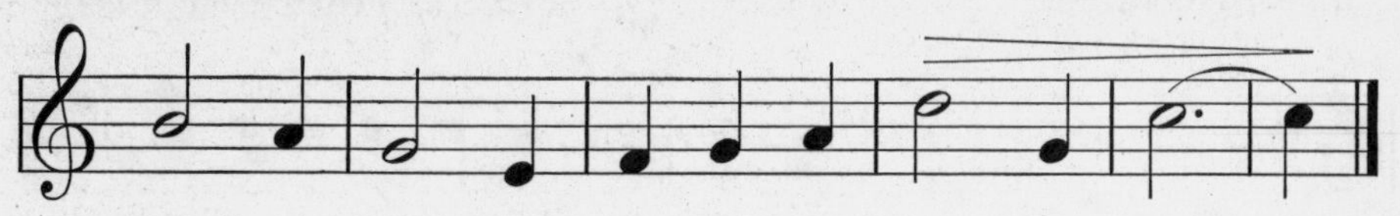

mile on mile Finds mo-tion and morn-ing fair. . .
on and on Through sum-mer-time's love-ly world. ·

EVENING PRAYER

MARY STANHOPE

MARY R. CARROLL

Andante

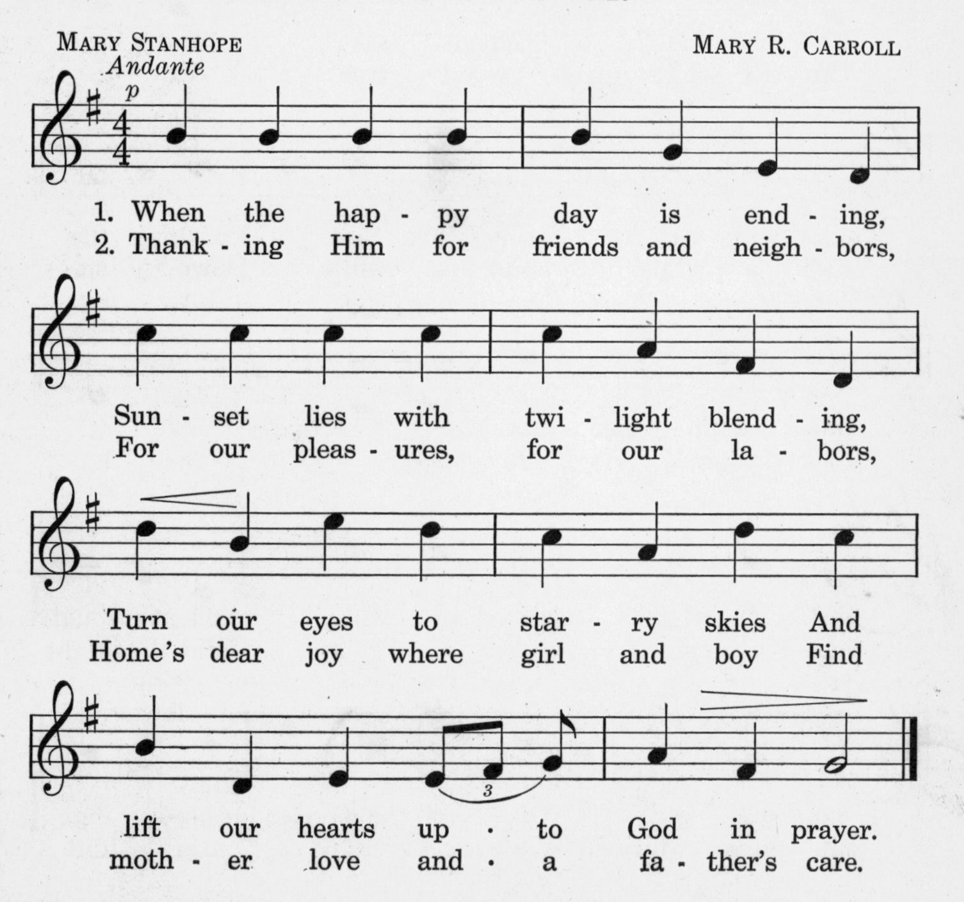

1. When the hap-py day is end-ing,
2. Thank-ing Him for friends and neigh-bors,

Sun-set lies with twi-light blend-ing,
For our pleas-ures, for our la-bors,

Turn our eyes to star-ry skies And
Home's dear joy where girl and boy Find

lift our hearts up · to God in prayer.
moth-er love and · a fa-ther's care.

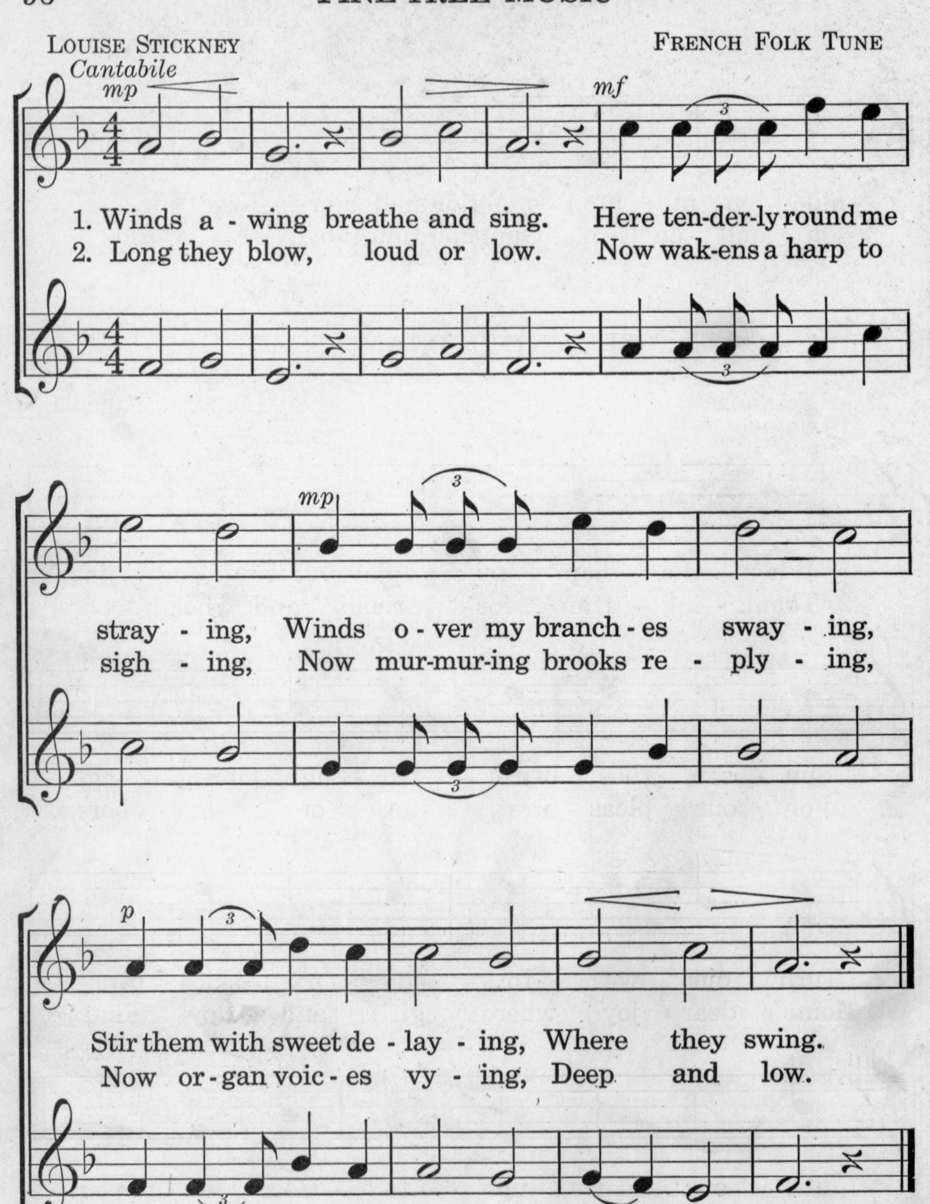

LOUISE STICKNEY

FRENCH FOLK TUNE

Cantabile

1. Winds a - wing breathe and sing.   Here ten-der-ly round me
2. Long they blow,   loud or low.   Now wak-ens a harp to

stray - ing,   Winds o - ver my branch - es   sway - ing,
sigh - ing,   Now mur-mur-ing brooks re - ply - ing,

Stir them with sweet de - lay - ing, Where   they swing.
Now or - gan voic - es   vy - ing, Deep   and low.

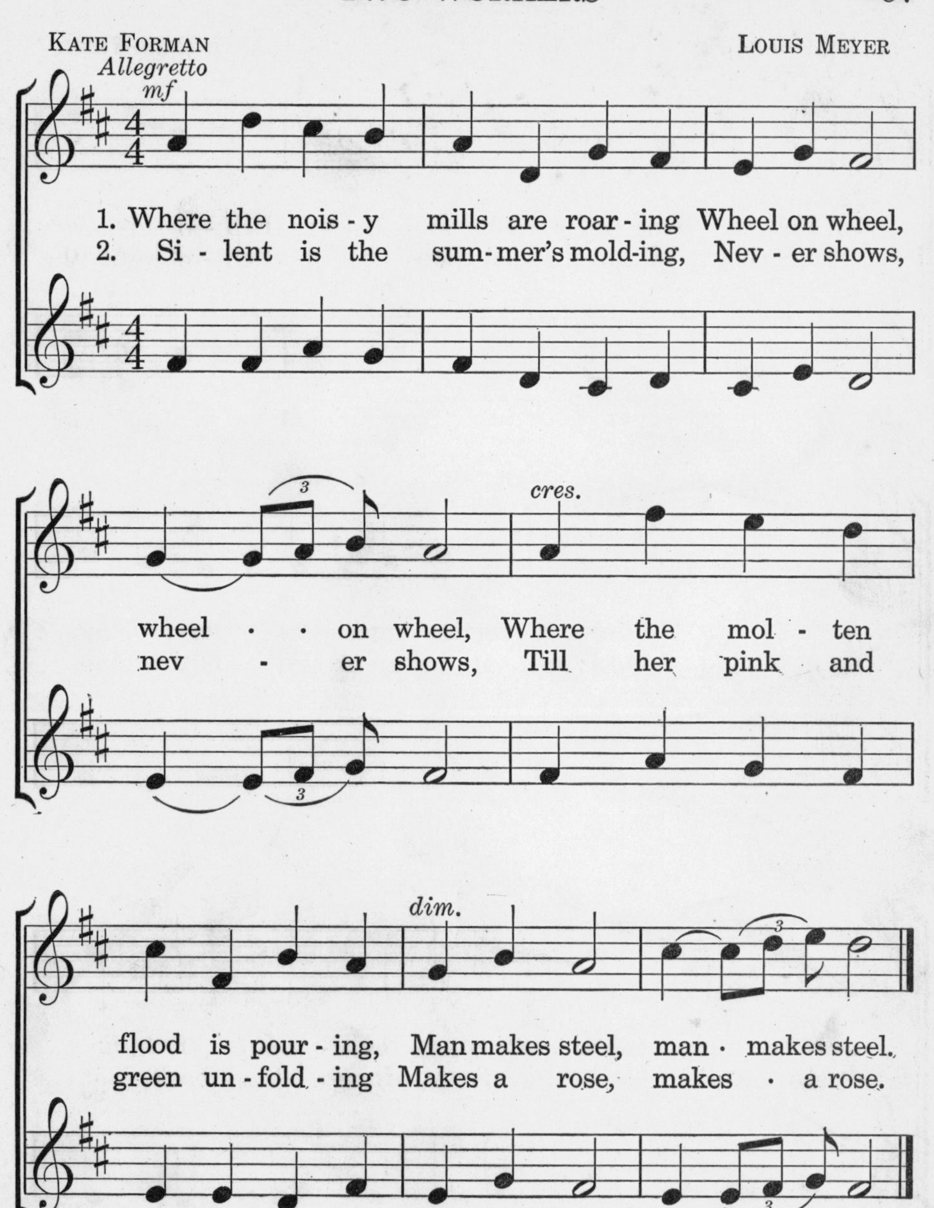

KATE FORMAN

LOUIS MEYER

Allegretto

1. Where the nois - y mills are roar - ing Wheel on wheel,
2. Si - lent is the sum - mer's mold-ing, Nev - er shows,

wheel · · on wheel, Where the mol - ten
nev - er shows, Till her pink and

flood is pour - ing, Man makes steel, man · makes steel.
green un - fold - ing Makes a rose, makes · a rose.

T

ECHO SONG

M. Louise Baum

Wilson-White

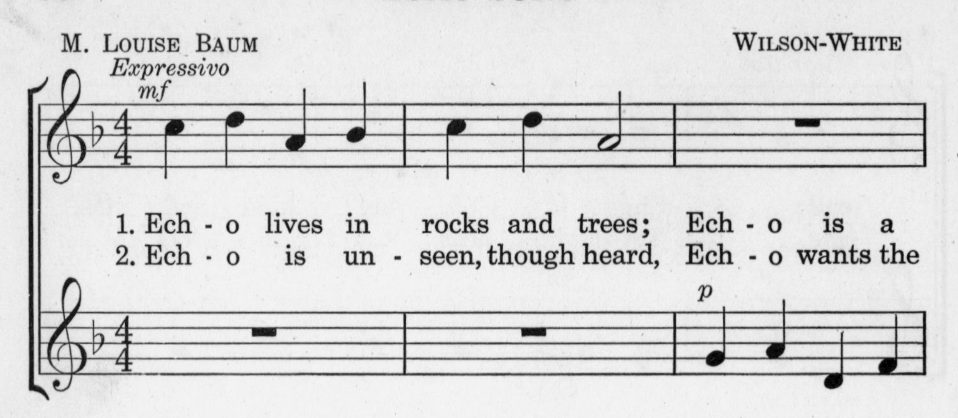

1. Ech - o lives in rocks and trees; Ech - o is a
2. Ech - o is un - seen, though heard, Ech - o wants the

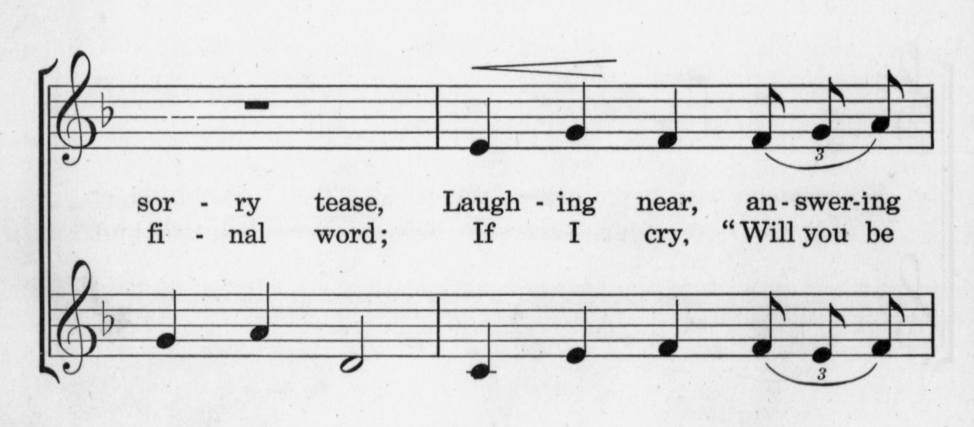

sor - ry tease, Laugh - ing near, an - swer - ing
fi - nal word; If I cry, "Will you be

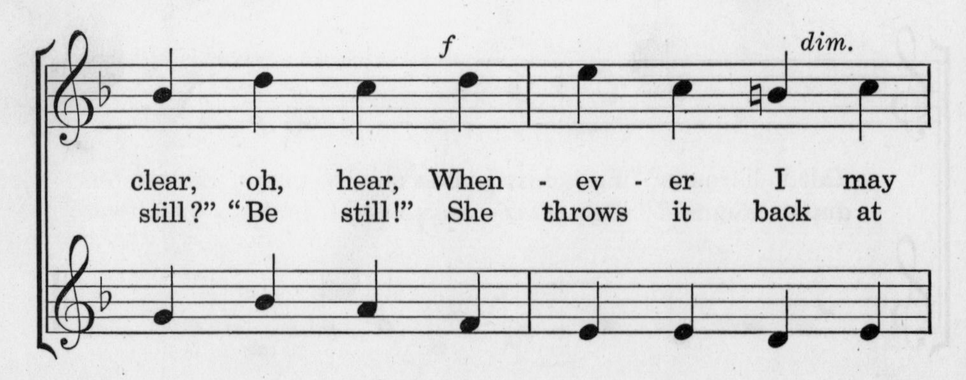

clear, oh, hear, When - ev - er I may
still?" "Be still!" She throws it back at

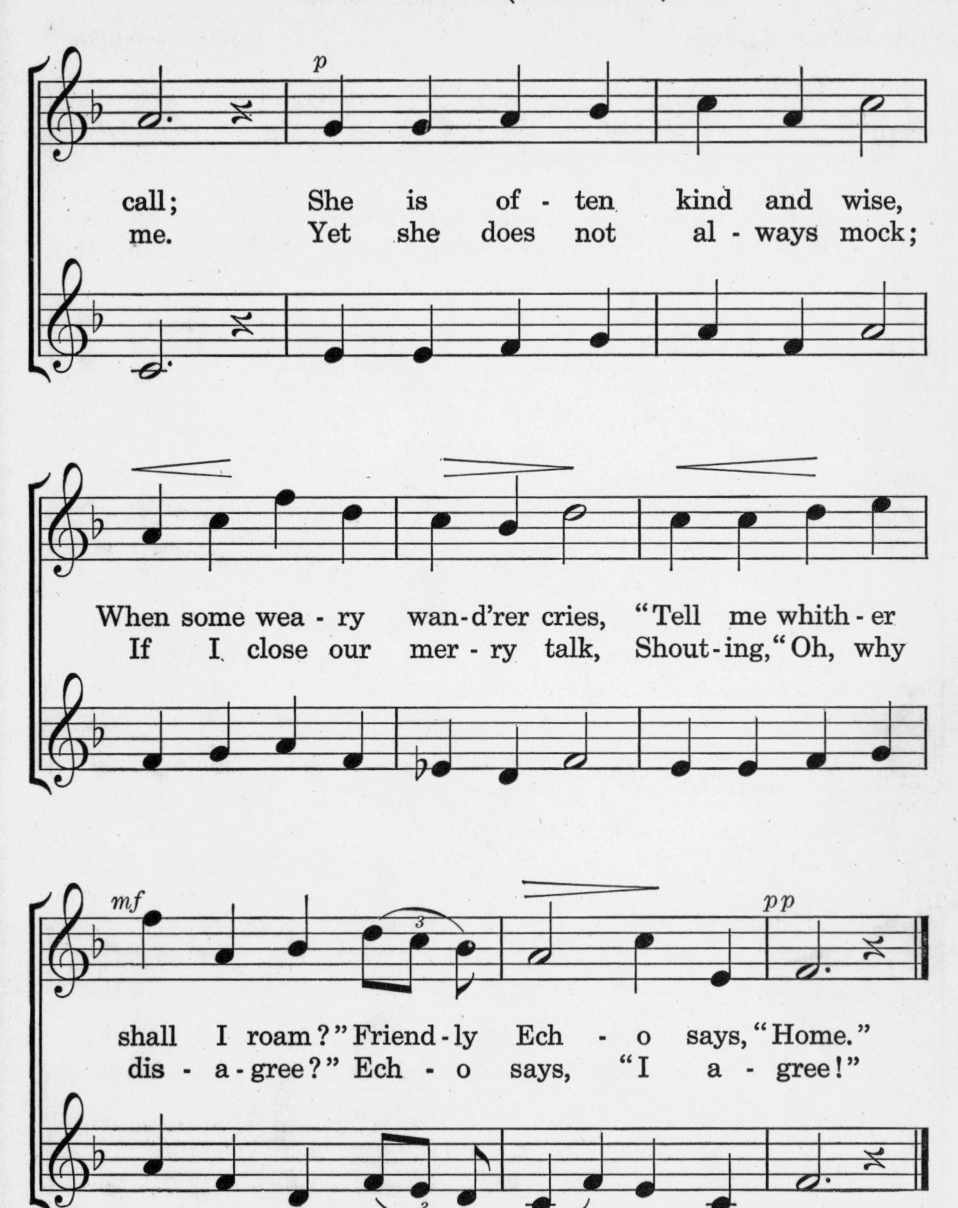

call; She is of-ten kind and wise,
me. Yet she does not al-ways mock;

When some wea-ry wan-d'rer cries, "Tell me whith-er
If I close our mer-ry talk, Shout-ing, "Oh, why

shall I roam?" Friend-ly Ech-o says, "Home."
dis-a-gree?" Ech-o says, "I a-gree!"

A SONG OF WHEELS

JOHN REED

STANLEY AVERY

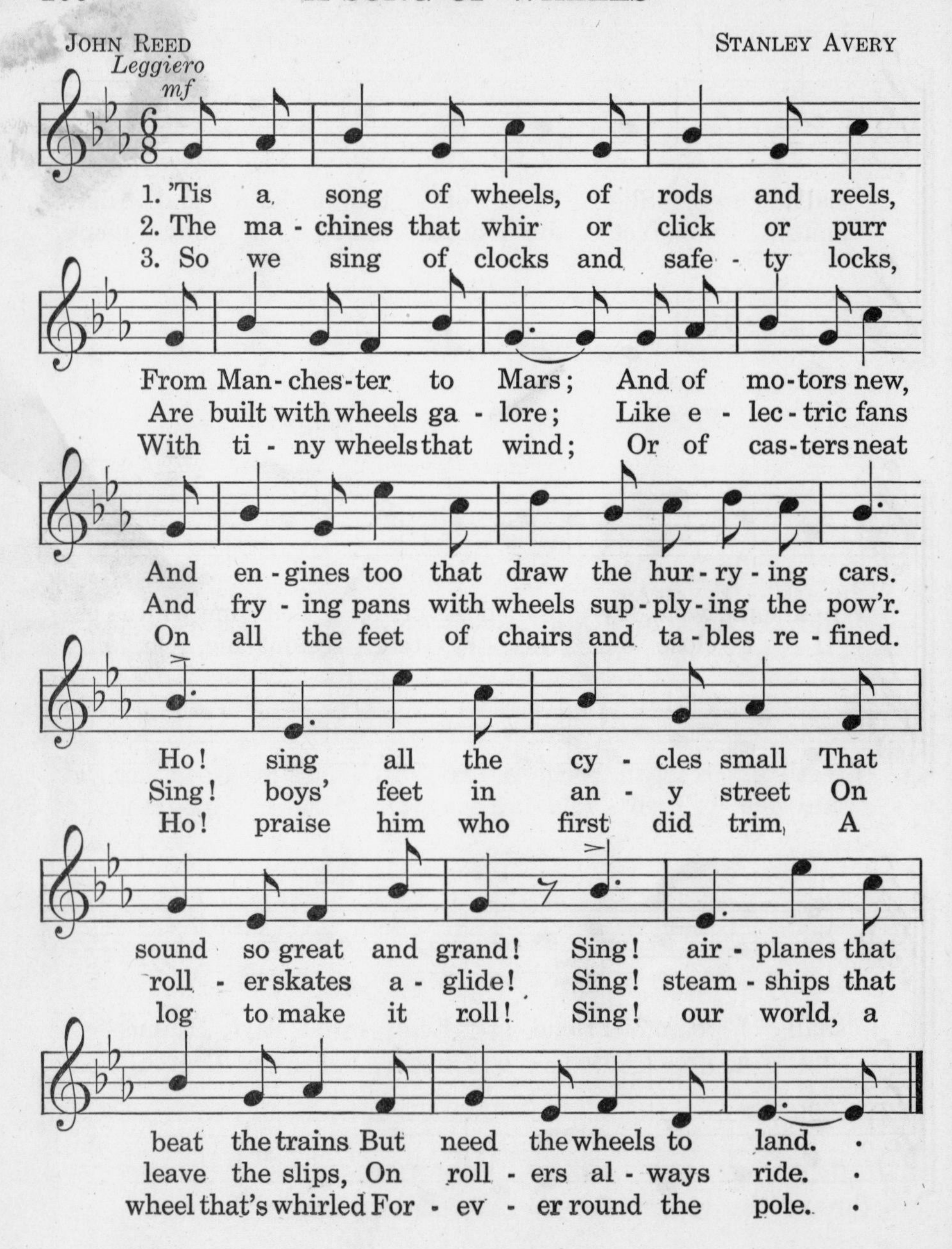

Leggiero
mf

1. 'Tis a song of wheels, of rods and reels,
2. The ma-chines that whir or click or purr
3. So we sing of clocks and safe-ty locks,

From Man-ches-ter to Mars; And of mo-tors new,
Are built with wheels ga-lore; Like e-lec-tric fans
With ti-ny wheels that wind; Or of cas-ters neat

And en-gines too that draw the hur-ry-ing cars.
And fry-ing pans with wheels sup-ply-ing the pow'r.
On all the feet of chairs and ta-bles re-fined.

Ho! sing all the cy-cles small That
Sing! boys' feet in an-y street On
Ho! praise him who first did trim, A

sound so great and grand! Sing! air-planes that
roll-er skates a-glide! Sing! steam-ships that
log to make it roll! Sing! our world, a

beat the trains But need the wheels to land.
leave the slips, On roll-ers al-ways ride.
wheel that's whirled For-ev-er round the pole.

MARY STANHOPE

WILL EARHART

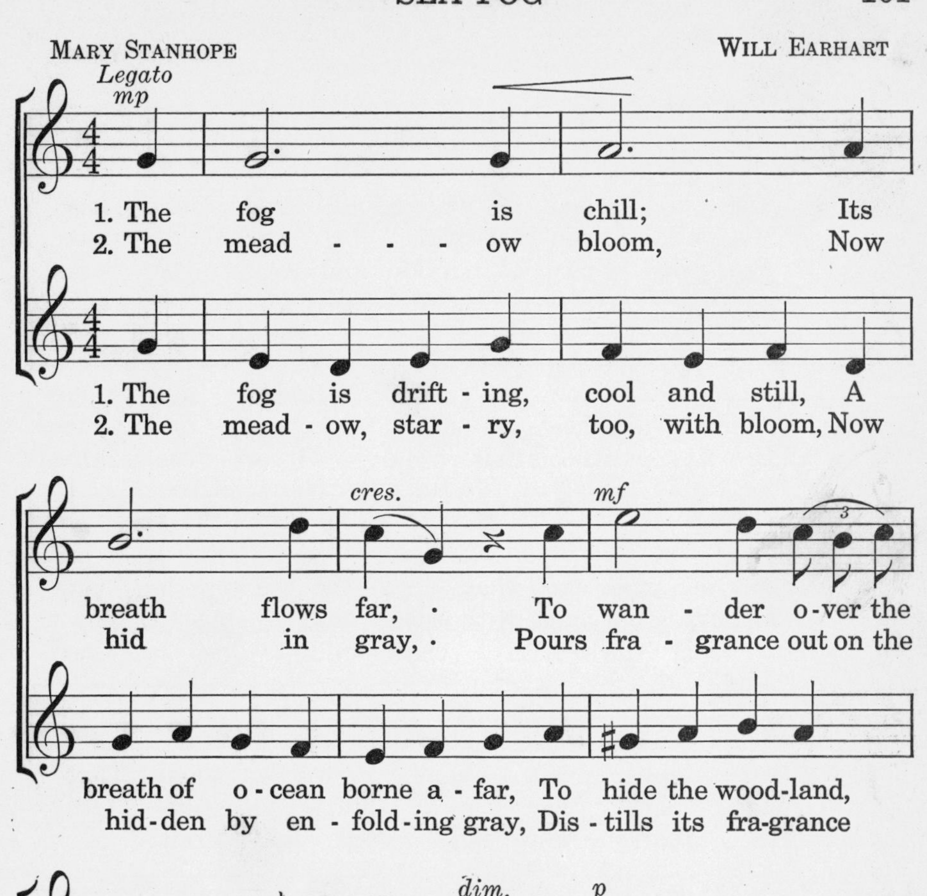

1. The fog is chill; Its
2. The mead - - - ow bloom, Now

1. The fog is drift - ing, cool and still, A
2. The mead - ow, star - ry, too, with bloom, Now

breath flows far, · To wan - der o - ver the
hid in gray, · Pours fra - grance out on the

breath of o - cean borne a - far, To hide the wood-land,
hid - den by en - fold-ing gray, Dis - tills its fra-grance

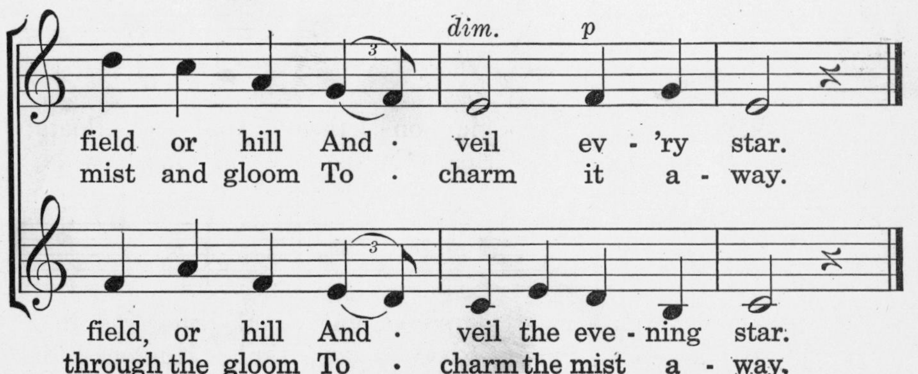

field or hill And · veil ev - 'ry star.
mist and gloom To · charm it a - way.

field, or hill And · veil the eve - ning star.
through the gloom To · charm the mist a - way.

ABBIE FARWELL BROWN   MARTHA WHITE

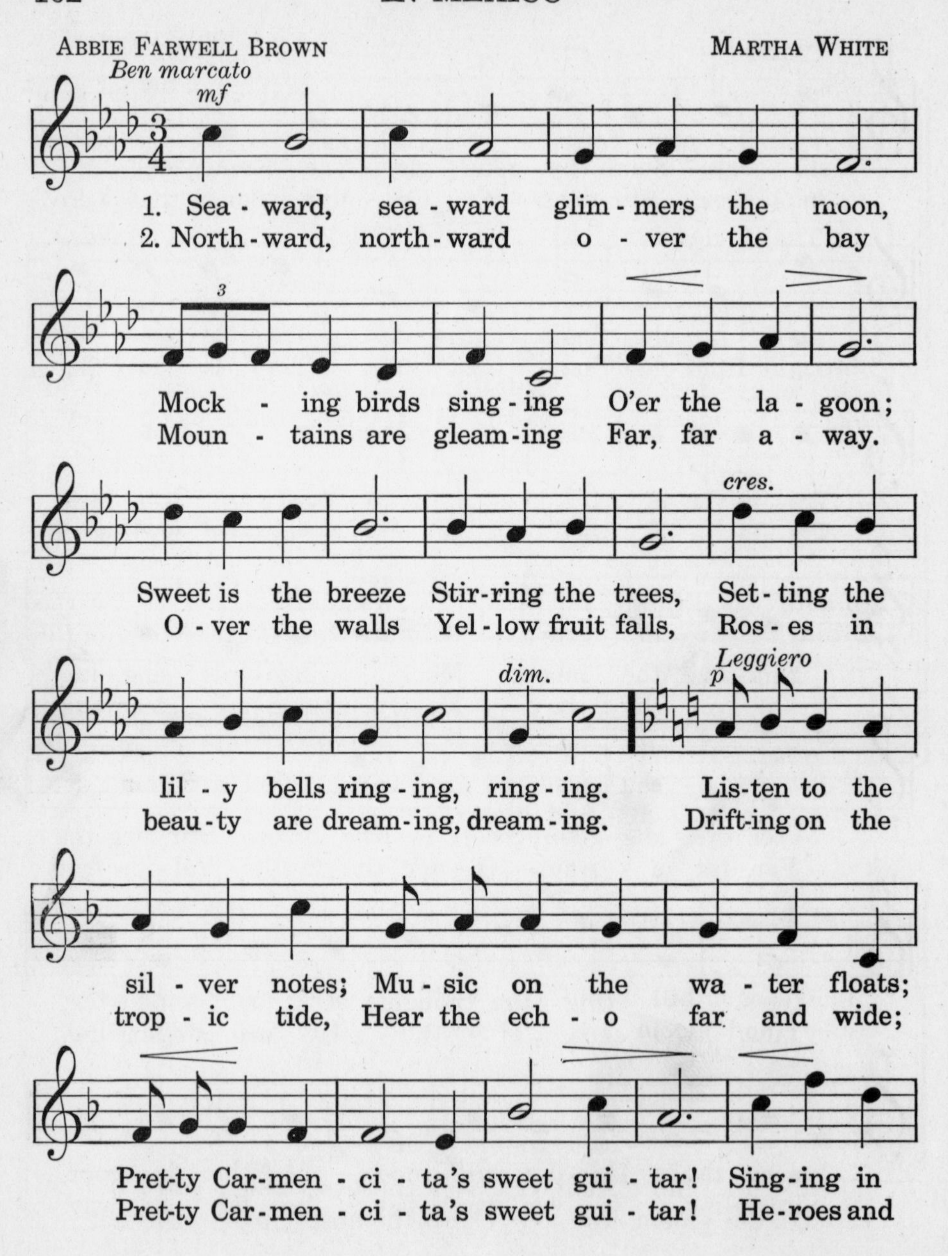

1. Sea - ward,   sea - ward   glim - mers   the   moon,
2. North - ward,   north - ward   o - ver   the   bay

Mock - ing birds sing - ing O'er the la - goon;
Moun - tains are gleam - ing Far, far a - way.

Sweet is   the breeze   Stir-ring the trees,   Set - ting the
O - ver   the walls   Yel - low fruit falls,   Ros - es   in

lil - y   bells ring - ing, ring - ing.   Lis-ten to the
beau - ty   are dream-ing, dream-ing.   Drift-ing on the

sil - ver   notes; Mu - sic   on   the   wa - ter floats;
trop - ic   tide, Hear the ech - o   far   and wide;

Pret-ty Car-men - ci - ta's sweet gui - tar! Sing-ing in
Pret-ty Car-men - ci - ta's sweet gui - tar! He-roes and

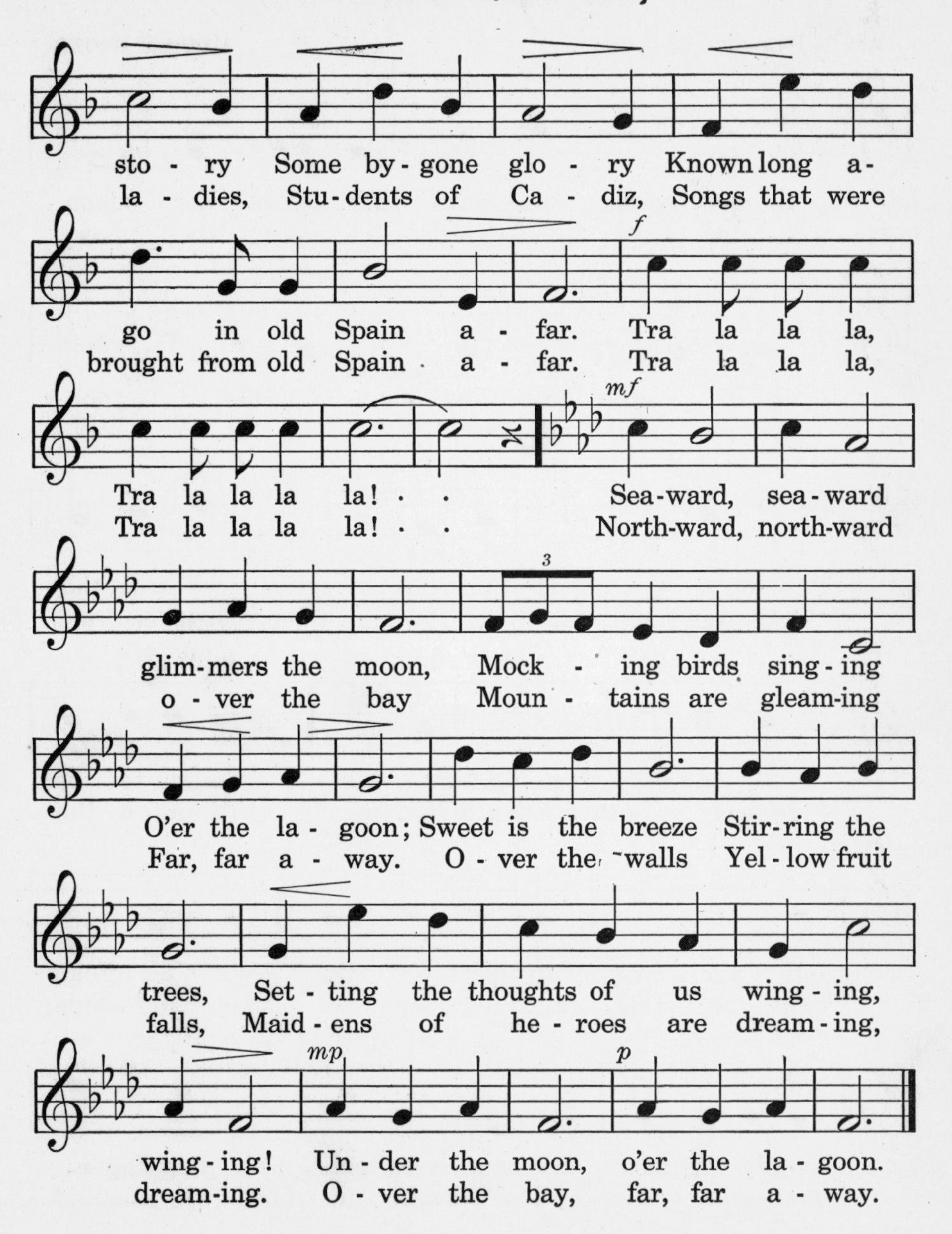

sto - ry Some by - gone glo - ry Known long a-
la - dies, Stu-dents of Ca - diz, Songs that were

go in old Spain a - far. Tra la la la,
brought from old Spain a - far. Tra la la la,

Tra la la la la! · · Sea-ward, sea-ward
Tra la la la la! · · North-ward, north-ward

glim-mers the moon, Mock - ing birds sing-ing
o - ver the bay Moun - tains are gleam-ing

O'er the la - goon; Sweet is the breeze Stir-ring the
Far, far a - way. O - ver the walls Yel-low fruit

trees, Set - ting the thoughts of us wing - ing,
falls, Maid - ens of he - roes are dream-ing,

wing - ing! Un - der the moon, o'er the la - goon.
dream-ing. O - ver the bay, far, far a - way.

PIONEERS

JEAN NEAL

STANLEY AVERY

Allegretto

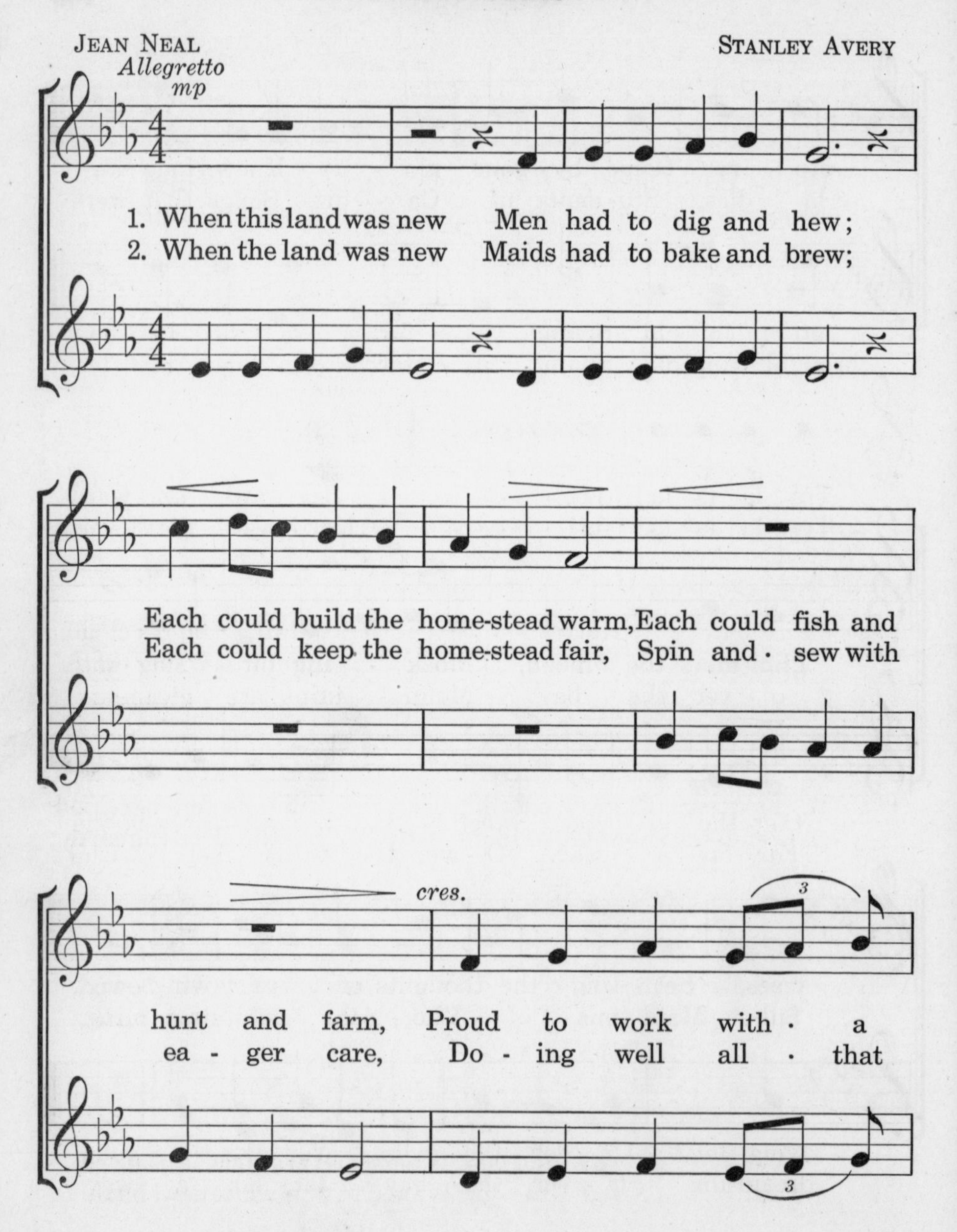

1. When this land was new   Men had to dig and hew;
2. When the land was new   Maids had to bake and brew;

Each could build the home-stead warm, Each could fish and
Each could keep the home-stead fair, Spin and · sew with

hunt and farm, Proud to work with · a
ea - ger care, Do - ing well all · that

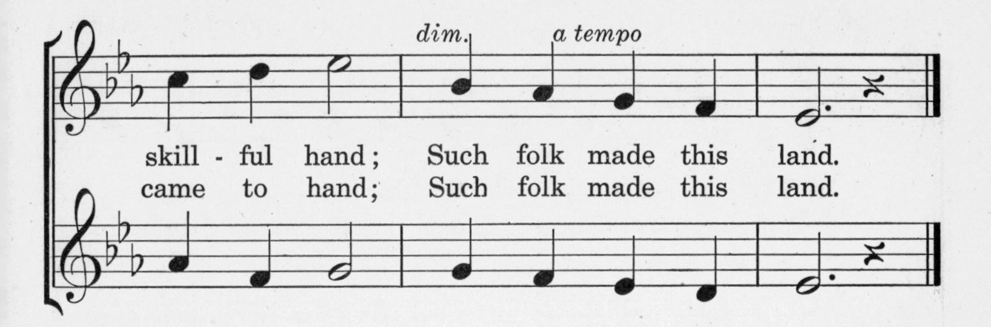

skill - ful hand; Such folk made this land.
came to hand; Such folk made this land.

SNOW CLOUD

M. Louise Baum

Elmer S. Hosmer

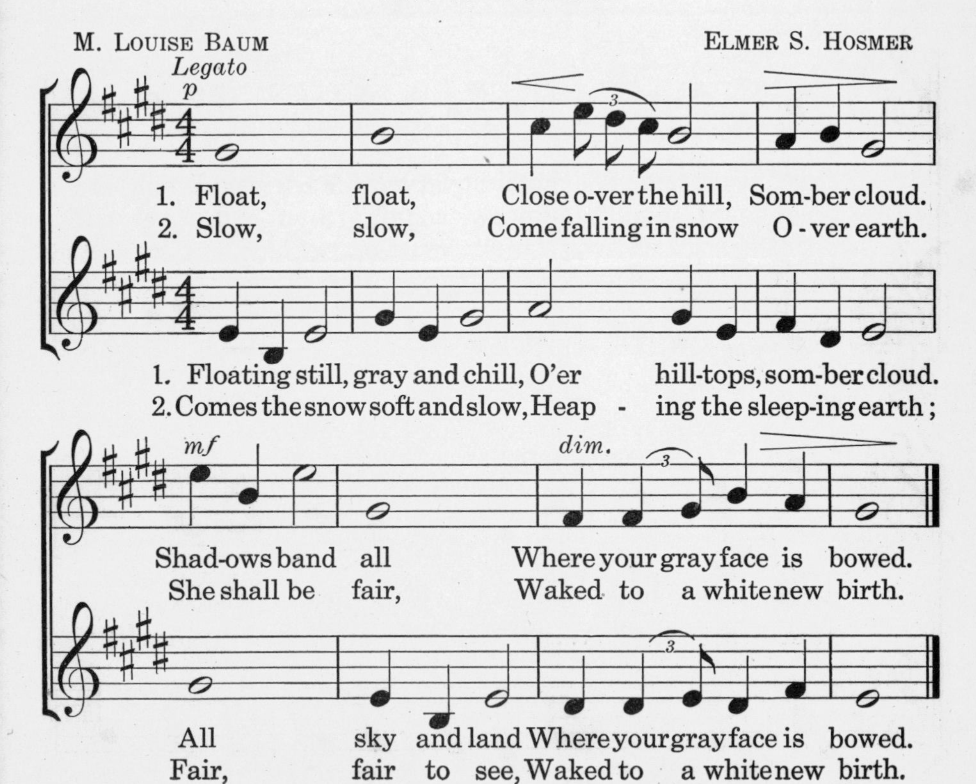

1. Float,   float,   Close o-ver the hill, Som-ber cloud.
2. Slow,   slow,   Come falling in snow O - ver earth.

1. Floating still, gray and chill, O'er hill-tops, som-ber cloud.
2. Comes the snow soft and slow, Heap - ing the sleep-ing earth;

Shad-ows band all Where your gray face is bowed.
She shall be fair, Waked to a white new birth.

All   sky and land Where your gray face is bowed.
Fair,   fair to see, Waked to a white new birth.

WHAT THEY DID

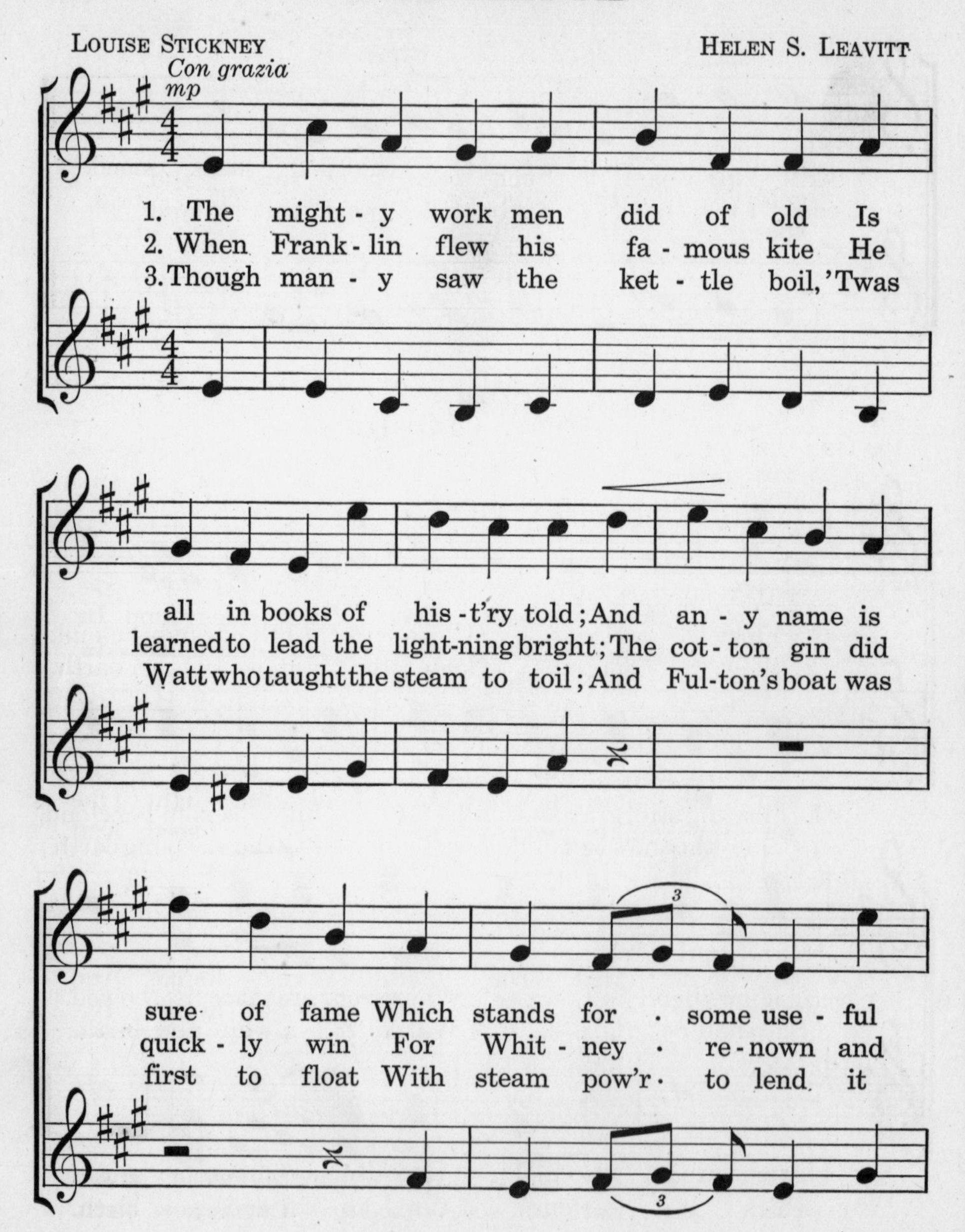

LOUISE STICKNEY

HELEN S. LEAVITT

Con grazia

1. The might-y work men did of old Is all in books of his-t'ry told; And an-y name is sure of fame Which stands for some use-ful
2. When Frank-lin flew his fa-mous kite He learned to lead the light-ning bright; The cot-ton gin did quick-ly win For Whit-ney re-nown and
3. Though man-y saw the ket-tle boil, 'Twas Watt who taught the steam to toil; And Ful-ton's boat was first to float With steam pow'r to lend it

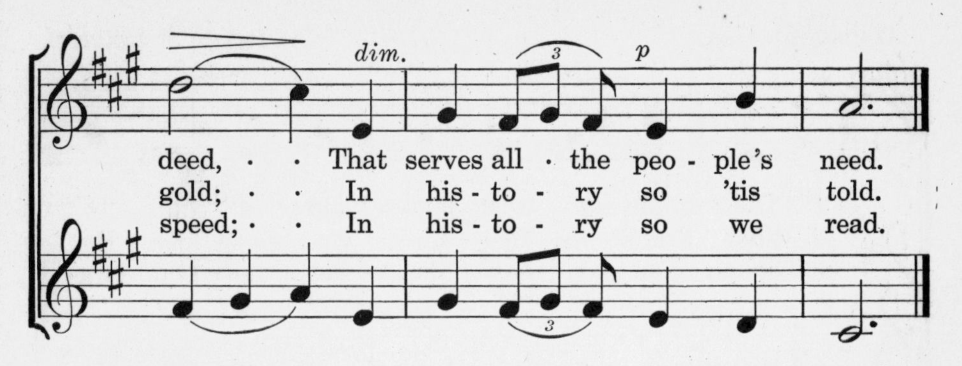

dim.   3   *p*

deed, · · That serves all · the peo - ple's need.
gold; · · In his - to - ry so 'tis told.
speed; · · In his - to - ry so we read.

SEEDS

PAULINE HILL   RUTH MAYNARD

Con espressione
mp   *cres.*

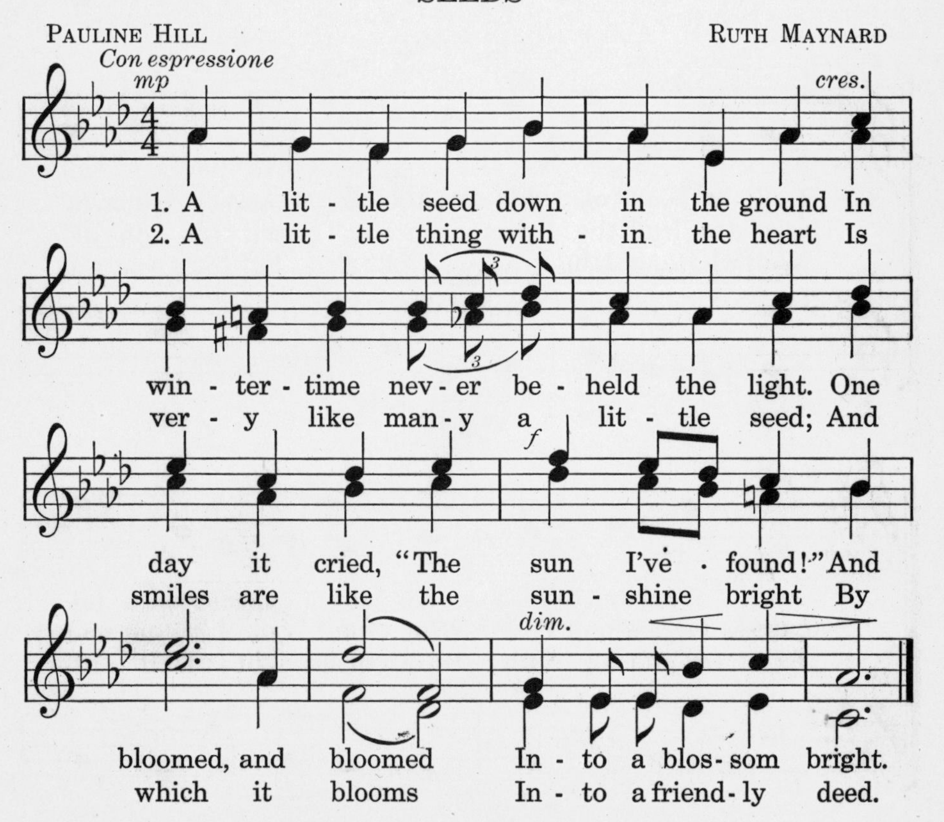

1. A lit - tle seed down in the ground In
2. A lit - tle thing with - in the heart Is

win - ter - time nev - er be - held the light. One
ver - y like man - y a lit - tle seed; And

day it cried, "The sun I've · found!" And
smiles are like the sun - shine bright By

f

dim.

bloomed, and bloomed In - to a blos - som bright.
which it blooms In - to a friend - ly deed.

HOLY, HOLY

FROM "THE HOLY CITY"

ALFRED GAUL

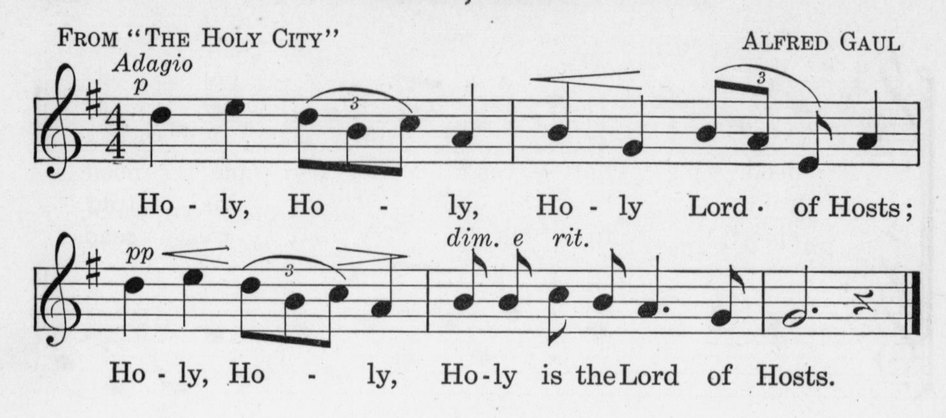

Ho - ly, Ho - ly, Ho - ly Lord · of Hosts;

Ho - ly, Ho - ly, Ho - ly is the Lord of Hosts.

INDIAN SUMMER

ROBERT BRIGHAM

KENNETH STRONG

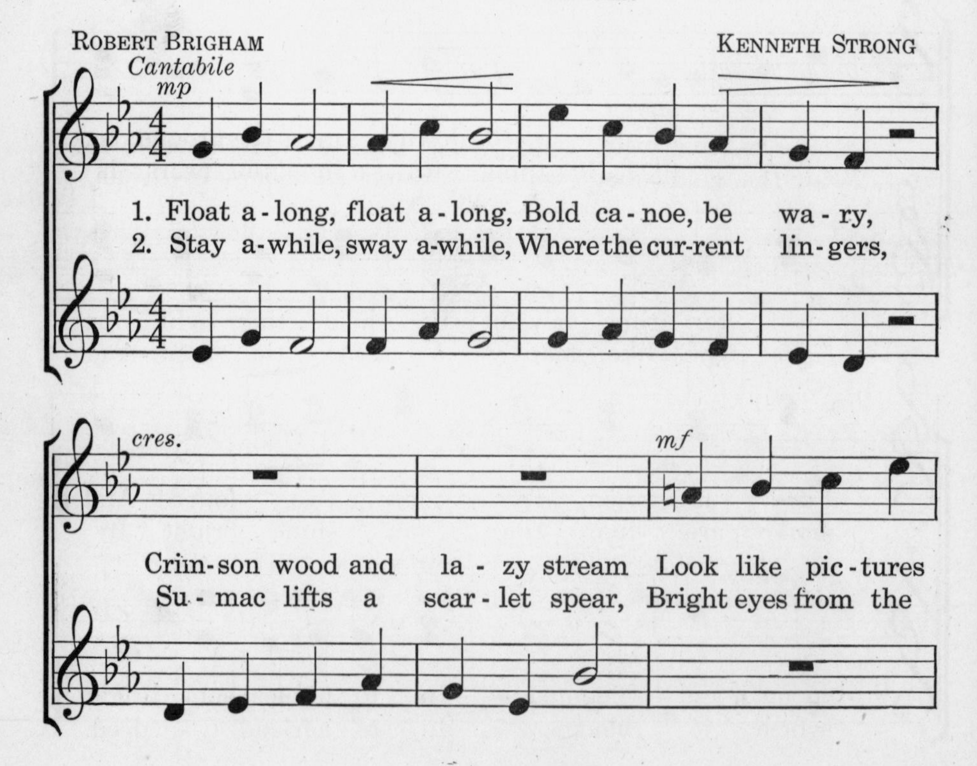

1. Float a - long, float a - long, Bold ca - noe, be wa - ry,
2. Stay a - while, sway a - while, Where the cur - rent lin - gers,

Crim - son wood and la - zy stream Look like pic - tures
Su - mac lifts a scar - let spear, Bright eyes from the

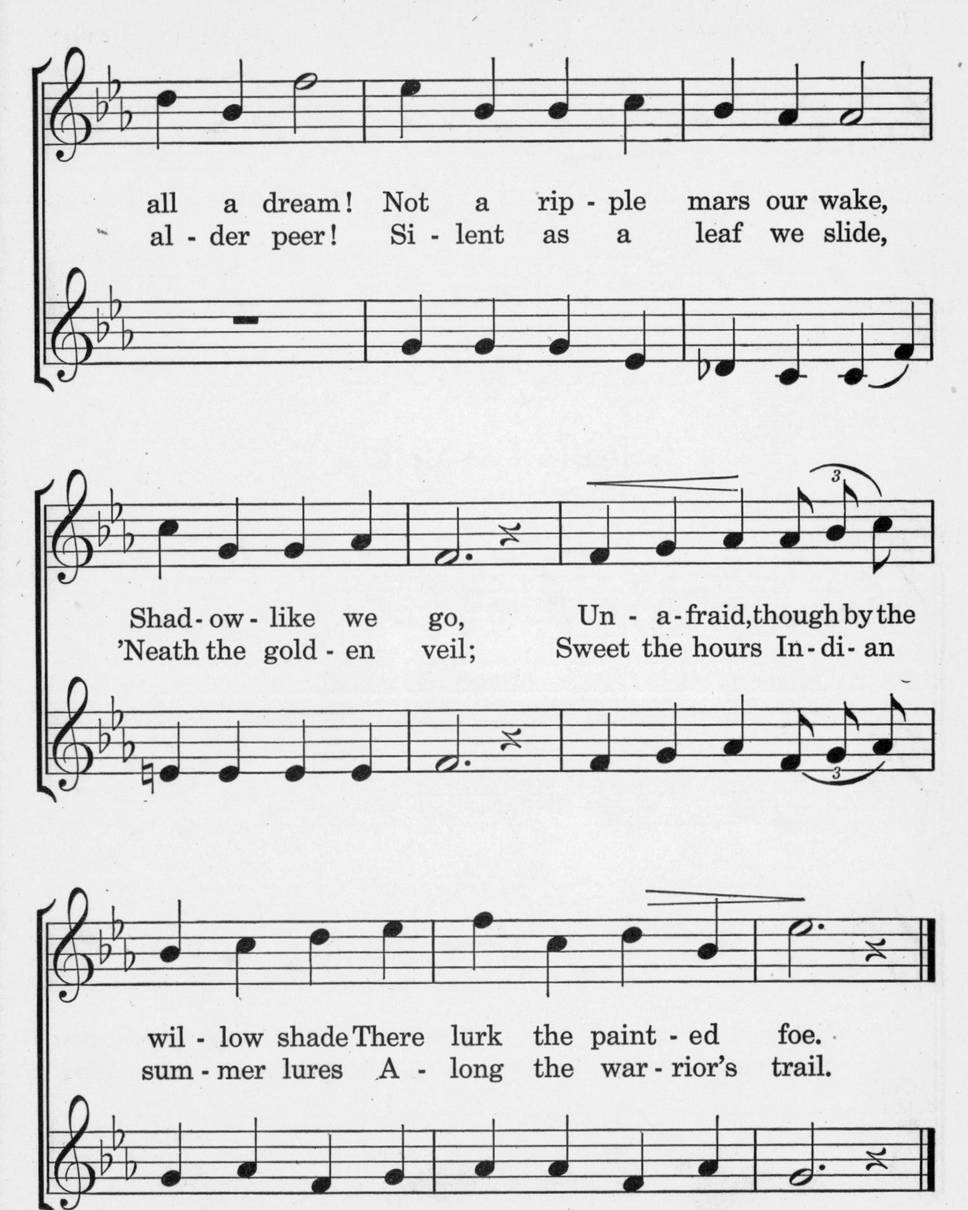

all a dream! Not a rip - ple mars our wake,
al - der peer! Si - lent as a leaf we slide,

Shad - ow - like we go, Un - a - fraid, though by the
'Neath the gold - en veil; Sweet the hours In - di - an

wil - low shade There lurk the paint - ed foe.
sum - mer lures A - long the war - rior's trail.

A TRIBUTE

NIXON WATERMAN

RALPH L. BALDWIN

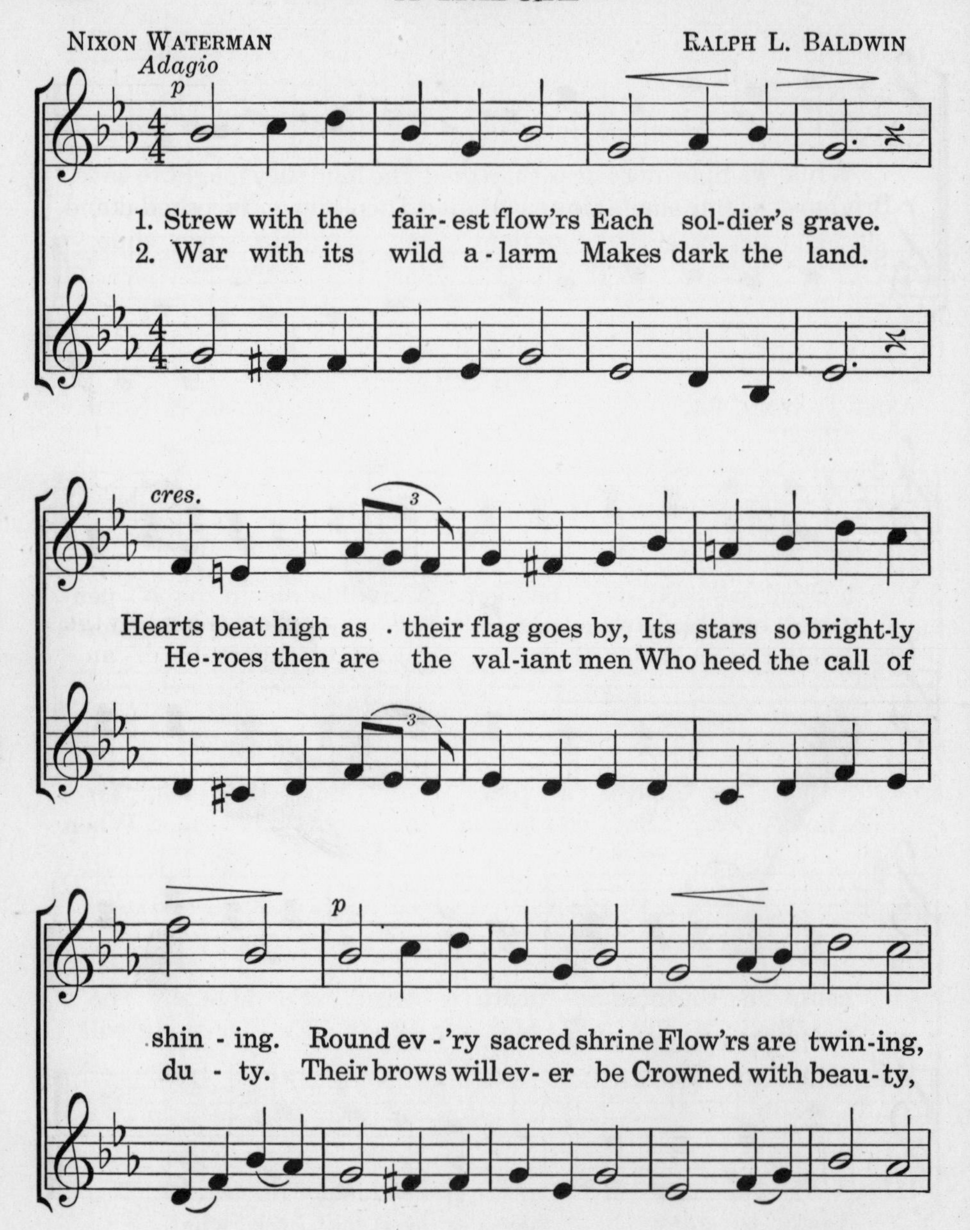

1. Strew with the fair-est flow'rs Each sol-dier's grave.
2. War with its wild a-larm Makes dark the land.

Hearts beat high as their flag goes by, Its stars so bright-ly
He-roes then are the val-iant men Who heed the call of

shin-ing. Round ev-'ry sacred shrine Flow'rs are twin-ing,
du-ty. Their brows will ev-er be Crowned with beau-ty,

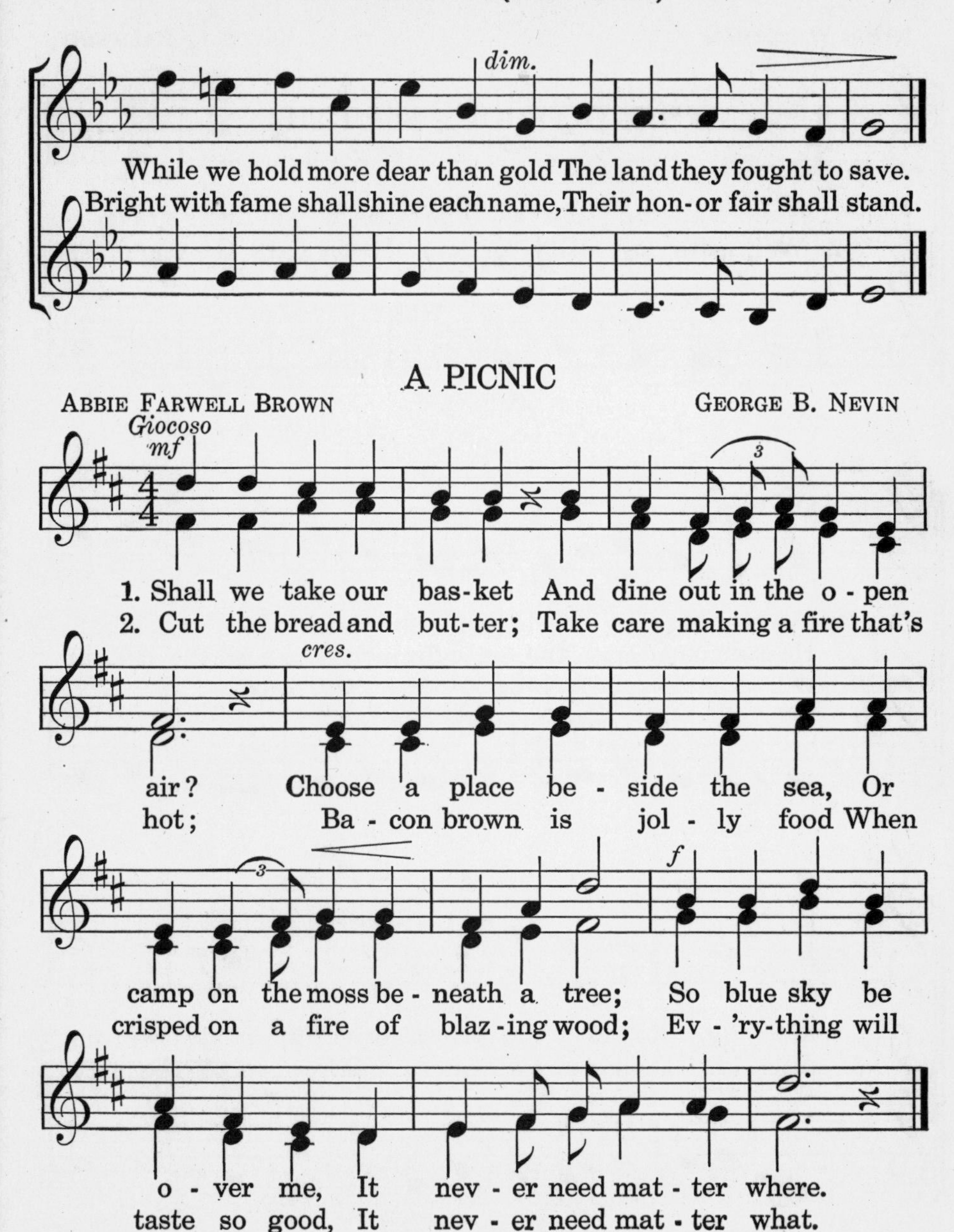

While we hold more dear than gold The land they fought to save.

Bright with fame shall shine each name, Their hon-or fair shall stand.

A PICNIC

ABBIE FARWELL BROWN   GEORGE B. NEVIN

Giocoso

1. Shall we take our bas-ket And dine out in the o - pen
2. Cut the bread and but-ter; Take care making a fire that's

air? Choose a place be - side the sea, Or

hot; Ba - con brown is jol - ly food When

camp on the moss be - neath a tree; So blue sky be

crisped on a fire of blaz -ing wood; Ev - 'ry-thing will

o - ver me, It nev - er need mat - ter where.

taste so good, It nev - er need mat - ter what.

PART II

THE GLORIOUS FOURTH

ELIZABETH NOXON

A. C. HORSFORD

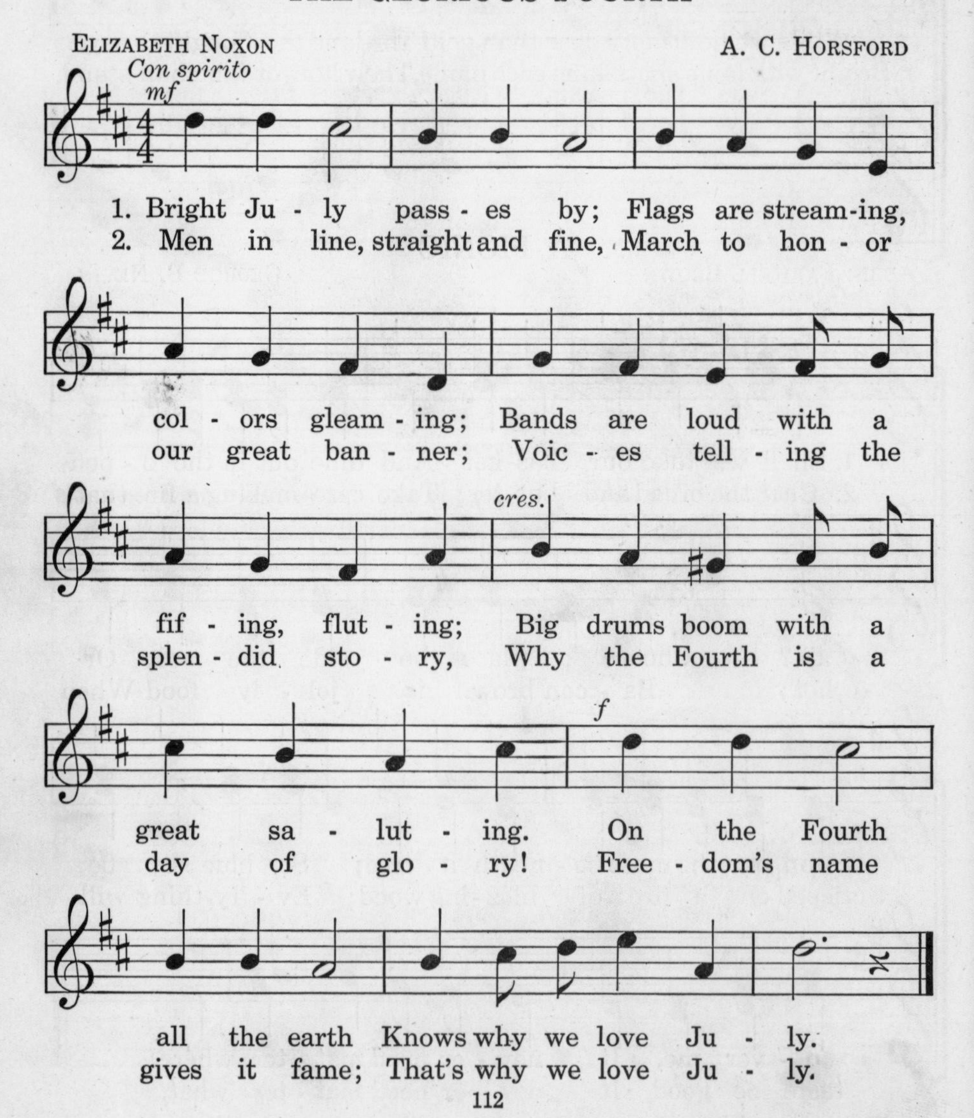

1. Bright Ju - ly pass - es by; Flags are stream-ing,
2. Men in line, straight and fine, March to hon - or

col - ors gleam - ing; Bands are loud with a
our great ban - ner; Voic - es tell - ing the

fif - ing, flut - ing; Big drums boom with a
splen - did sto - ry, Why the Fourth is a

great sa - lut - ing. On the Fourth
day of glo - ry! Free - dom's name

all the earth Knows why we love Ju - ly.
gives it fame; That's why we love Ju - ly.

JOHN REED

MAY ANDRUS

Andante
mp

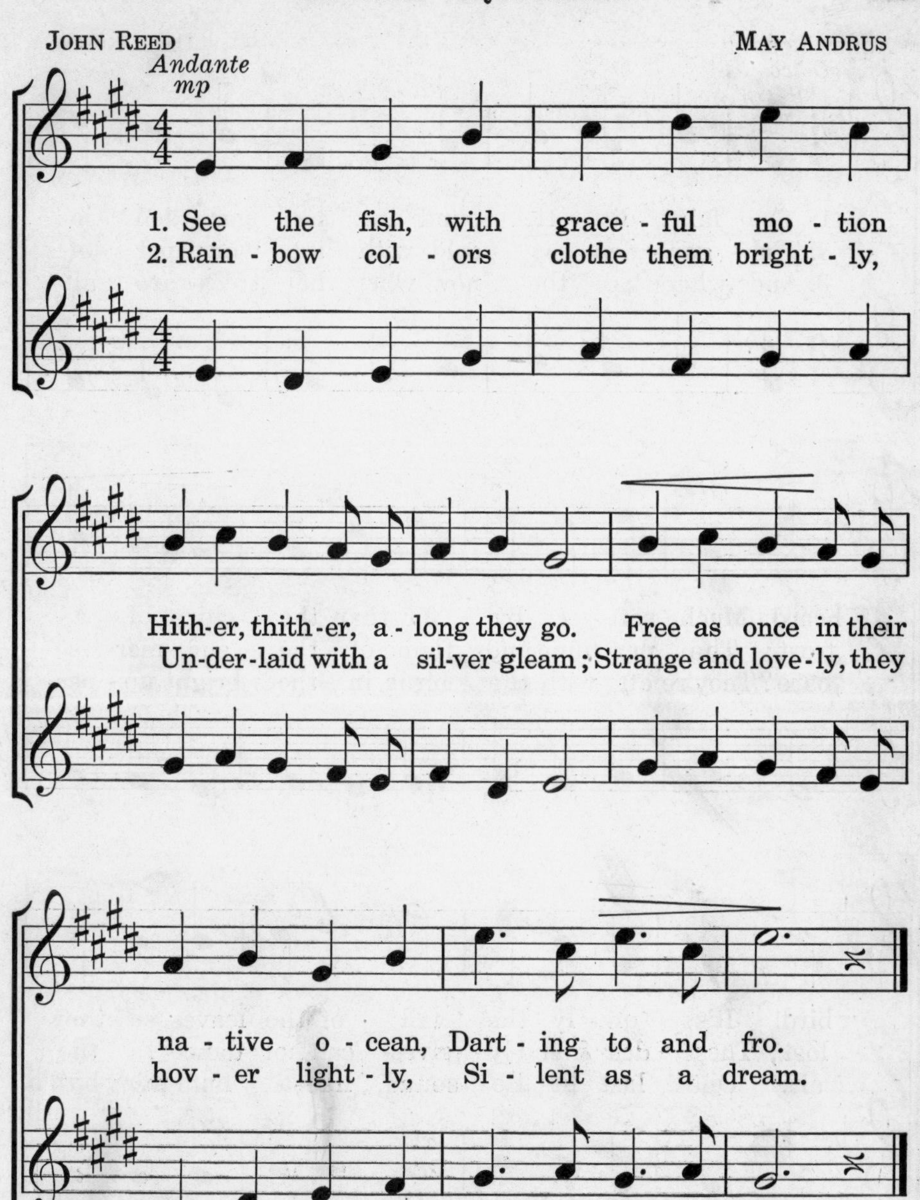

1. See the fish, with grace - ful mo - tion
2. Rain - bow col - ors clothe them bright - ly,

Hith-er, thith-er, a - long they go.   Free as once in their
Un-der-laid with a sil-ver gleam; Strange and love-ly, they

na - tive o - cean, Dart - ing to and fro.
hov - er light - ly, Si - lent as a dream.

T

THE FAIRIES' GOOD-BY

Agnes Ross

Carl Busch

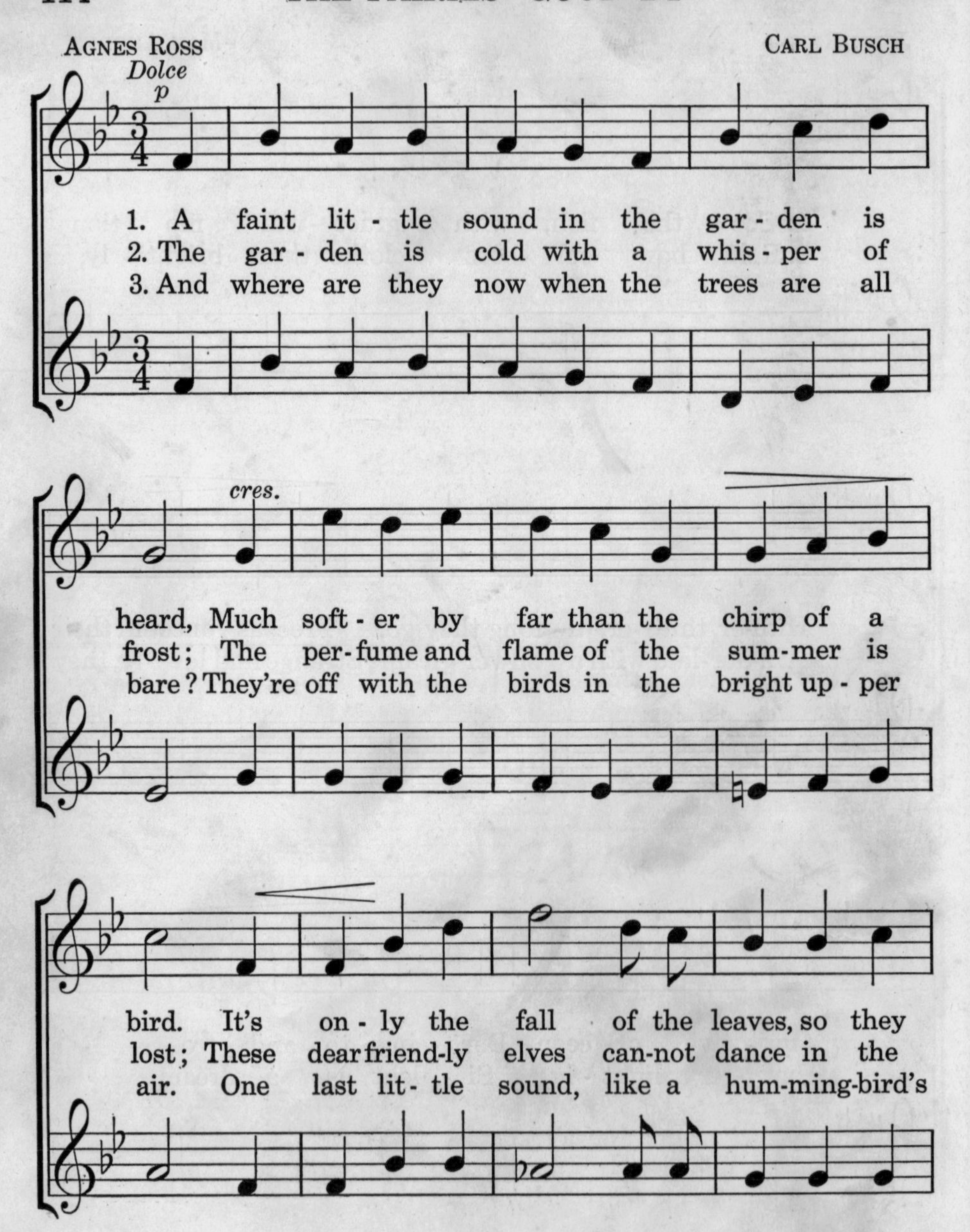

1. A faint lit - tle sound in the gar - den is
2. The gar - den is cold with a whis - per of
3. And where are they now when the trees are all

heard, Much soft - er by far than the chirp of a
frost; The per - fume and flame of the sum - mer is
bare? They're off with the birds in the bright up - per

bird. It's on - ly the fall of the leaves, so they
lost; These dear friend - ly elves can - not dance in the
air. One last lit - tle sound, like a hum - ming - bird's

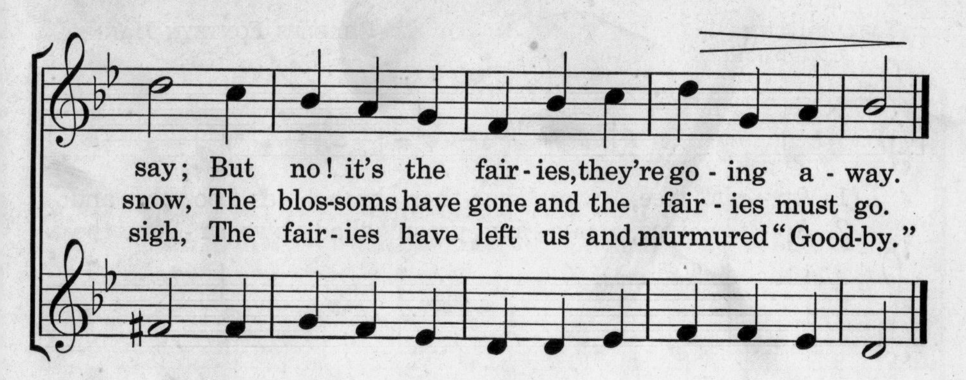

say; But no! it's the fair-ies, they're go-ing a-way.
snow, The blos-soms have gone and the fair-ies must go.
sigh, The fair-ies have left us and murmured "Good-by."

ELECTRIC SIGNS

LOUISE STICKNEY

ENGLISH FOLK TUNE

Animato
mf

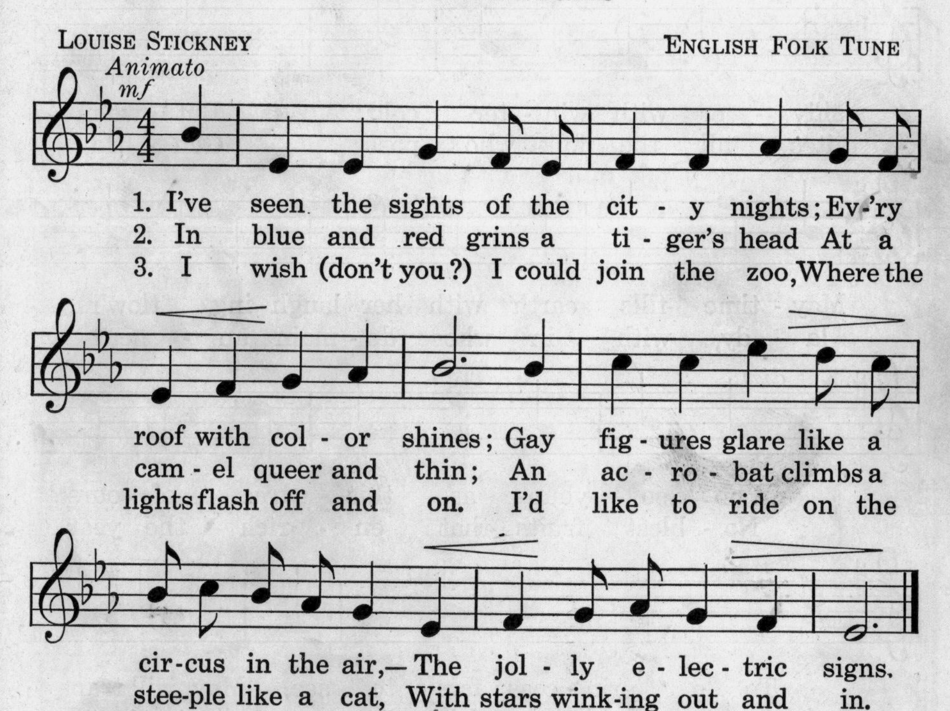

1. I've seen the sights of the cit-y nights; Ev-'ry
2. In blue and red grins a ti-ger's head At a
3. I wish (don't you?) I could join the zoo, Where the

roof with col-or shines; Gay fig-ures glare like a
cam-el queer and thin; An ac-ro-bat climbs a
lights flash off and on. I'd like to ride on the

cir-cus in the air,—The jol-ly e-lec-tric signs.
stee-ple like a cat, With stars wink-ing out and in.
ti-ger, if he's tied,—Oh, cit-ies at night are fun!

A WAYSIDE PRINCESS

TAYLOR-BAUM

CHARLES FONTEYN MANNEY

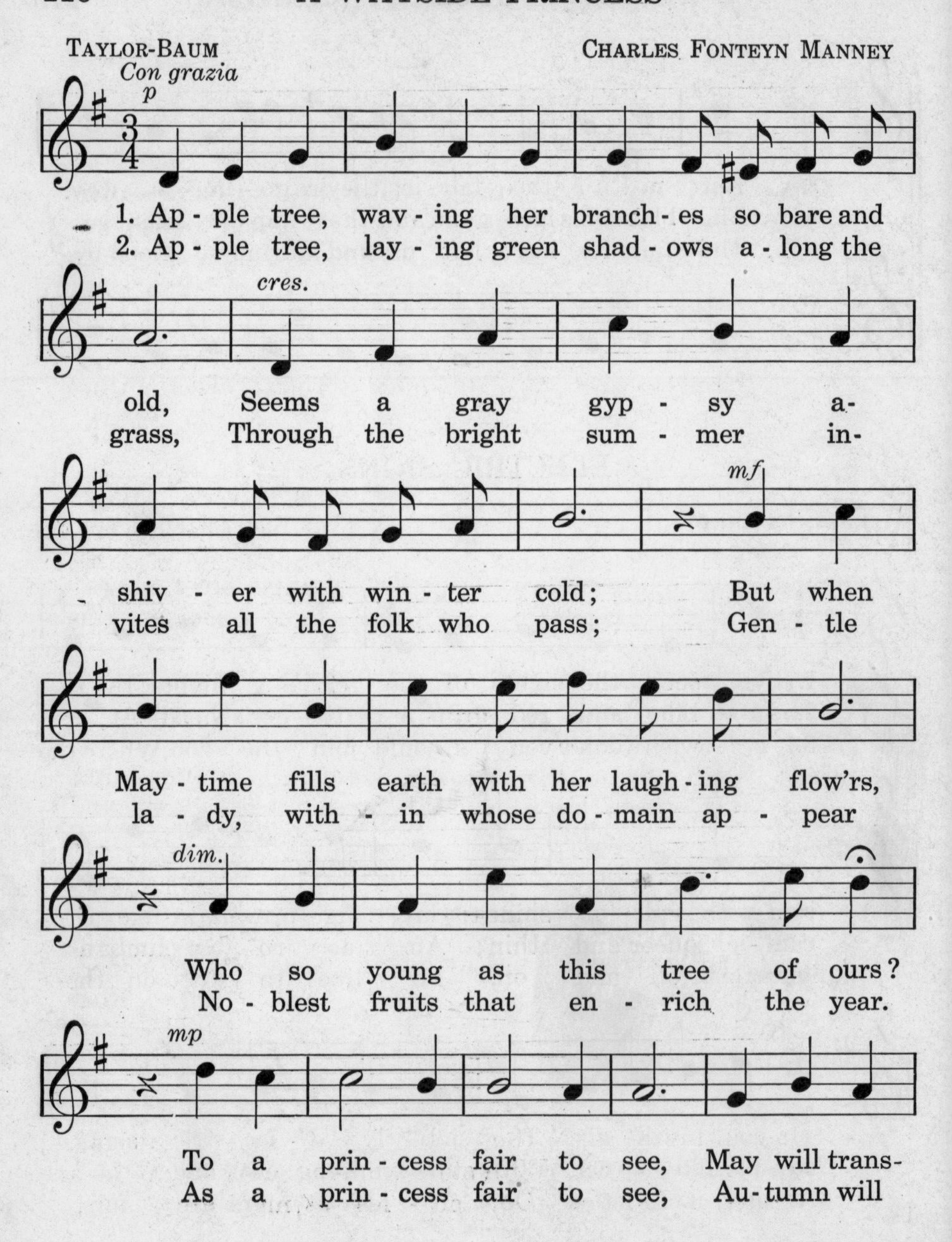

1. Ap - ple tree, wav - ing her branch - es so bare and
2. Ap - ple tree, lay - ing green shad - ows a - long the

old, Seems a gray gyp - sy a-
grass, Through the bright sum - mer in-

_ shiv - er with win - ter cold; But when
vites all the folk who pass; Gen - tle

May - time fills earth with her laugh - ing flow'rs,
la - dy, with - in whose do - main ap - pear

Who so young as this tree of ours?
No - blest fruits that en - rich the year.

To a prin - cess fair to see, May will trans-
As a prin - cess fair to see, Au - tumn will

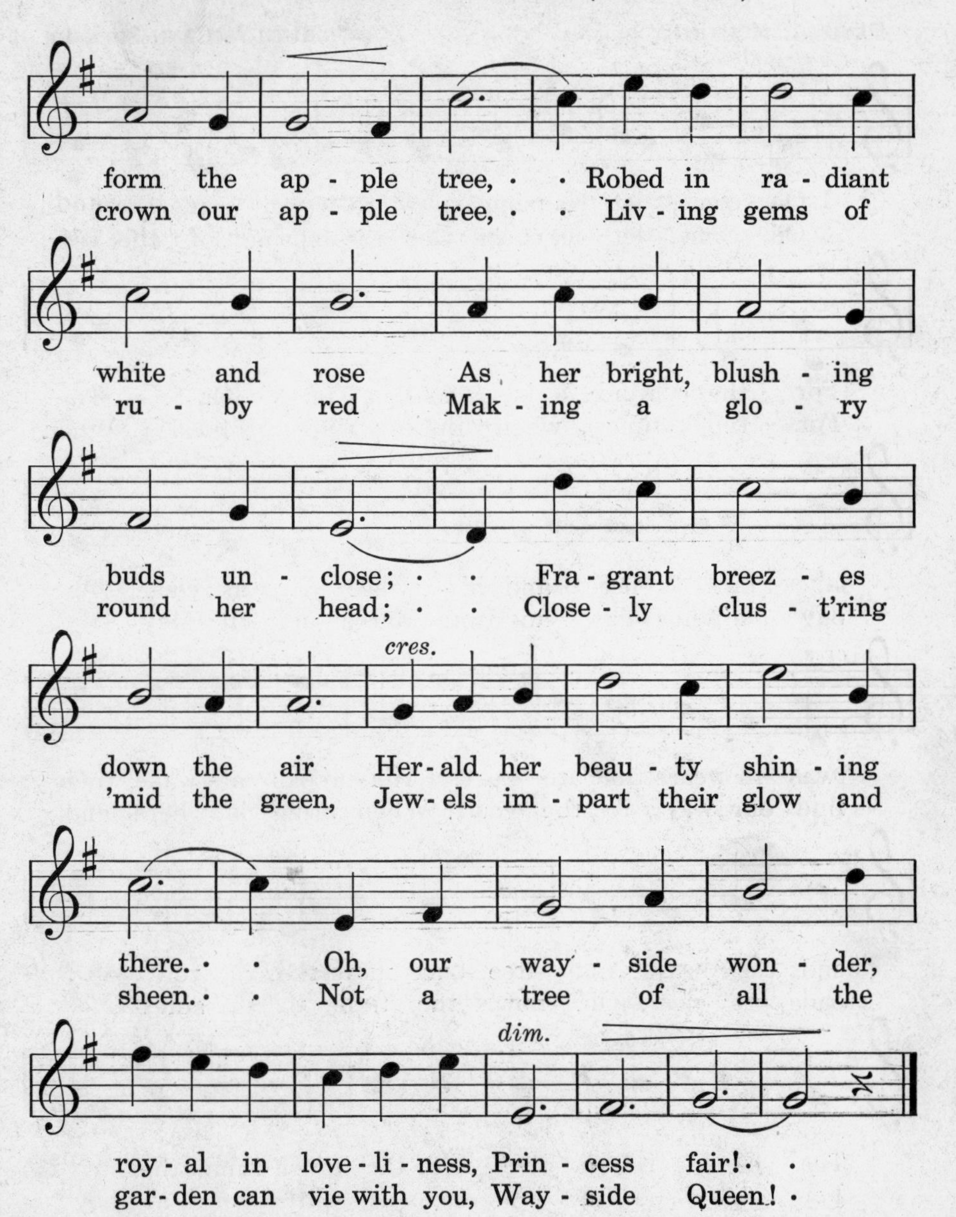

form the ap - ple tree, · · Robed in ra - diant
crown our ap - ple tree, · · Liv - ing gems of

white and rose As her bright, blush - ing
ru - by red Mak - ing a glo - ry

buds un - close; · · Fra - grant breez - es
round her head; · · Close - ly clus - t'ring

down the air Her - ald her beau - ty shin - ing
'mid the green, Jew - els im - part their glow and

there. · · Oh, our way - side won - der,
sheen. · · Not a tree of all the

roy - al in love - li - ness, Prin - cess fair! · ·
gar - den can vie with you, Way - side Queen! ·

TO WELCOME SPRING

DENIS A. MCCARTHY

RUTH MCCONN SPENCER

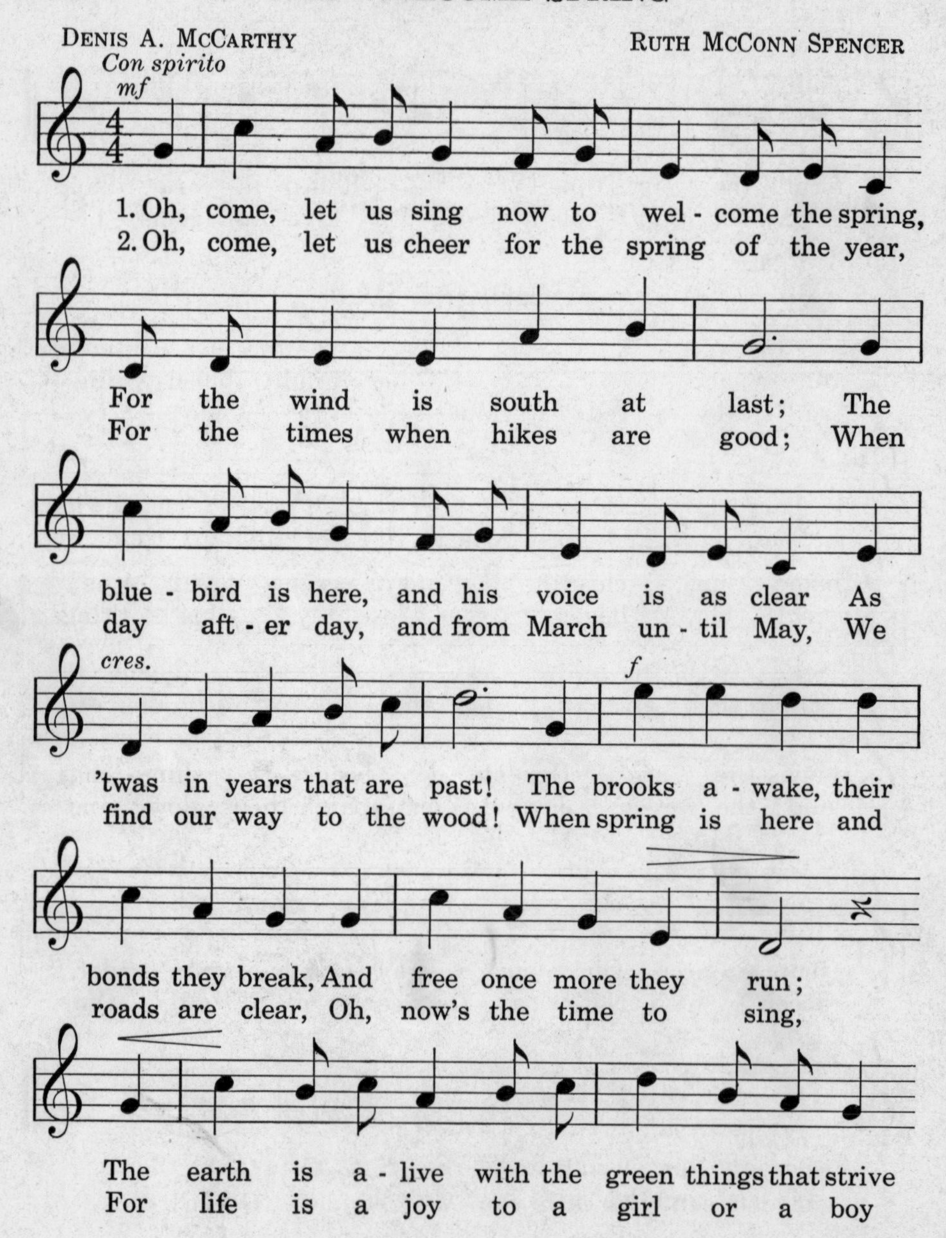

1. Oh, come, let us sing now to wel - come the spring,
2. Oh, come, let us cheer for the spring of the year,

For the wind is south at last; The
For the times when hikes are good; When

blue - bird is here, and his voice is as clear As
day aft - er day, and from March un - til May, We

'twas in years that are past! The brooks a - wake, their
find our way to the wood! When spring is here and

bonds they break, And free once more they run;
roads are clear, Oh, now's the time to sing,

The earth is a - live with the green things that strive
For life is a joy to a girl or a boy

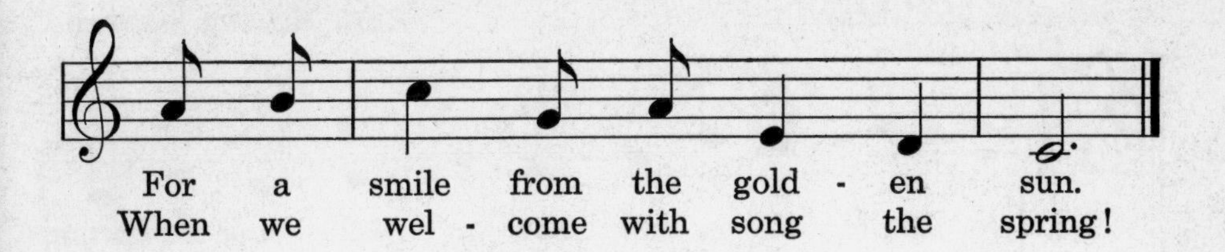

For a smile from the gold - en sun.
When we wel - come with song the spring!

MEMORIAL DAY

Robert Brigham

Ludwig van Beethoven

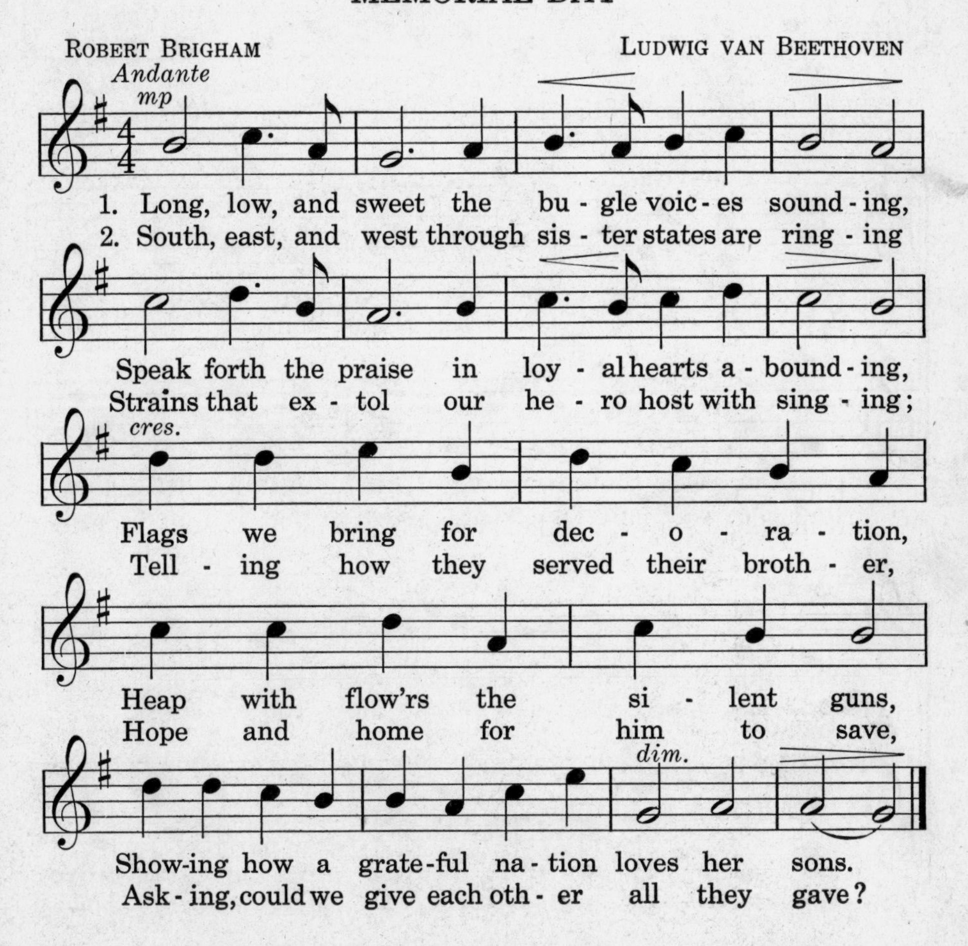

1. Long, low, and sweet the bu - gle voic - es sound - ing,
2. South, east, and west through sis - ter states are ring - ing

Speak forth the praise in loy - al hearts a - bound - ing,
Strains that ex - tol our he - ro host with sing - ing;

Flags we bring for dec - o - ra - tion,
Tell - ing how they served their broth - er,

Heap with flow'rs the si - lent guns,
Hope and home for him to save,

Show-ing how a grate-ful na - tion loves her sons.
Ask - ing, could we give each oth - er all they gave?

LULLABY

Mary Stanhope

Evelyn Sprague

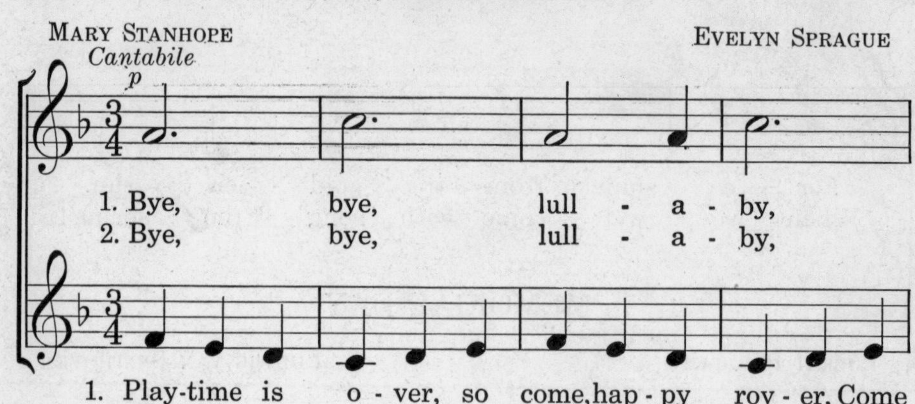

1. Bye, bye, lull - a - by,
2. Bye, bye, lull - a - by,

1. Play-time is o - ver, so come, hap - py rov - er, Come
2. Come, let us num - ber the hours of our slum - ber By

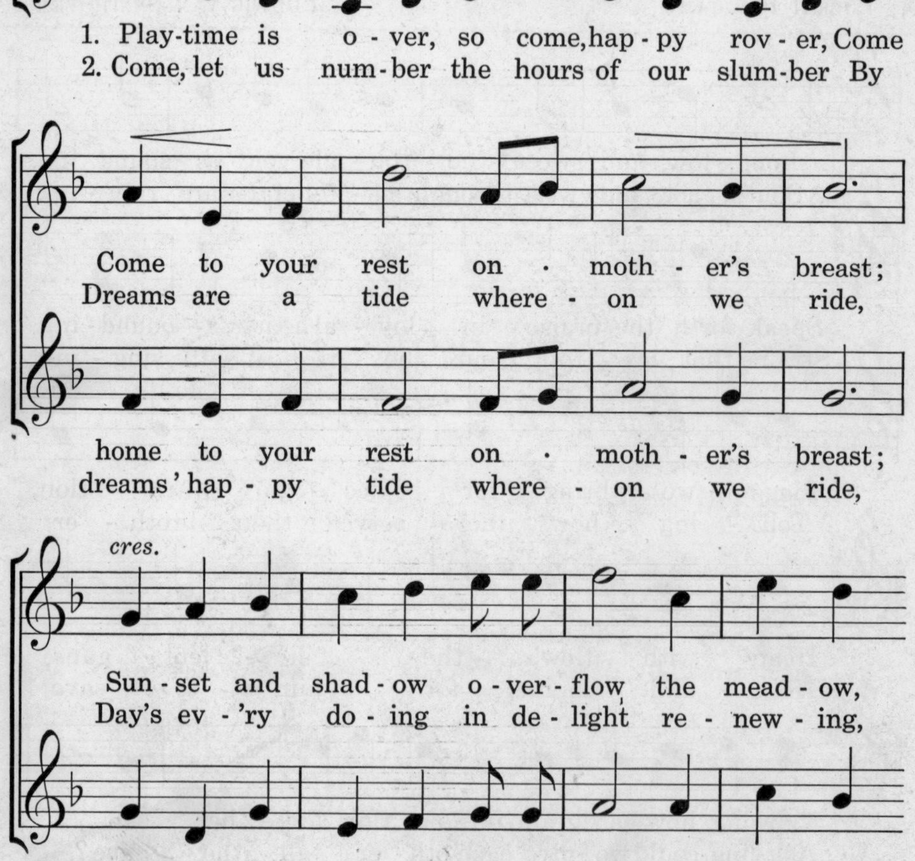

Come to your rest on · moth - er's breast;
Dreams are a tide where - on we ride,

home to your rest on · moth - er's breast;
dreams' hap - py tide where - on we ride,

cres.

Sun - set and shad - ow o - ver - flow the mead - ow,
Day's ev - 'ry do - ing in de - light re - new - ing,

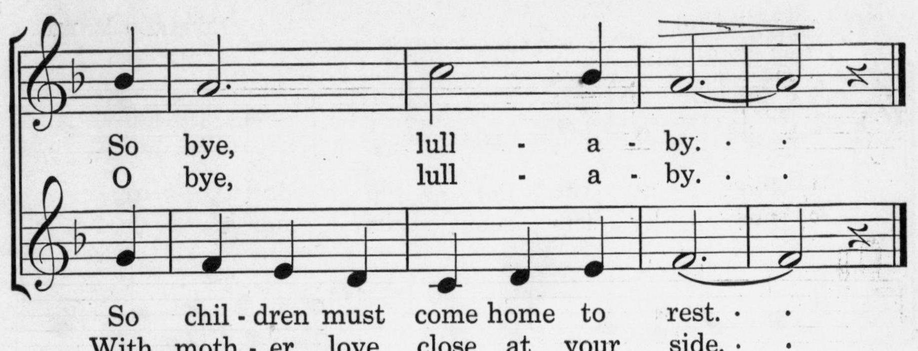

So bye,   lull - a - by. . .
O bye,   lull - a - by. . .

So chil - dren must come home to rest. . .
With moth - er love close at your side. . .

STARS

PHILIP ADAMS   HARRY HARTS

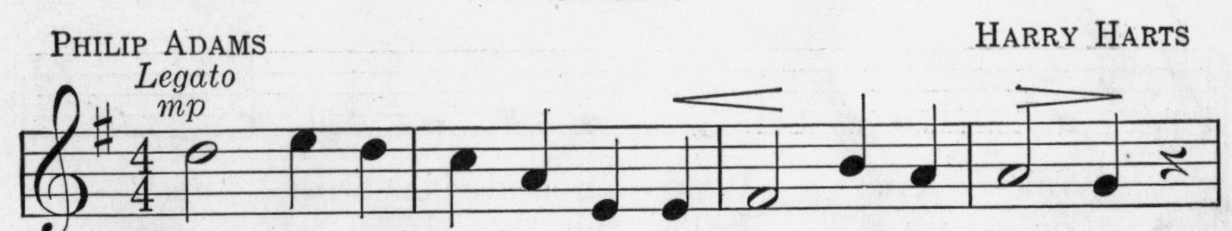

1. Night-long the stars on high that fail not in glo - ry
2. Day - long the stars shine on, while sunlight flows un - der;

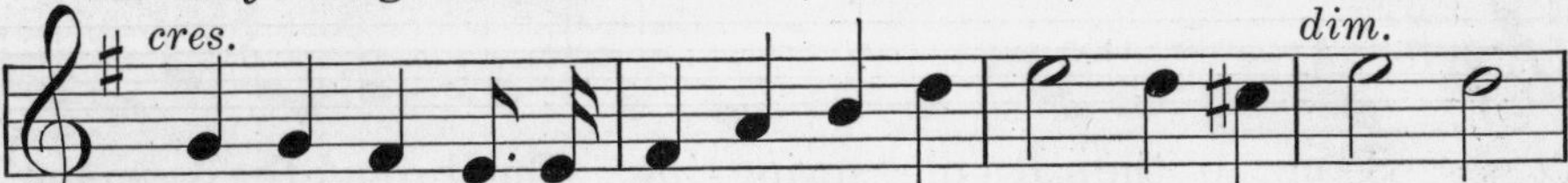

Print in gold on the az - ure sky a won-der-ful sto - ry.
Darkness comes to re - veal a - non their beau - ty and won - der.

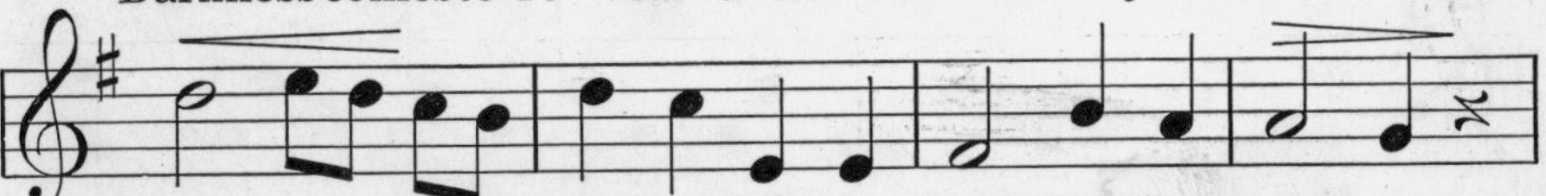

Bright con - stel - la-tions gild the heav'ns' end-less spac - es;
Stars crowd the Milk - y Way, or stand pure and lone - ly,

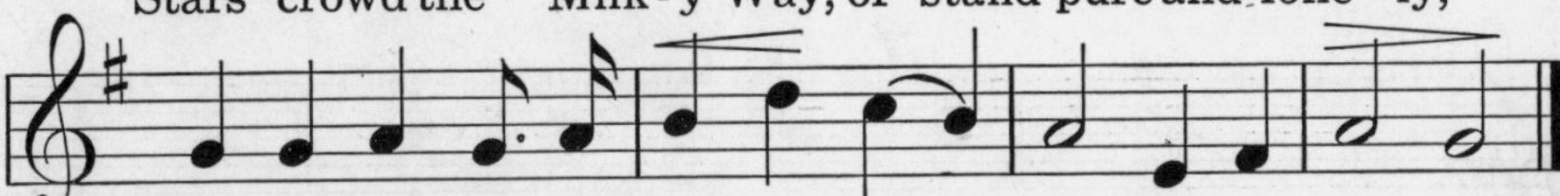

Pag-es fair with the ra-diant word God's fin-ger trac - es.
All re-cord-ing by night and day · God's prais-es on - ly.

THE MORNING RIDE

M. Louise Baum

Eduardo Marzo

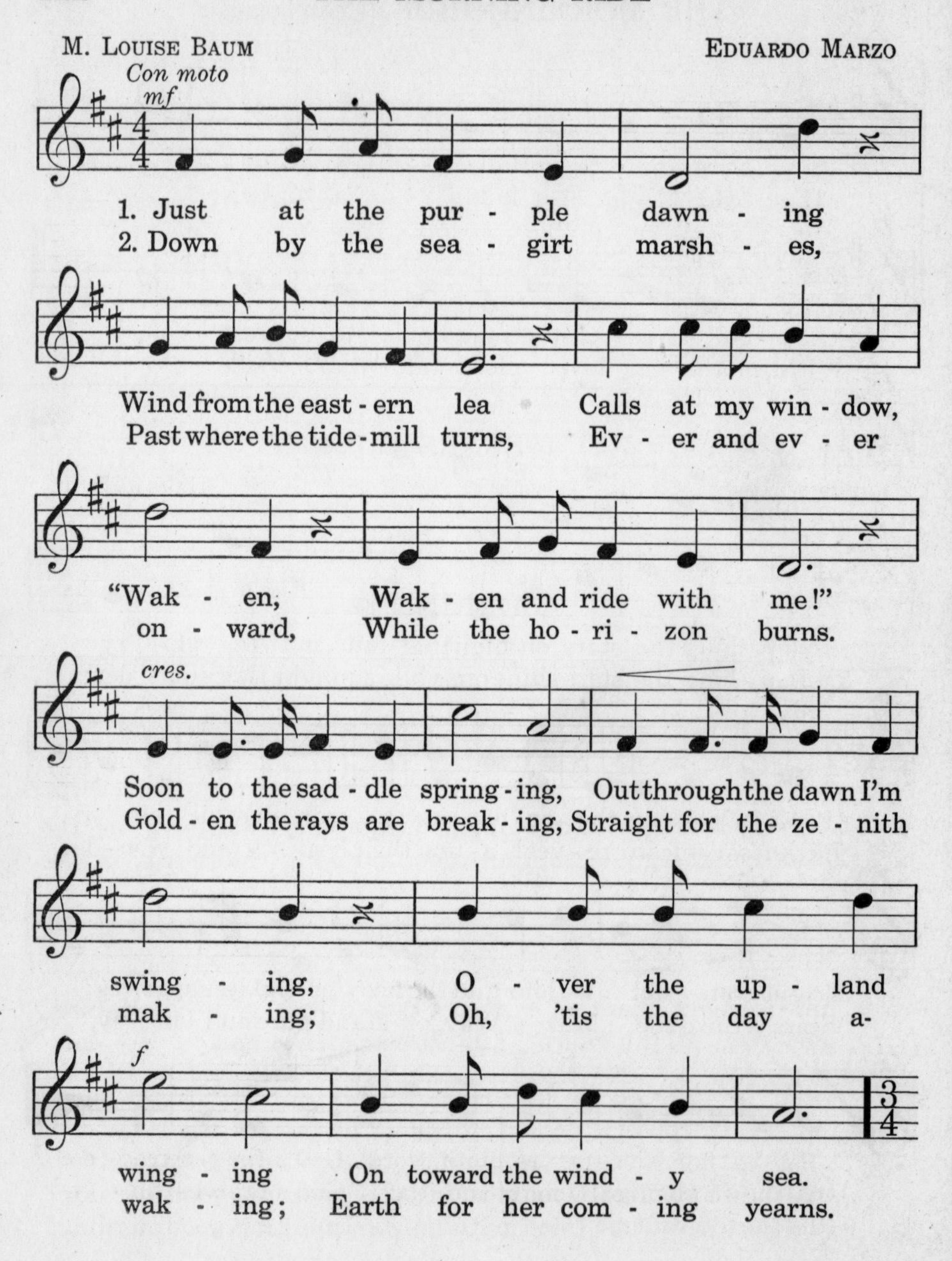

1. Just at the pur - ple dawn - ing
2. Down by the sea - girt marsh - es,

Wind from the east - ern lea Calls at my win - dow,
Past where the tide - mill turns, Ev - er and ev - er

"Wak - en, Wak - en and ride with me!"
on - ward, While the ho - ri - zon burns.

Soon to the sad - dle spring - ing, Out through the dawn I'm
Gold - en the rays are break - ing, Straight for the ze - nith

swing - ing, O - ver the up - land
mak - ing; Oh, 'tis the day a-

wing - ing On toward the wind - y sea.
wak - ing; Earth for her com - ing yearns.

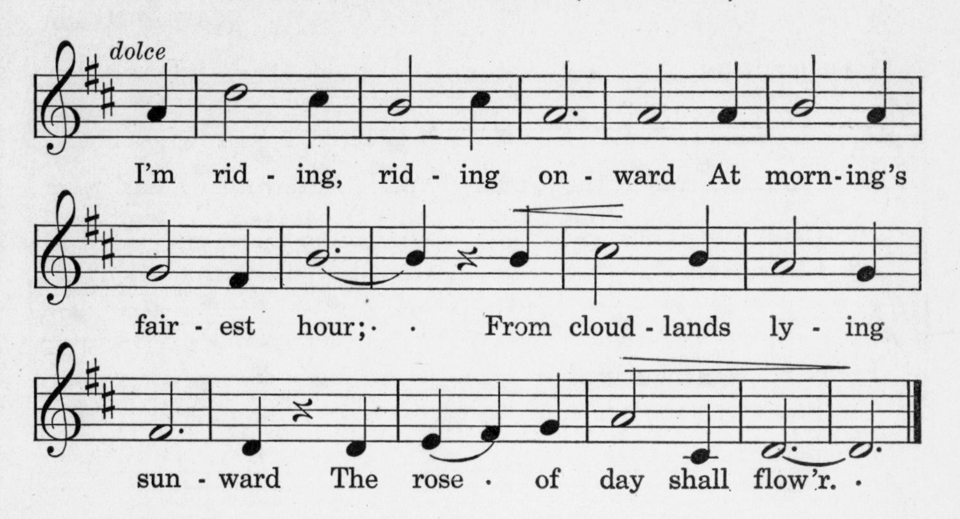

dolce

I'm rid - ing, rid - ing on - ward At morn-ing's

fair - est hour; · · From cloud - lands ly - ing

sun - ward The rose · of day shall flow'r. ·

MORNING

Mary Root Kern   Mary Root Kern

Allegretto

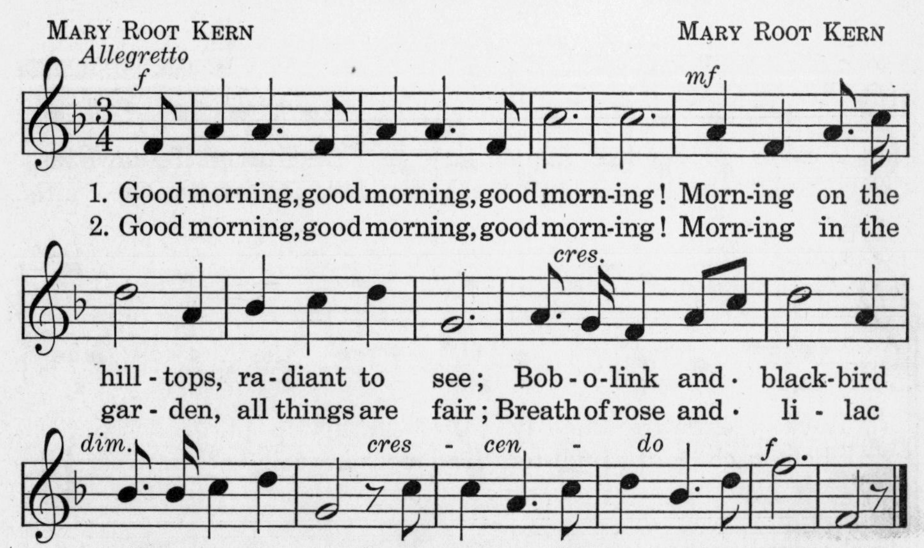

1. Good morning, good morning, good morn-ing! Morn-ing on the
2. Good morning, good morning, good morn-ing! Morn-ing in the

cres.

hill - tops, ra - diant to   see; Bob - o - link and · black-bird
gar - den, all things are   fair; Breath of rose and · li - lac

dim.   *cres - cen - do*   *f*

trill-ing on the tree. Good morning, good morning, good morning!
fills the fragrant air. Good morning, good morning, good morning!

CALM FLOWING RIVER

English version by
M. LOUISE BAUM

FRENCH FOLK SONG

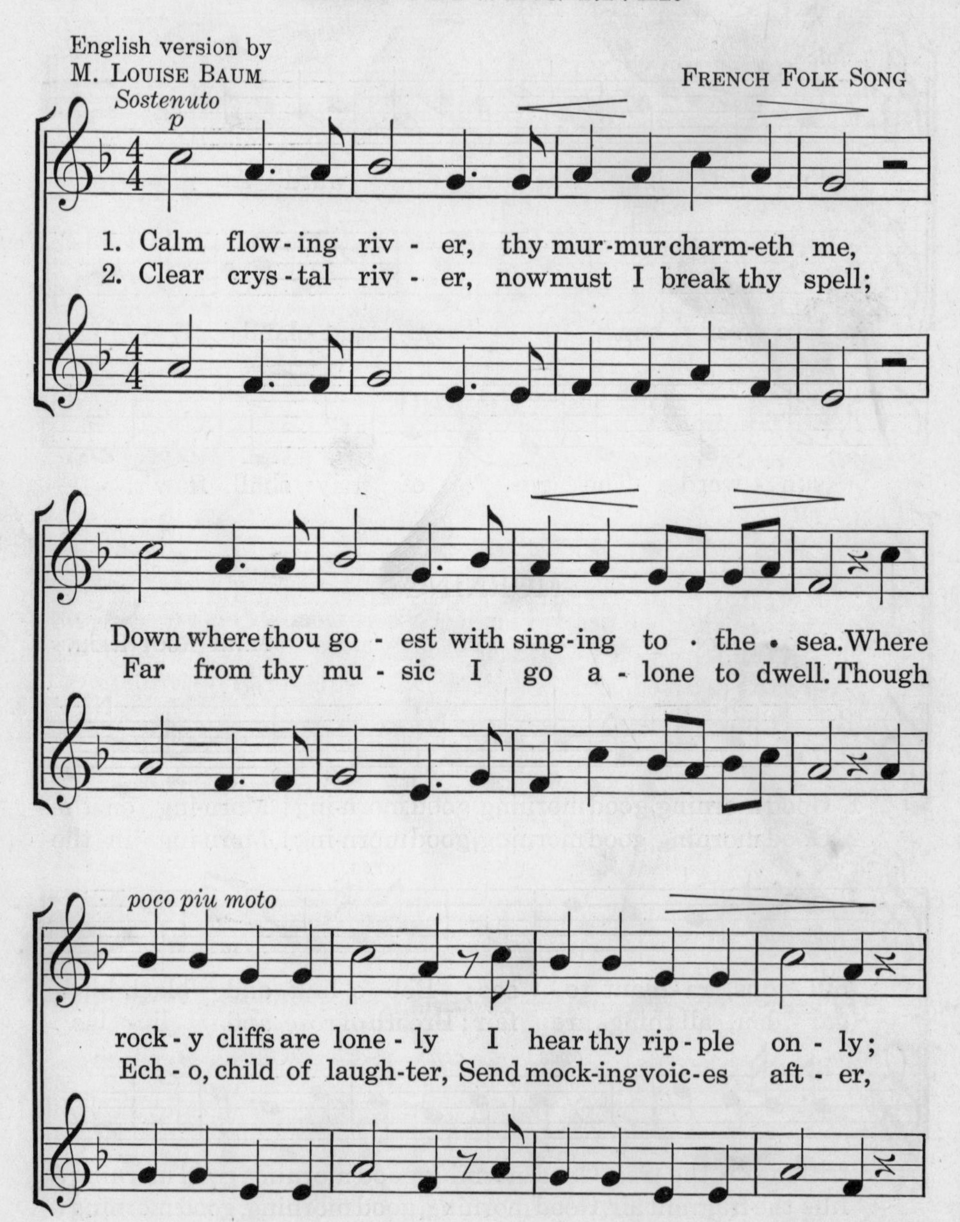

1. Calm flow-ing riv - er, thy mur-mur charm-eth me,
2. Clear crys-tal riv - er, now must I break thy spell;

Down where thou go - est with sing-ing to the sea. Where
Far from thy mu - sic I go a - lone to dwell. Though

rock - y cliffs are lone - ly I hear thy rip - ple on - ly;
Ech - o, child of laugh-ter, Send mock-ing voic-es aft - er,

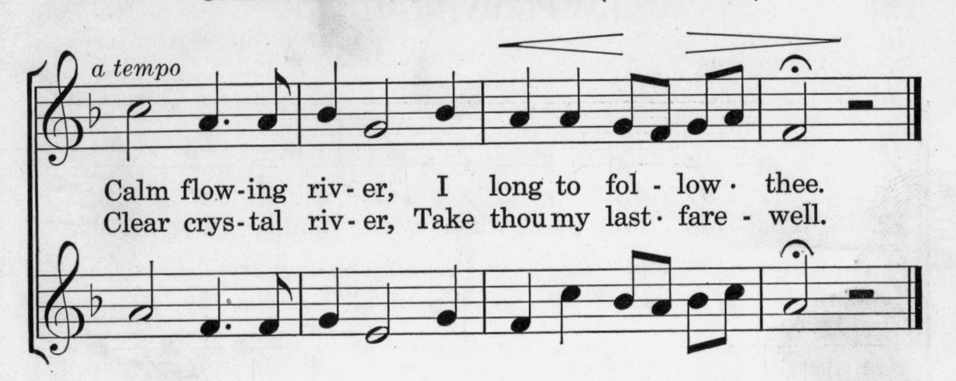

a tempo

Calm flow-ing riv-er, I long to fol-low thee.
Clear crys-tal riv-er, Take thou my last fare-well.

CAMP FIRE

ABBIE FARWELL BROWN

ENGLISH FOLK TUNE

Animato

mf

cres.

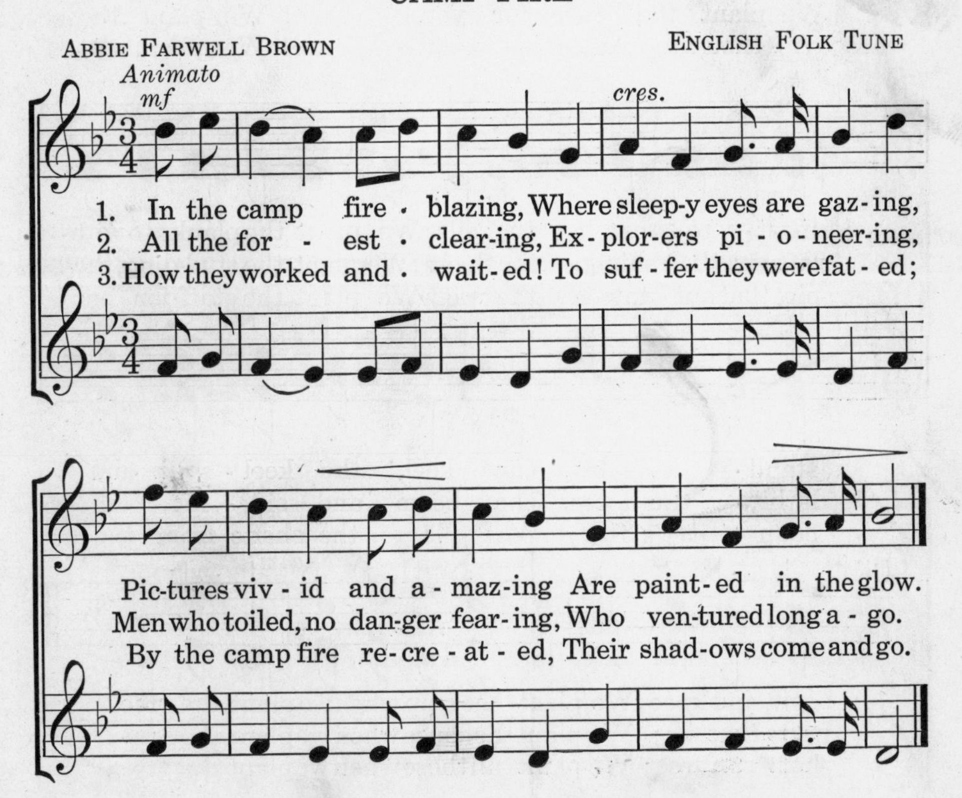

1. In the camp fire blazing, Where sleep-y eyes are gaz-ing,
2. All the for-est clear-ing, Ex-plor-ers pi-o-neer-ing,
3. How they worked and wait-ed! To suf-fer they were fat-ed;

Pic-tures viv-id and a-maz-ing Are paint-ed in the glow.
Men who toiled, no dan-ger fear-ing, Who ven-tured long a-go.
By the camp fire re-cre-at-ed, Their shad-ows come and go.

HENRY ABBEY

FANNY SNOW KNOWLTON

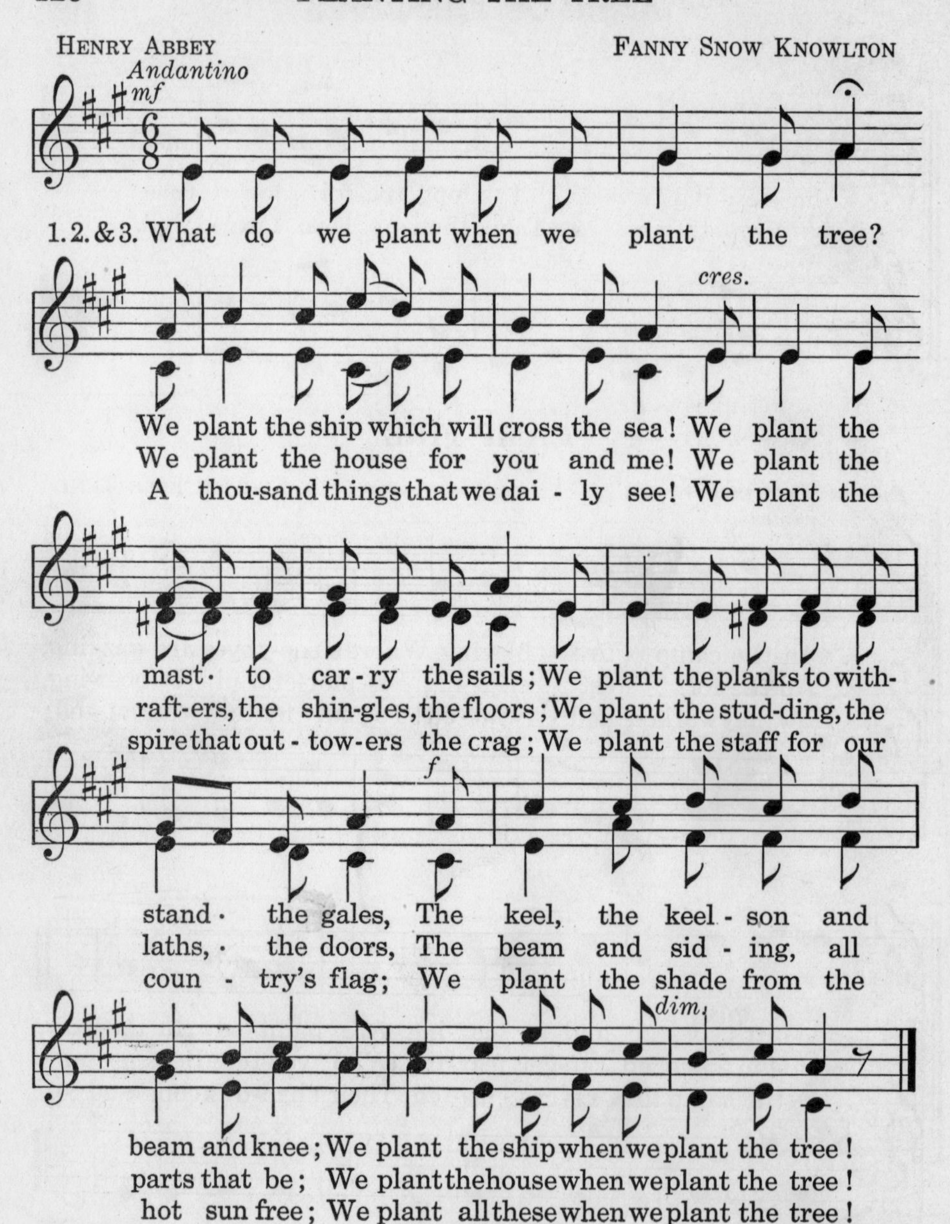

1.2.&3. What do we plant when we plant the tree?

We plant the ship which will cross the sea! We plant the
We plant the house for you and me! We plant the
A thou-sand things that we dai - ly see! We plant the

mast · to car - ry the sails; We plant the planks to with-
raft-ers, the shin-gles, the floors; We plant the stud-ding, the
spire that out - tow-ers the crag; We plant the staff for our

stand · the gales, The keel, the keel - son and
laths, · the doors, The beam and sid - ing, all
coun - try's flag; We plant the shade from the

beam and knee; We plant the ship when we plant the tree!
parts that be; We plant the house when we plant the tree!
hot sun free; We plant all these when we plant the tree!

STANLEY MARTIN

LAURETTA V. SWEESY

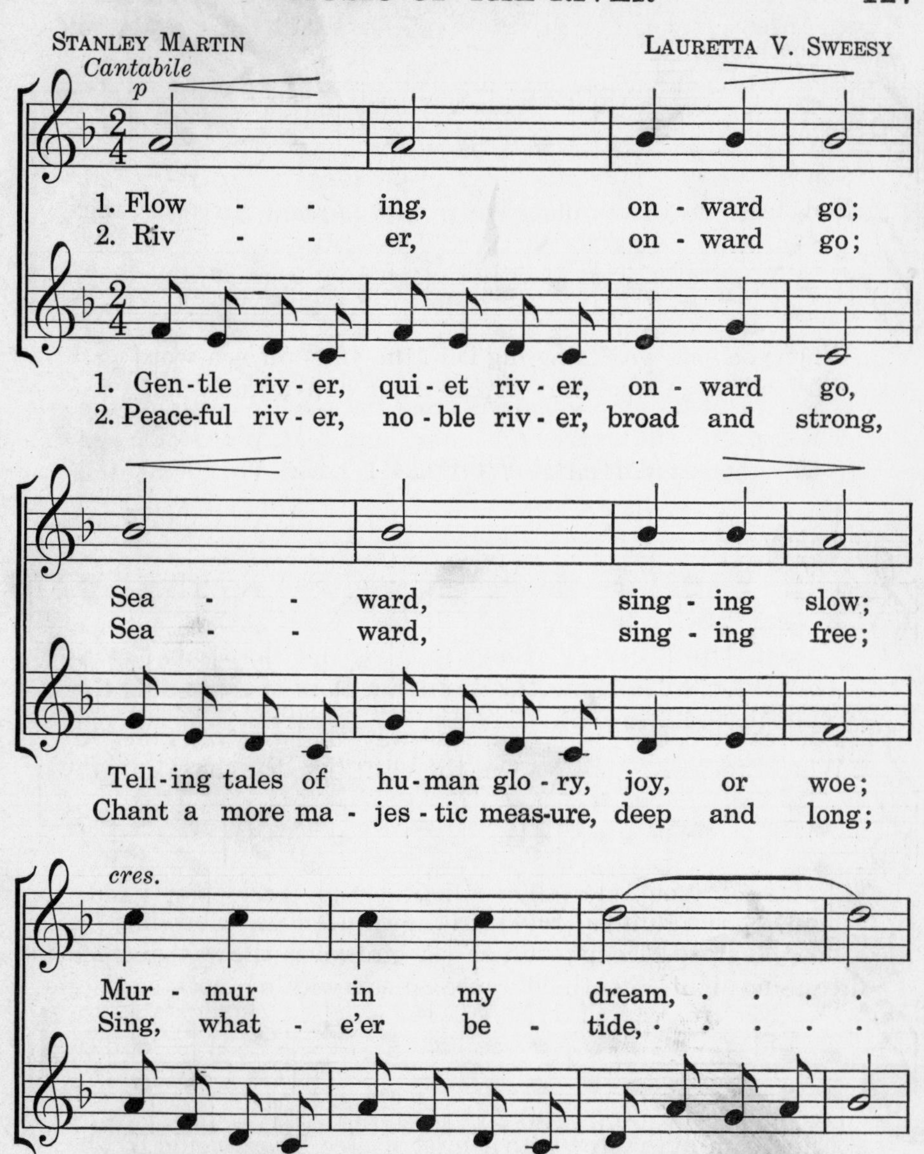

1. Flow - - ing, on - ward go;
2. Riv - - er, on - ward go;

1. Gen-tle riv-er, qui-et riv-er, on-ward go,
2. Peace-ful riv-er, no-ble riv-er, broad and strong,

Sea - - ward, sing-ing slow;
Sea - - ward, sing-ing free;

Tell-ing tales of hu-man glo-ry, joy, or woe;
Chant a more ma-jes-tic meas-ure, deep and long;

Mur - mur in my dream, ...
Sing, what-e'er be-tide, ...

Tell-ing tales of new ad-ven-tures Yon-der that a-wait,
Stead-y keep your on-ward flow-ing; It shall end-ed be,

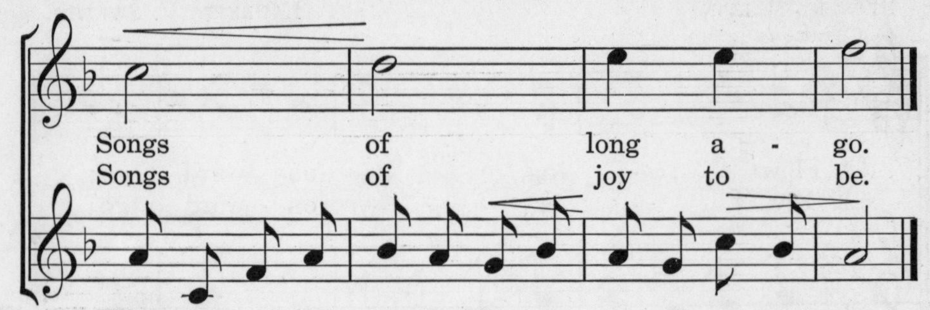

Songs   of   long a - go.
Songs   of   joy to be.

When you pass with sing-ing Thro' the far - off sea-ward gate.
Like all true en - deav-or, In some hap-py shin - ing sea.

WHERE WOULD I BE?

KARL ZÖLLNER

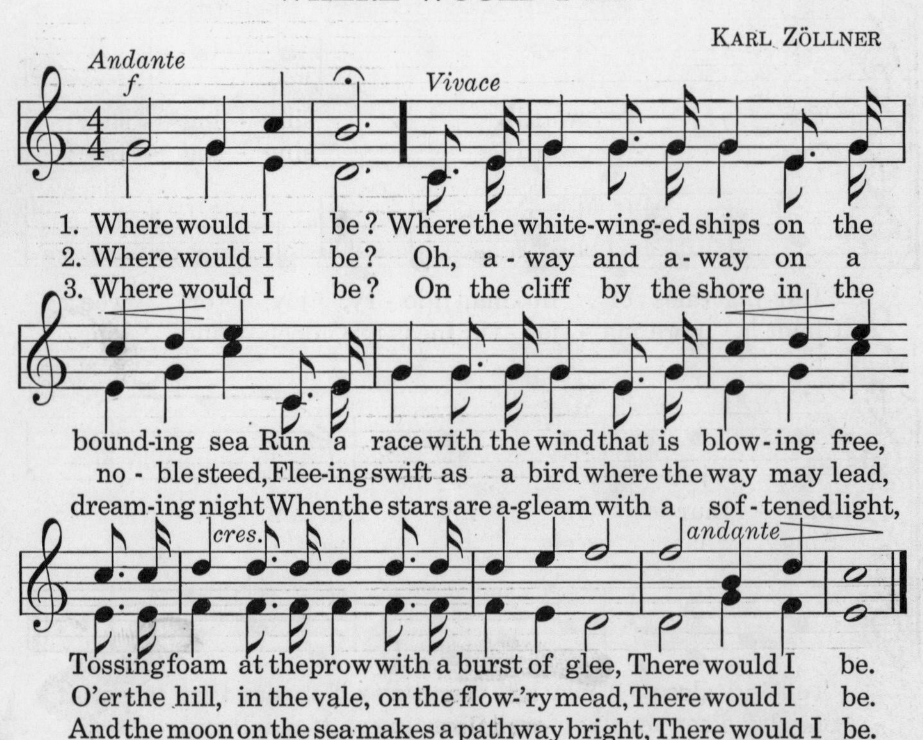

1. Where would I be? Where the white-wing-ed ships on the
2. Where would I be? Oh, a - way and a - way on a
3. Where would I be? On the cliff by the shore in the

bound-ing sea Run a race with the wind that is blow-ing free,
no - ble steed, Flee-ing swift as a bird where the way may lead,
dream-ing night When the stars are a-gleam with a sof - tened light,

Tossing foam at the prow with a burst of glee, There would I be.
O'er the hill, in the vale, on the flow-'ry mead, There would I be.
And the moon on the sea makes a pathway bright, There would I be.

MY FARM

KATE FORMAN
Con moto

MARY STRAWN VERNON

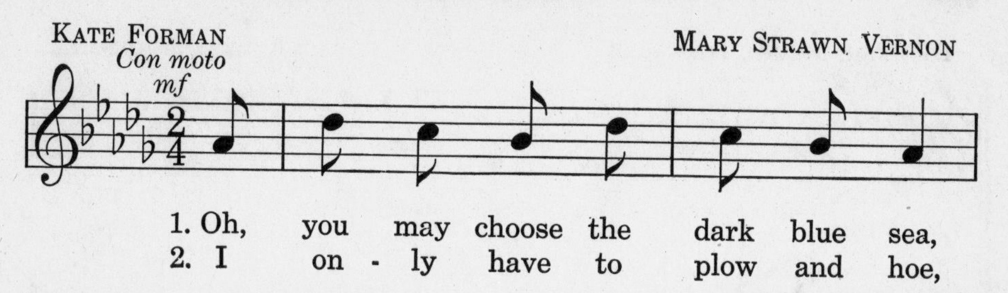

1. Oh, you may choose the dark blue sea,
2. I on - ly have to plow and hoe,

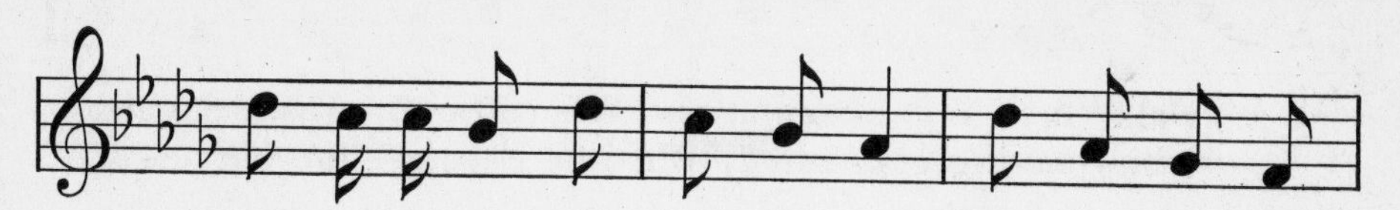

Life on the brown old earth for me! On - ly let me
On - ly the gold - en seed to sow, Keep the weeds a-

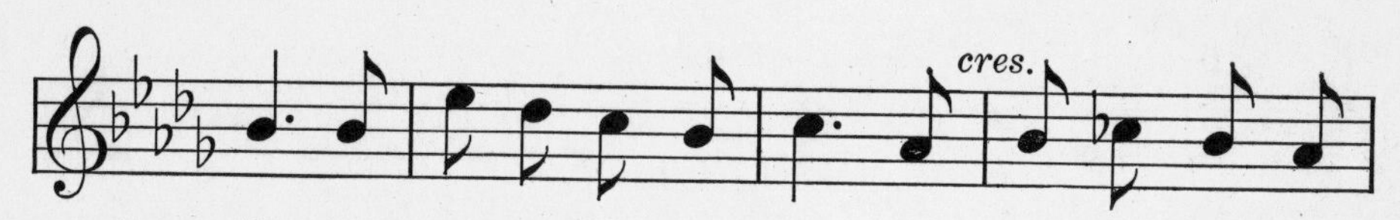

own a lit - tle farm a - lone, Oh, let me have a
way with pa - tient care each day. When small green leaves be-

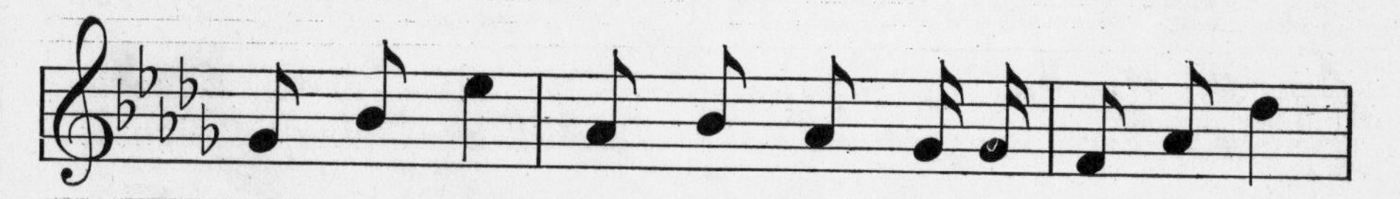

spade and plow; Wait and watch till I show you how
gin to show, All so fresh in a live - ly row,

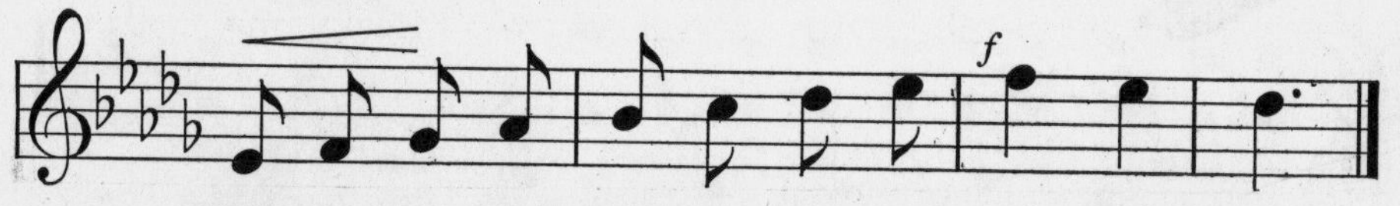

This be - nign and fer - tile earth will work for me!
Then the won - der - work - ing earth will make them grow.

T

IN THE GARDEN

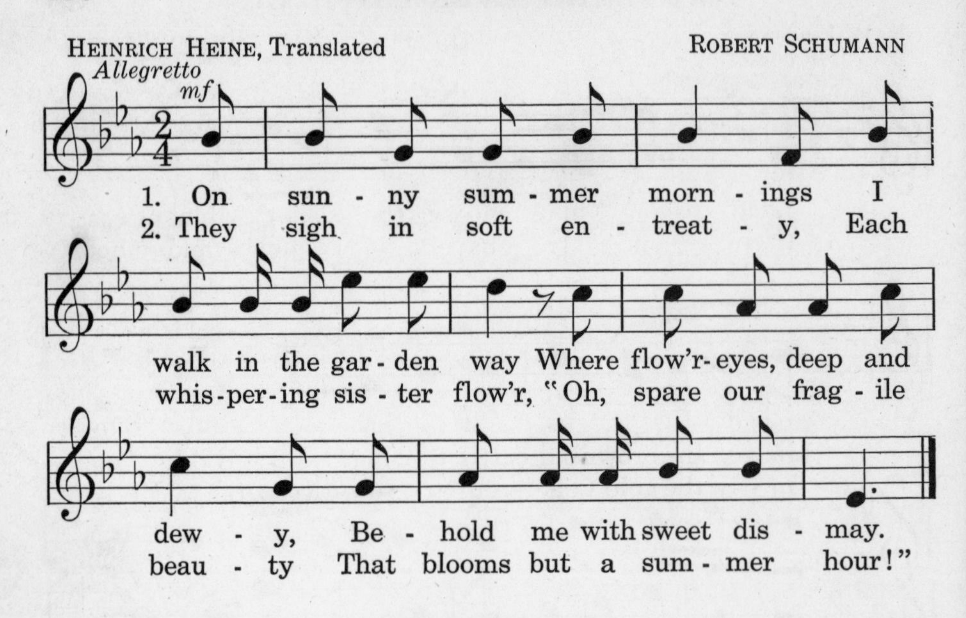

HEINRICH HEINE, Translated

ROBERT SCHUMANN

Allegretto
mf

1. On sun - ny sum - mer morn - ings I
2. They sigh in soft en - treat - y, Each

walk in the gar - den way Where flow'r- eyes, deep and
whis -per-ing sis - ter flow'r, "Oh, spare our frag - ile

dew - y, Be - hold me with sweet dis - may.
beau - ty That blooms but a sum - mer hour!"

REFLECTIONS

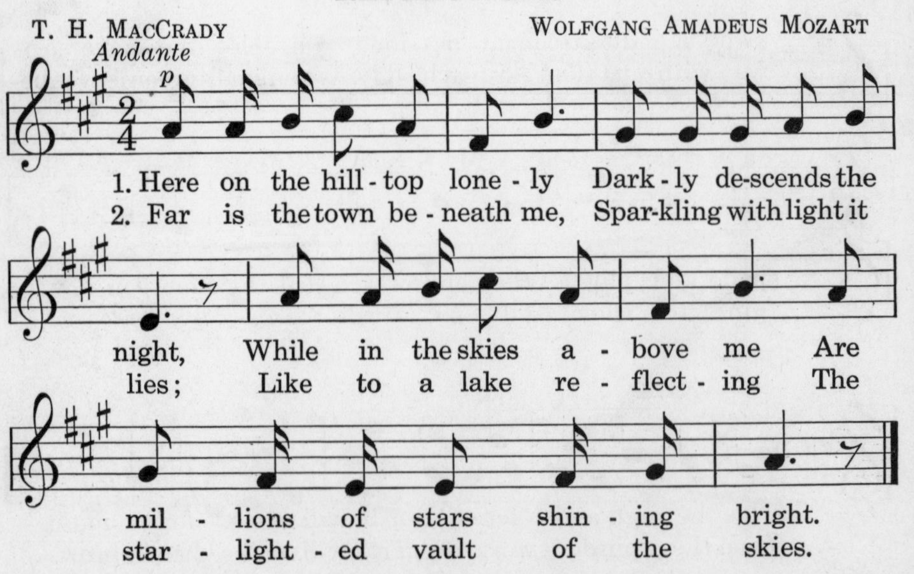

T. H. MacCrady

WOLFGANG AMADEUS MOZART

Andante
p

1. Here on the hill - top lone - ly Dark - ly de-scends the
2. Far is the town be - neath me, Spar-kling with light it

night, While in the skies a - bove me Are
lies; Like to a lake re - flect - ing The

mil - lions of stars shin - ing bright.
star - light - ed vault of the skies.

JOHN SEBASTIAN BACH

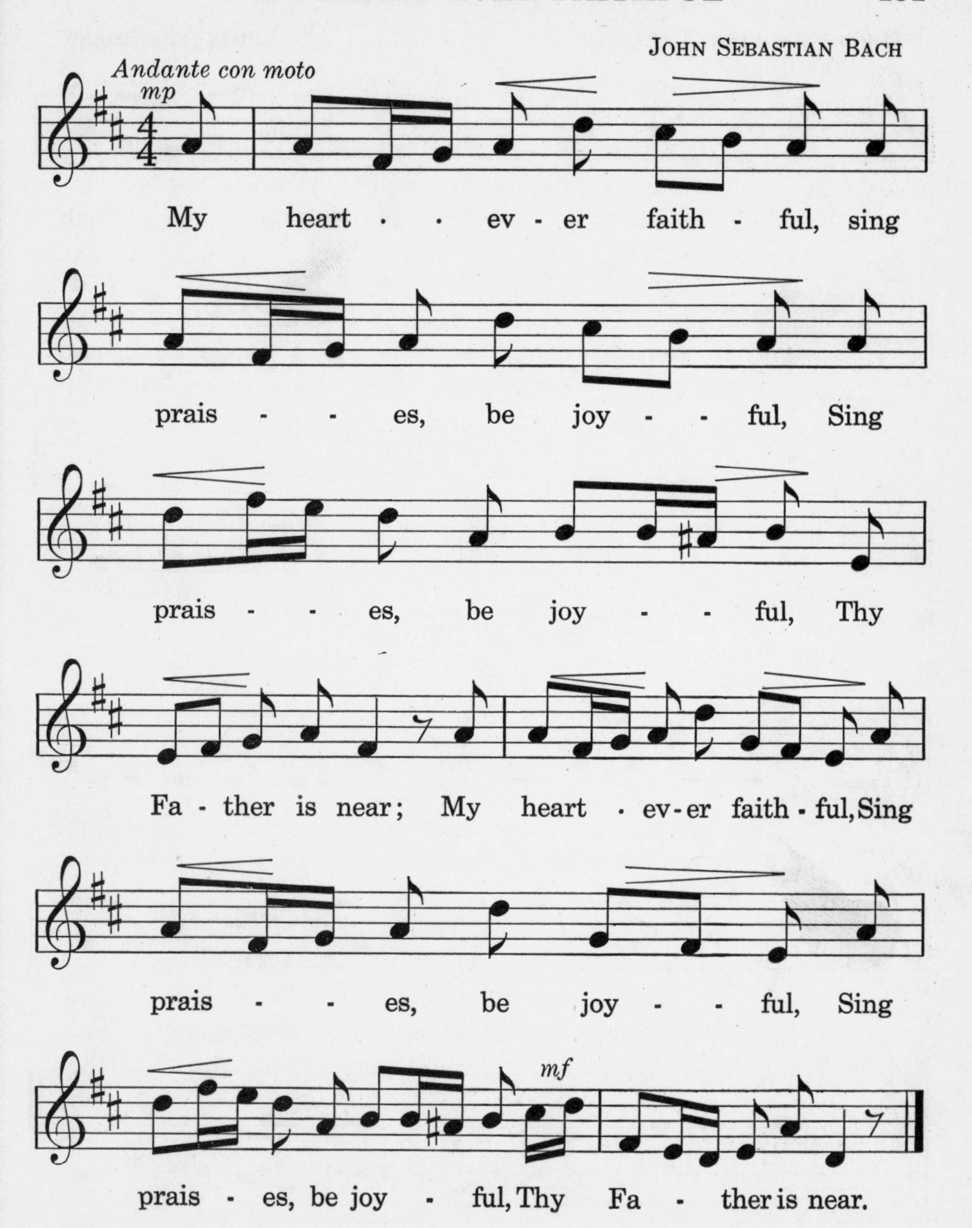

Andante con moto
mp

My   heart · · ev - er   faith - ful, sing

prais - - es,   be   joy - - ful,   Sing

prais - - es,   be   joy - - ful,   Thy

Fa - ther is near;   My   heart · ev - er   faith - ful, Sing

prais - - es,   be   joy - - ful,   Sing

mf

prais - - es,   be joy - - ful, Thy   Fa - ther is near.

THE RACE

ROBERT BRIGHAM

STANLEY AVERY

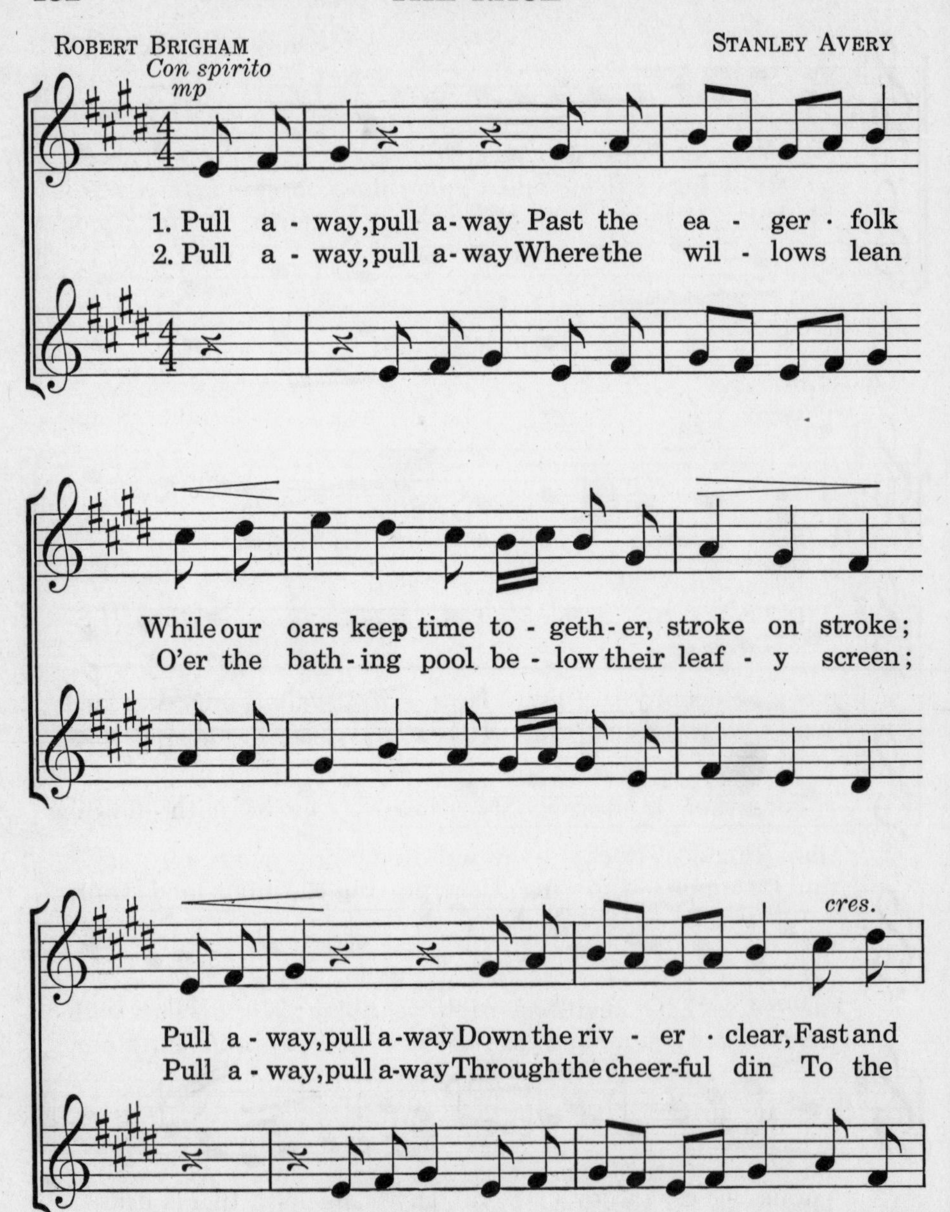

Con spirito

1. Pull a - way, pull a - way Past the ea - ger - folk
2. Pull a - way, pull a - way Where the wil - lows lean

While our oars keep time to - geth - er, stroke on stroke;
O'er the bath - ing pool be - low their leaf - y screen;

Pull a - way, pull a - way Down the riv - er - clear, Fast and
Pull a - way, pull a - way Through the cheer - ful din To the

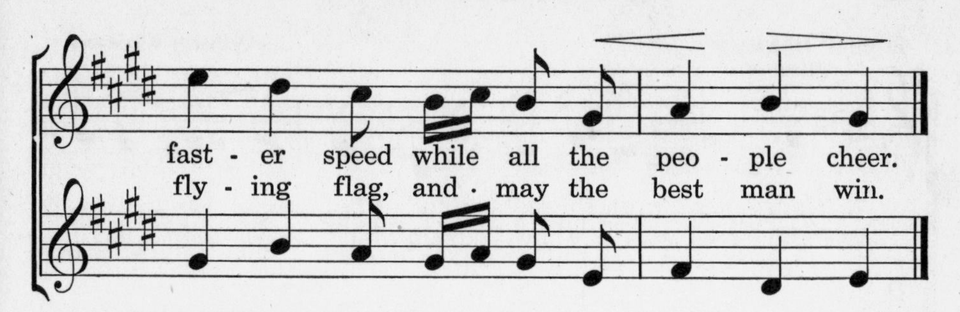

fast - er speed while all the peo - ple cheer.
fly - ing flag, and may the best man win.

THE EXILES

Louise Stickney

Frances Rittenhouse

Adagio
mp

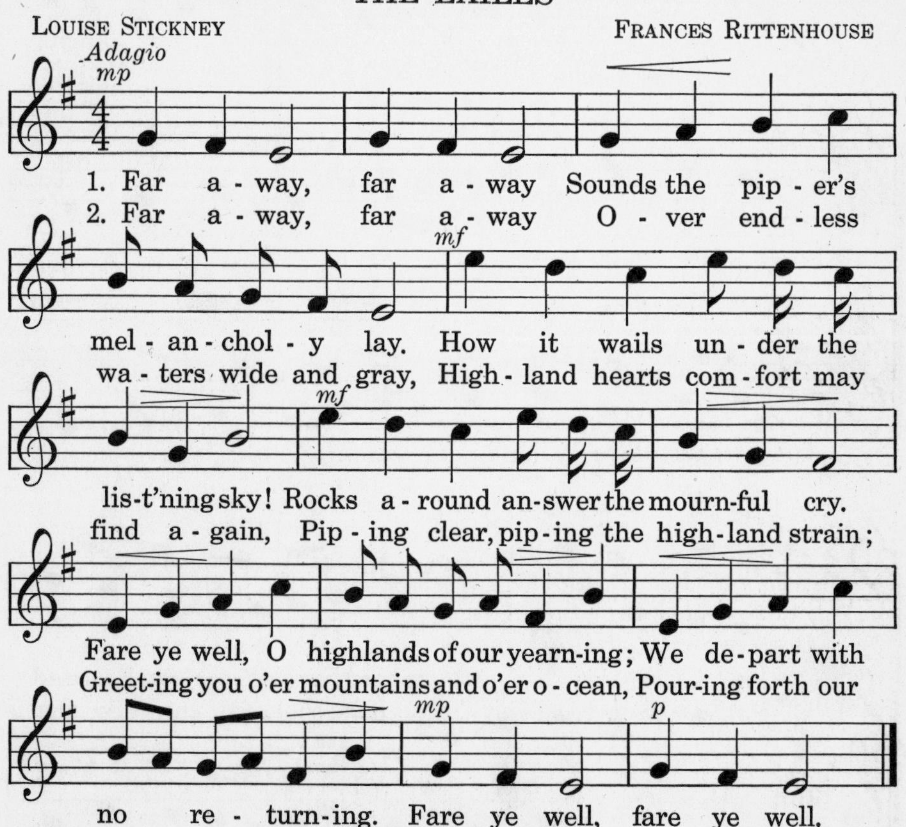

1. Far a - way, far a - way Sounds the pip - er's
2. Far a - way, far a - way O - ver end - less

mel - an - chol - y lay. How it wails un - der the
wa - ters wide and gray, High - land hearts com - fort may

lis-t'ning sky! Rocks a - round an-swer the mourn-ful cry.
find a - gain, Pip - ing clear, pip-ing the high-land strain;

Fare ye well, O highlands of our yearn-ing; We de-part with
Greet-ing you o'er mountains and o'er o - cean, Pour-ing forth our

no re - turn-ing. Fare ye well, fare ye well.
long - de - vo - tion. Fare ye well, fare ye well.

WHEN NIGHT IS FALLING

MARIE CONDÉ

ARTHUR TARGETT

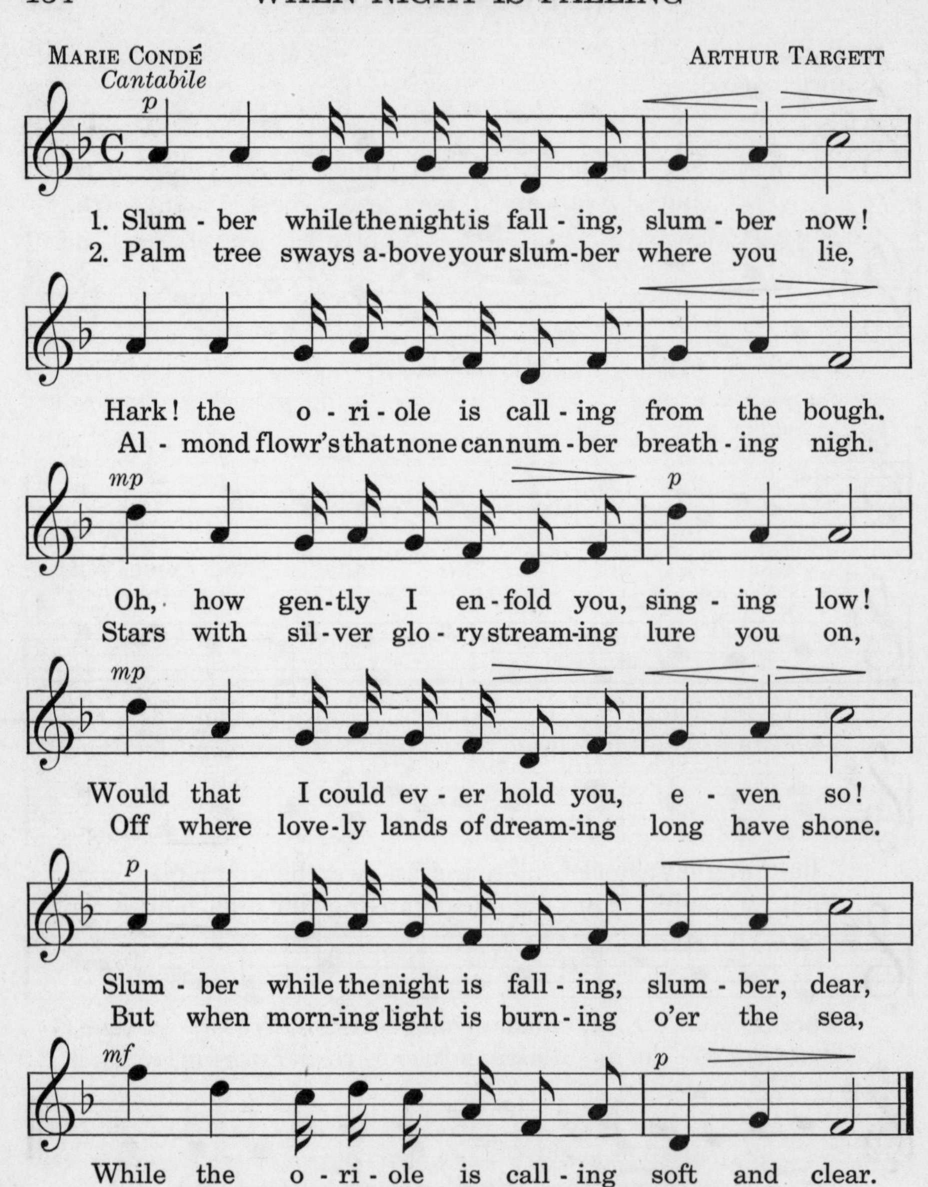

1. Slum - ber while the night is fall - ing, slum - ber now!
2. Palm tree sways a-bove your slum-ber where you lie,

Hark! the o - ri - ole is call - ing from the bough.
Al - mond flowr's that none can num - ber breath - ing nigh.

Oh, how gen - tly I en - fold you, sing - ing low!
Stars with sil - ver glo - ry stream-ing lure you on,

Would that I could ev - er hold you, e - ven so!
Off where love-ly lands of dream-ing long have shone.

Slum - ber while the night is fall - ing, slum - ber, dear,
But when morn-ing light is burn - ing o'er the sea,

While the o - ri - ole is call - ing soft and clear.
Dear one, you will be re - turn - ing home to me.

M. Louise Baum

Mary Turner Salter

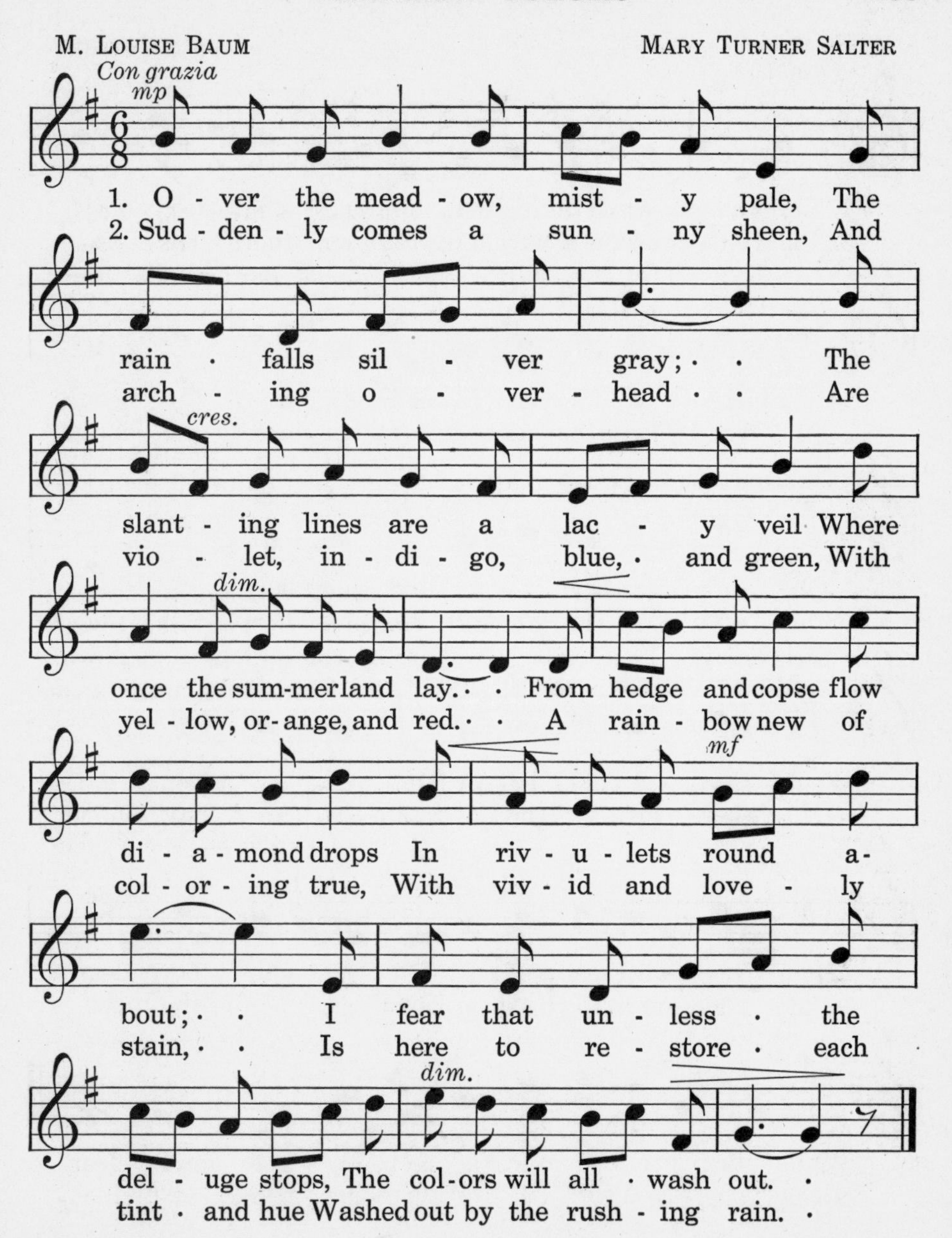

1. O - ver the mead - ow, mist - y pale, The
2. Sud - den - ly comes a sun - ny sheen, And

rain · falls sil - ver gray; · · The
arch - ing o - ver - head · · Are

slant - ing lines are a lac - y veil Where
vio - let, in - di - go, blue, · and green, With

once the sum-merland lay. · · From hedge and copse flow
yel - low, or - ange, and red. · · A rain - bow new of

di - a - mond drops In riv - u - lets round a -
col - or - ing true, With viv - id and love - ly

bout; · · I fear that un - less · the
stain, · · Is here to re - store · each

del - uge stops, The col - ors will all · wash out. ·
tint · and hue Washed out by the rush - ing rain. ·

LA BELLE DEMOISELLE

ABBIE FARWELL BROWN

FRENCH FOLK TUNE

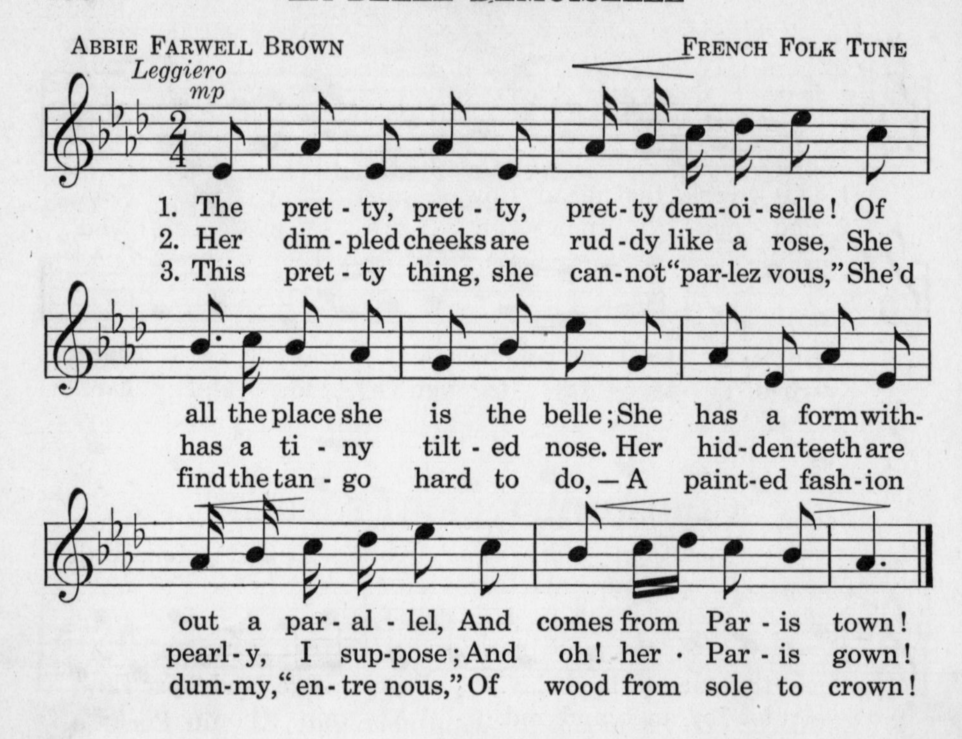

Leggiero
mp

1. The pret - ty, pret - ty, pret - ty dem - oi - selle! Of
2. Her dim - pled cheeks are rud - dy like a rose, She
3. This pret - ty thing, she can - not "par - lez vous," She'd

all the place she is the belle; She has a form with-
has a ti - ny tilt - ed nose. Her hid - den teeth are
find the tan - go hard to do, — A paint - ed fash - ion

out a par - al - lel, And comes from Par - is town!
pearl - y, I sup - pose; And oh! her · Par - is gown!
dum - my, "en - tre nous," Of wood from sole to crown!

PRAYER

Translated

CARL M. VON WEBER

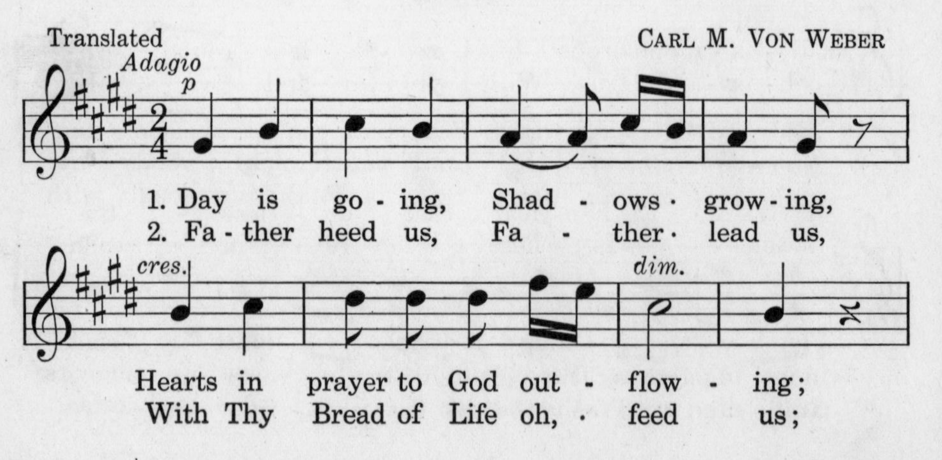

Adagio
p

1. Day is go - ing, Shad - ows · grow - ing,
2. Fa - ther heed us, Fa - ther · lead us,

cres.

dim.

Hearts in prayer to God out - flow - ing;
With Thy Bread of Life oh, · feed us;

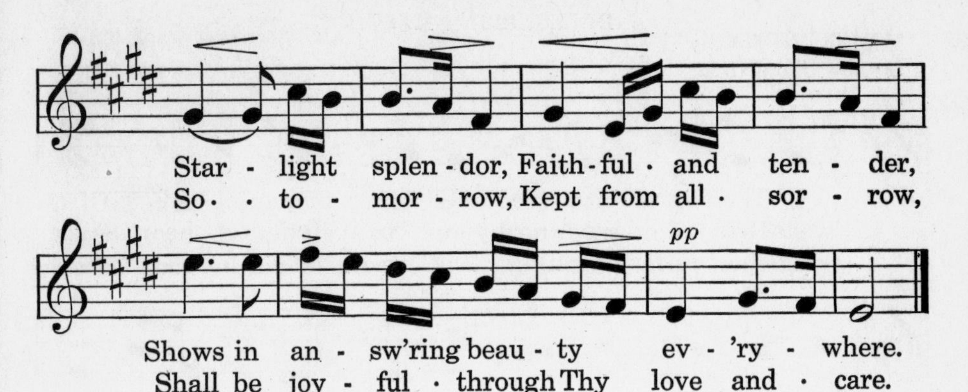

Star - light splen - dor, Faith - ful · and ten - der,
So · · to - mor - row, Kept from all · sor - row,

Shows in an - sw'ring beau - ty ev - 'ry - where.
Shall be joy - ful · through Thy love and · care.

A MIDSUMMER NIGHT'S DREAM

M. Louise Baum

Felix Mendelssohn

Con grazia

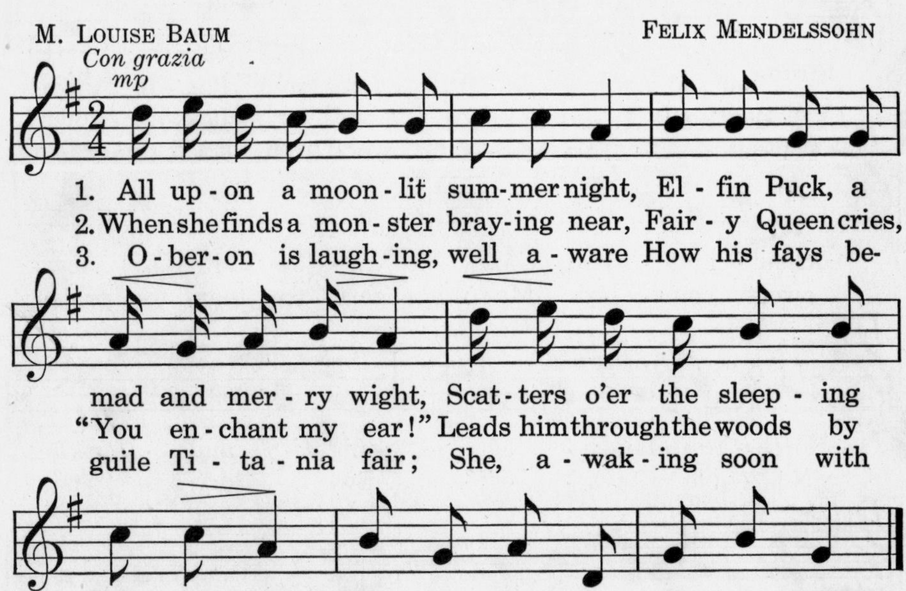

1. All up - on a moon - lit sum - mer night, El - fin Puck, a
2. When she finds a mon - ster bray - ing near, Fair - y Queen cries,
3. O - ber - on is laugh - ing, well a - ware How his fays be-

mad and mer - ry wight, Scat - ters o'er the sleep - ing
"You en - chant my ear!" Leads him through the woods by
guile Ti - ta - nia fair; She, a - wak - ing soon with

Fair - y Queen Mag - ic juic - es, quite un - seen.
chains of flow'rs, Feeds him hon - ey - dew in show'rs.
clear - er eyes, Views poor Nick in sore sur - prise.

SONGS OF SWEDEN

DALECARLIAN MARCH

English Version by
LOUISE STICKNEY

SCANDINAVIAN FOLK SONG

Vivace

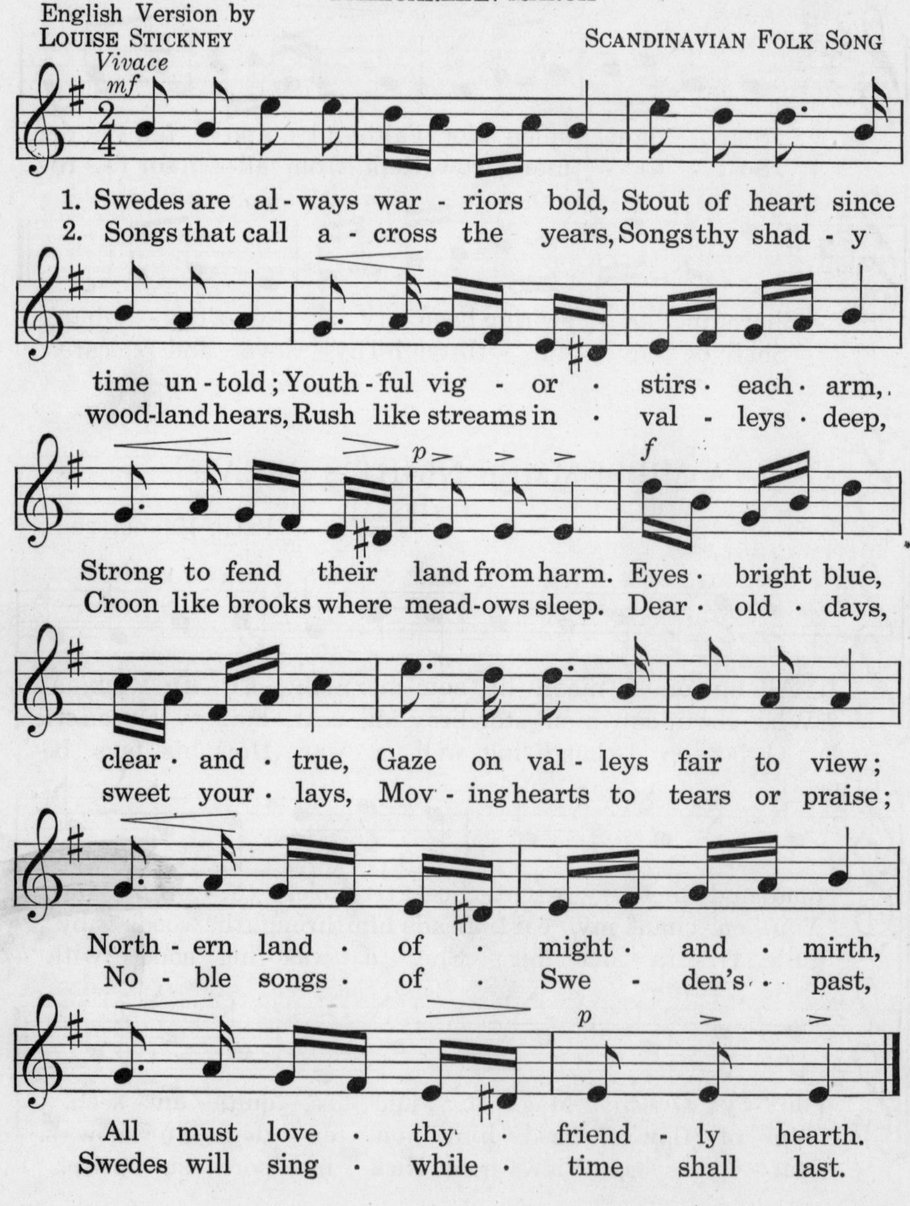

1. Swedes are al - ways war - riors bold, Stout of heart since
2. Songs that call a - cross the years, Songs thy shad - y

time un - told; Youth - ful vig - or · stirs · each · arm,,
wood-land hears, Rush like streams in · val - leys · deep,

Strong to fend their land from harm. Eyes · bright blue,
Croon like brooks where mead-ows sleep. Dear · old · days,

clear · and · true, Gaze on val - leys fair to view;
sweet your · lays, Mov - ing hearts to tears or praise;

North - ern land · of · might · and · mirth,
No - ble songs · of · Swe - den's · · past,

All must love · thy · friend - ly hearth.
Swedes will sing · while · time shall last.

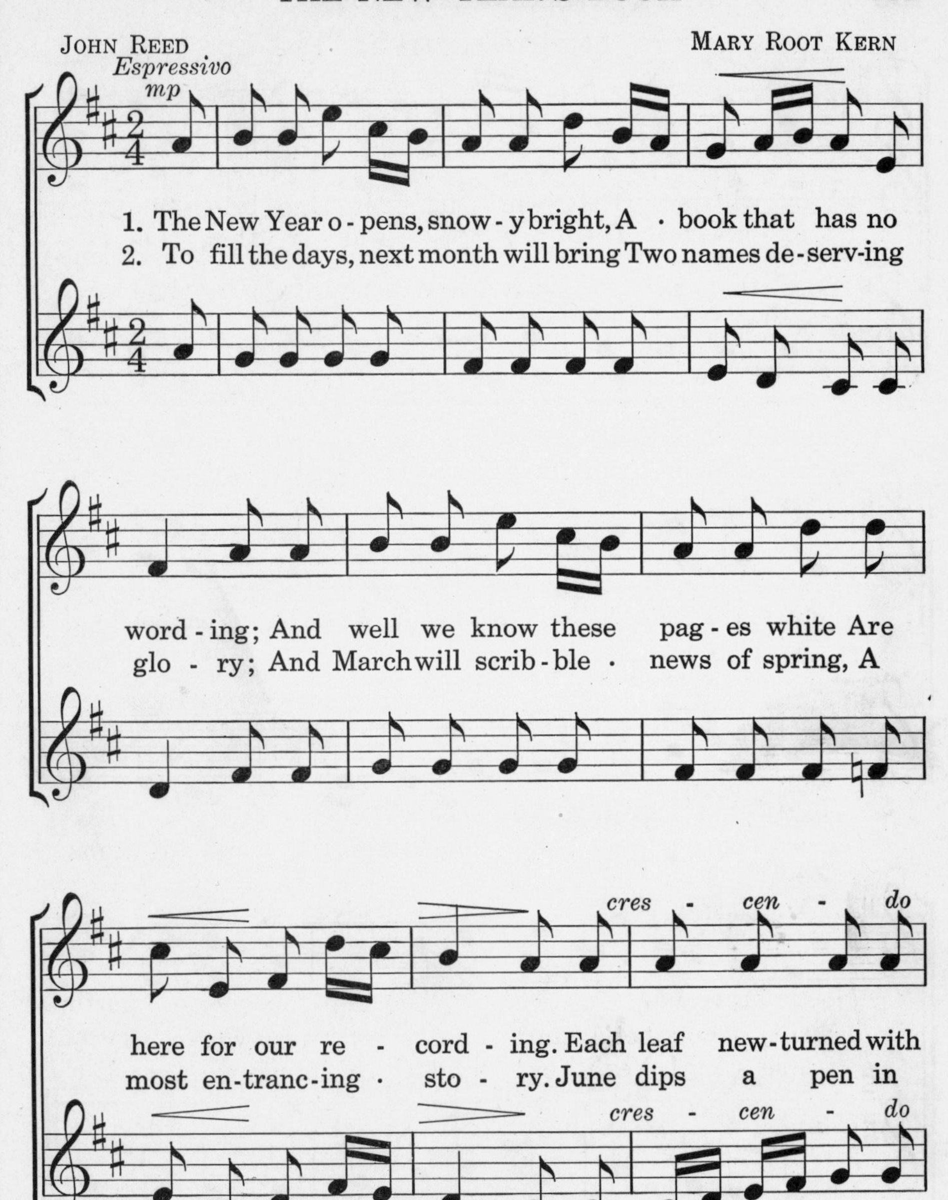

JOHN REED
Espressivo
mp

MARY ROOT KERN

1. The New Year o-pens, snow-y bright, A · book that has no
2. To fill the days, next month will bring Two names de-serv-ing

word-ing; And well we know these pag-es white Are
glo-ry; And March will scrib-ble · news of spring, A

here for our re-cord-ing. Each leaf new-turned with
most en-tranc-ing · sto-ry. June dips a pen in

cres - cen - do

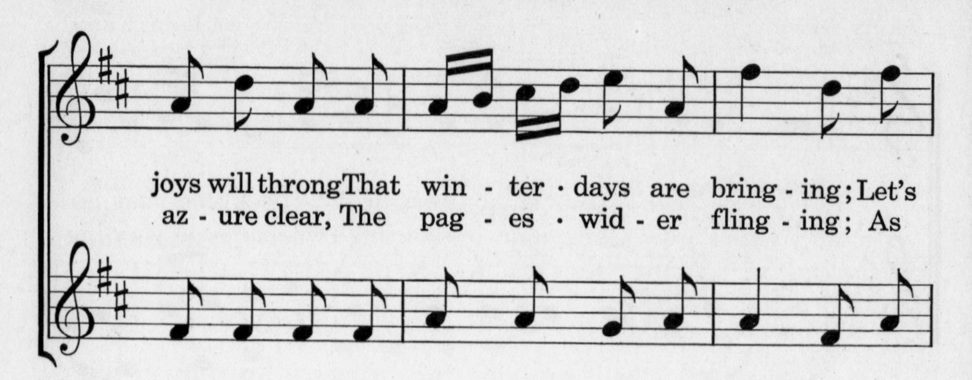

joys will throng That win - ter · days are bring - ing; Let's
az - ure clear, The pag - es · wid - er fling - ing; As

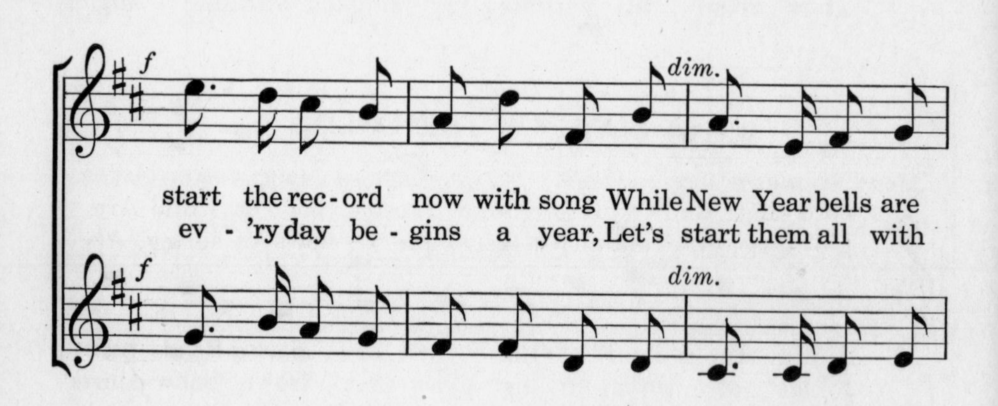

start the rec - ord now with song While New Year bells are
ev - 'ry day be - gins a year, Let's start them all with

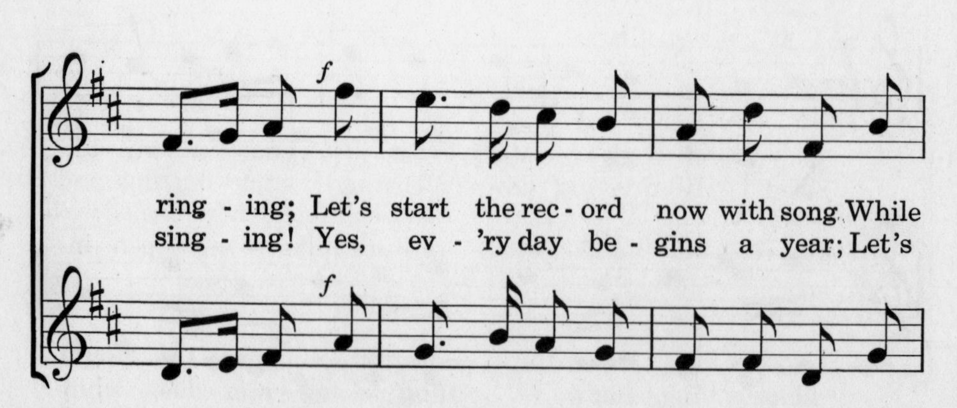

ring - ing; Let's start the rec - ord now with song While
sing - ing! Yes, ev - 'ry day be - gins a year; Let's

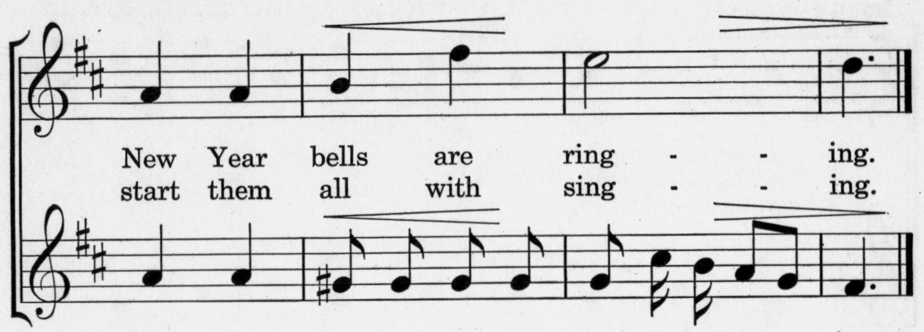

New Year bells are ring - - ing.
start them all with sing - - ing.

New Year bells are ring-ing, ring-ing, are ring - ing.
start them all with sing-ing, sing-ing, with sing - ing.

A SONG OF THE COLD

Mary Stanhope

Charles Camille Saint-Saëns

Energico
mf

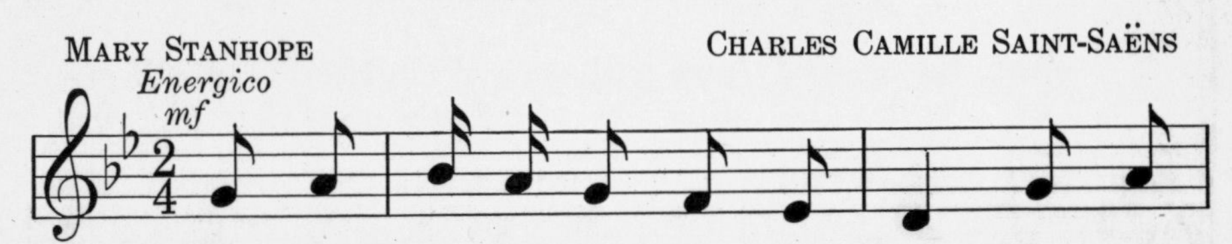

1. 'Mid the shud-der-ing win - ter dark Roads turn
2. Out of threat-en-ing skies that frown Snow comes

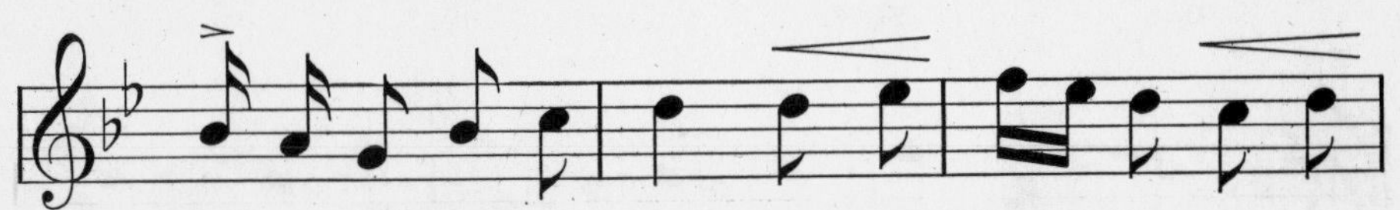

i - ci - er, trees are stark, Frost is bold - er, win - ter
stead-i - ly driv-ing down; Sharp and sting - ing, fine and

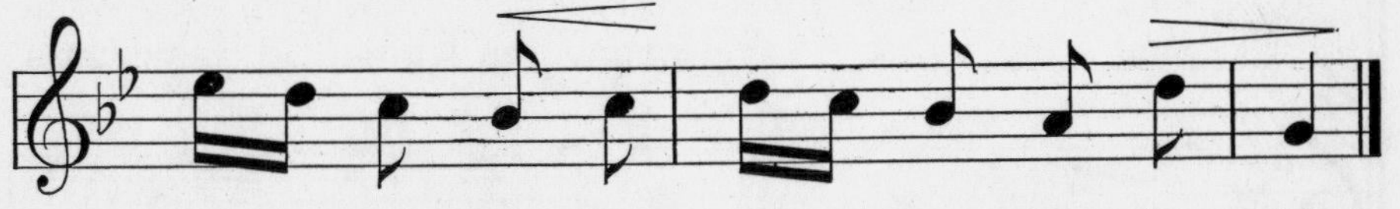

old - er, Dawn is cold - er than the night.
cling - ing, Snow is fling - ing star - dust white.

FRIENDSHIP

LOUISE STICKNEY

WOLFGANG AMADEUS MOZART

Andante grazioso

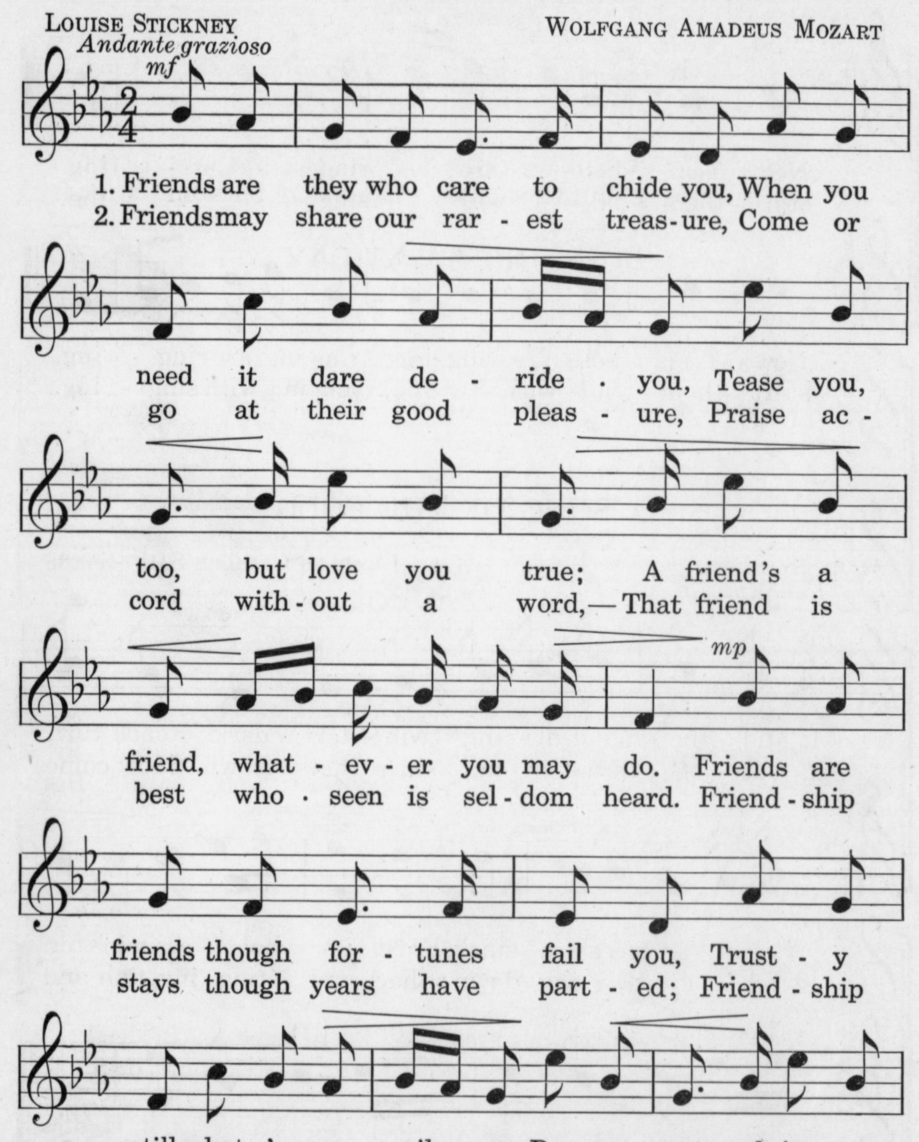

1. Friends are they who care to chide you, When you need it dare deride you, Tease you, too, but love you true; A friend's a friend, what-ev-er you may do. Friends are friends though for-tunes fail you, Trust-y still, what-e'er as-sail-you; Do your part and give your

2. Friends may share our rar-est treas-ure, Come or go at their good pleas-ure, Praise ac-cord with-out a word,— That friend is best who-seen is sel-dom heard. Friend-ship stays though years have part-ed; Friend-ship finds the loy-al-heart-ed; Gives, not lends, and nev-er

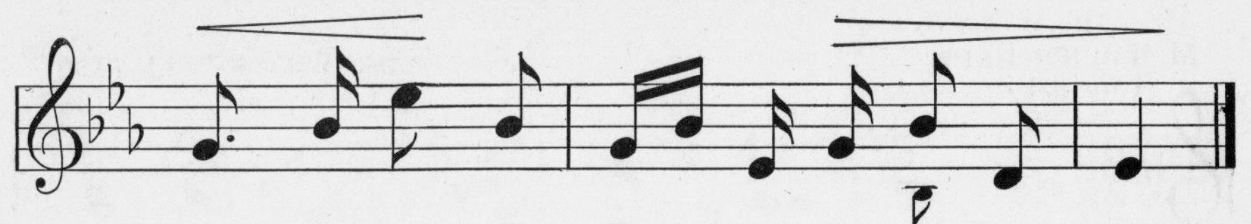

heart, To be a friend is the fin - est art.
ends, — No gift more cher - ished than faith-ful friends.

FOR CHRISTMAS DAY

English Version by
JOHN REED

PETER CORNELIUS

Allegro moderato

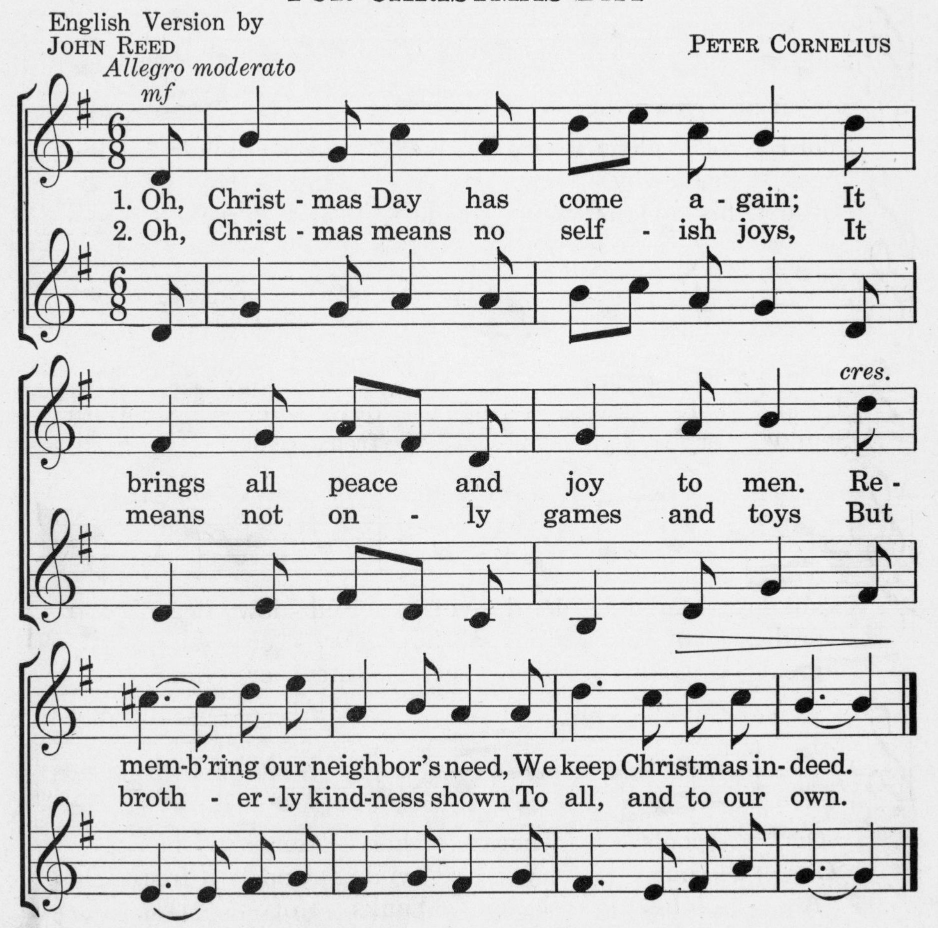

1. Oh, Christ - mas Day has come a - gain; It
2. Oh, Christ - mas means no self - ish joys, It

brings all peace and joy to men. Re -
means not on - ly games and toys But

mem-b'ring our neighbor's need, We keep Christmas in-deed.
broth - er-ly kind-ness shown To all, and to our own.

OWEN GLENDOWER

After the Welsh by
M. LOUISE BAUM

WELSH FOLK SONG

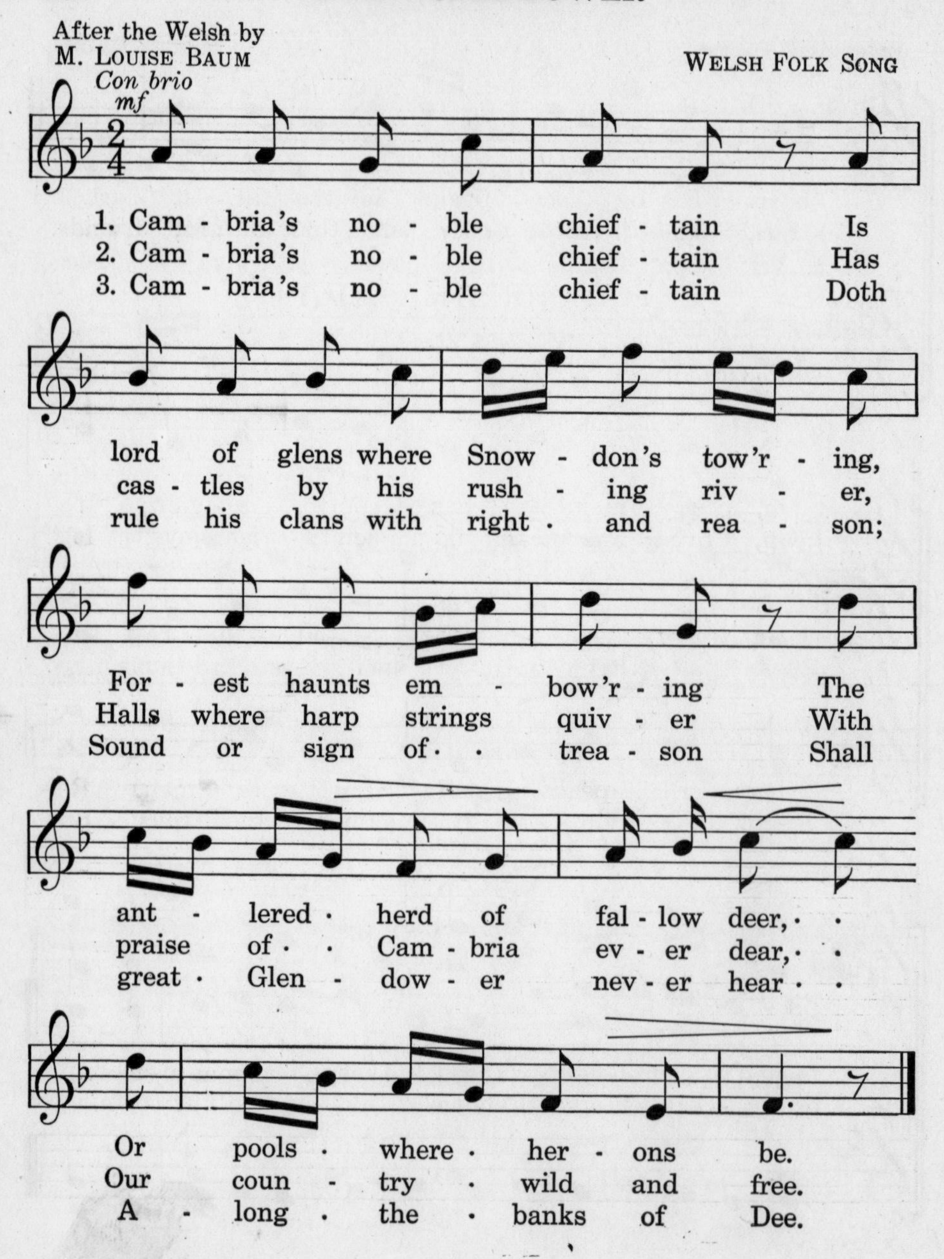

1. Cam - bria's no - ble chief - tain Is
2. Cam - bria's no - ble chief - tain Has
3. Cam - bria's no - ble chief - tain Doth

lord of glens where Snow - don's tow'r - ing,
cas - tles by his rush - ing riv - er,
rule his clans with right and rea - son;

For - est haunts em - bow'r - ing The
Halls where harp strings quiv - er With
Sound or sign of trea - son Shall

ant - lered herd of fal - low deer,
praise of Cam - bria ev - er dear,
great Glen - dow - er nev - er hear

Or pools where her - ons be.
Our coun - try wild and free.
A - long the banks of Dee.

SWEET THE ANGELUS IS RINGING

FREDERICK ENOCH

HENRY SMART

Larghetto

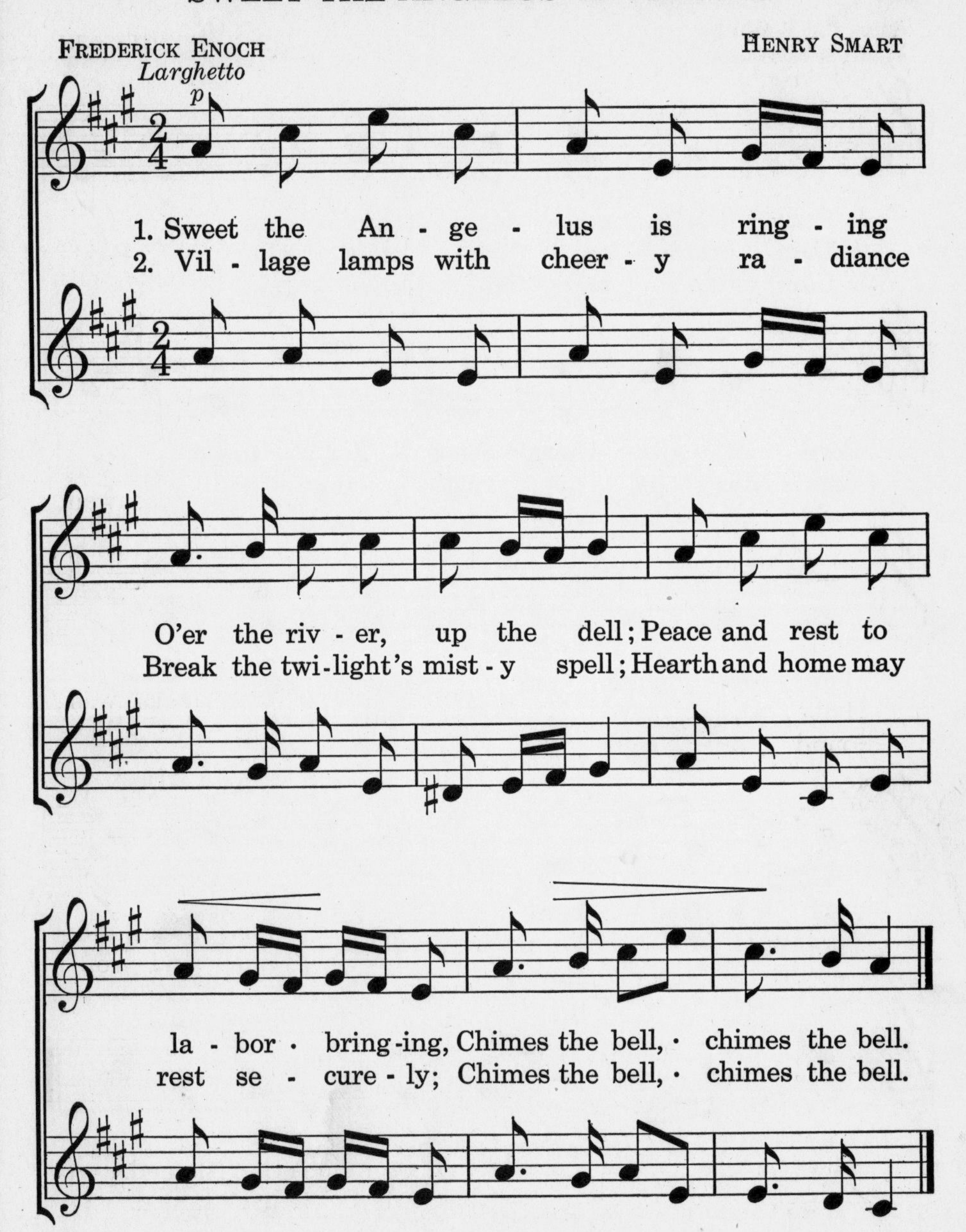

1. Sweet the An - ge - lus is ring - ing
2. Vil - lage lamps with cheer - y ra - diance

O'er the riv - er, up the dell; Peace and rest to
Break the twi - light's mist - y spell; Hearth and home may

la - bor - bring-ing, Chimes the bell, · chimes the bell.
rest se - cure - ly; Chimes the bell, · chimes the bell.

T

BRIDGING THE ANDES

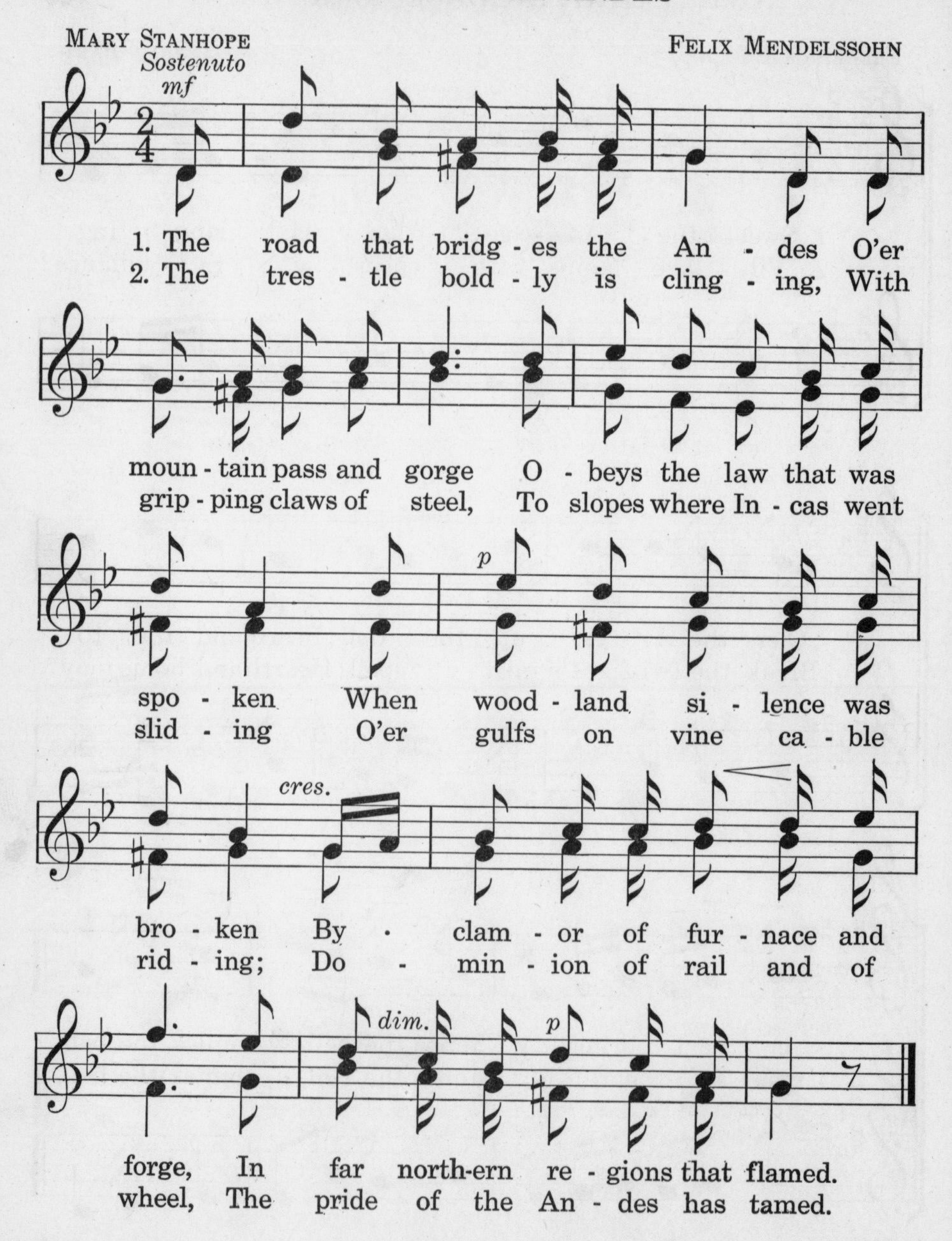

MARY STANHOPE

FELIX MENDELSSOHN

Sostenuto
mf

1. The road that bridg - es the An - des O'er
2. The tres - tle bold - ly is cling - ing, With

moun - tain pass and gorge O - beys the law that was
grip - ping claws of steel, To slopes where In - cas went

spo - ken When wood - land si - lence was
slid - ing O'er gulfs on vine ca - ble

cres.

bro - ken By clam - or of fur - nace and
rid - ing; Do - min - ion of rail and of

dim. *p*

forge, In far north-ern re - gions that flamed.
wheel, The pride of the An - des has tamed.

ALICE BARD

WELSH FOLK TUNE

Animato

mp

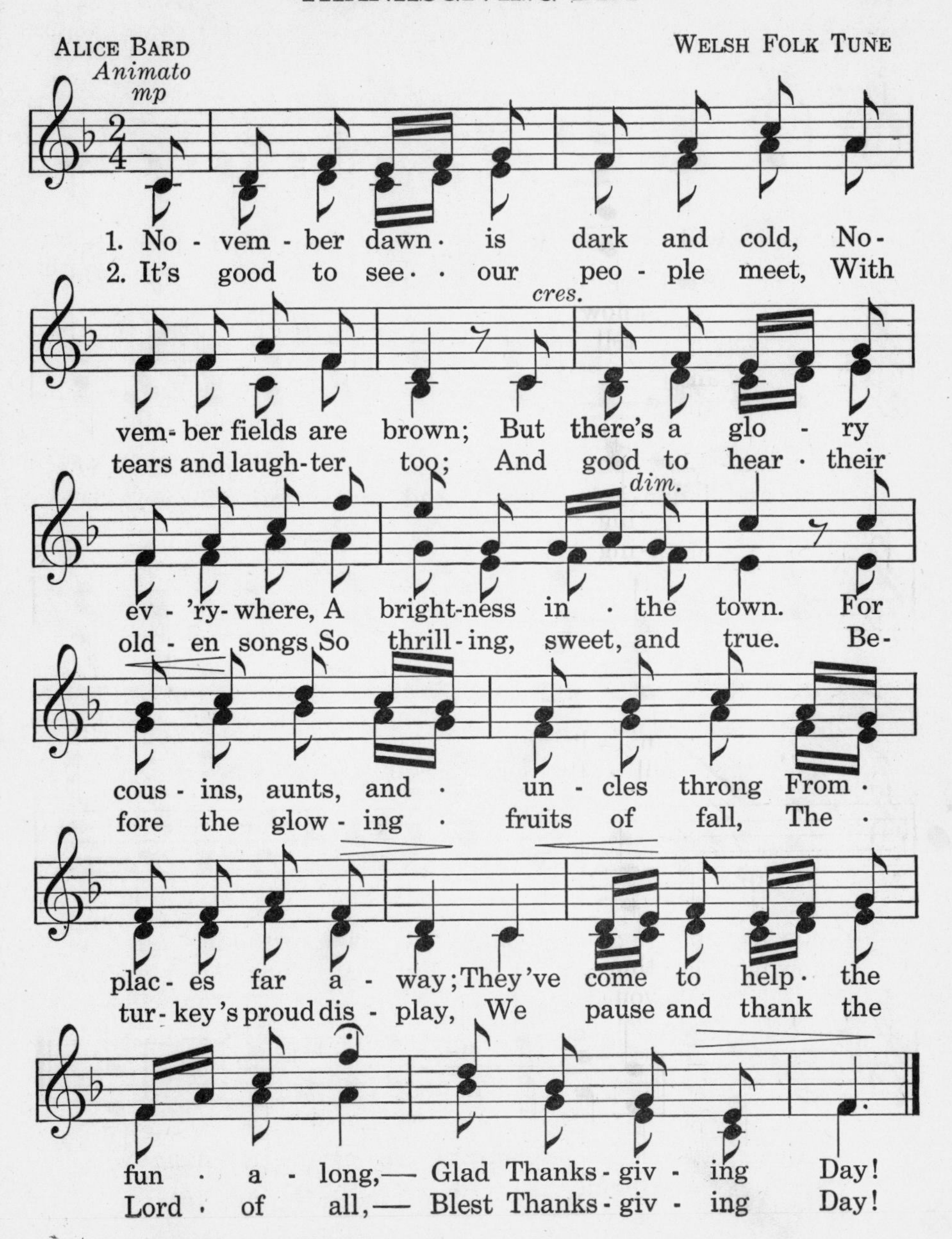

1. No - vem - ber dawn · is dark and cold, No -
2. It's good to see · · our peo - ple meet, With

cres.

vem - ber fields are brown; But there's a glo - ry
tears and laugh - ter · too; And good to hear · their

dim.

ev - 'ry - where, A bright-ness in · the town. For
old - en songs So thrill - ing, sweet, and true. Be -

cous - ins, aunts, and · un - cles throng From ·
fore the glow - ing · fruits of fall, The ·

plac - es far a - way; They've come to help · the
tur - key's proud dis - play, We pause and thank the

fun · a - long, — Glad Thanks - giv - ing Day!
Lord · of all, — Blest Thanks - giv - ing Day!

LADY MAY

HERBERT RANDALL

MARY STRAWN VERNON

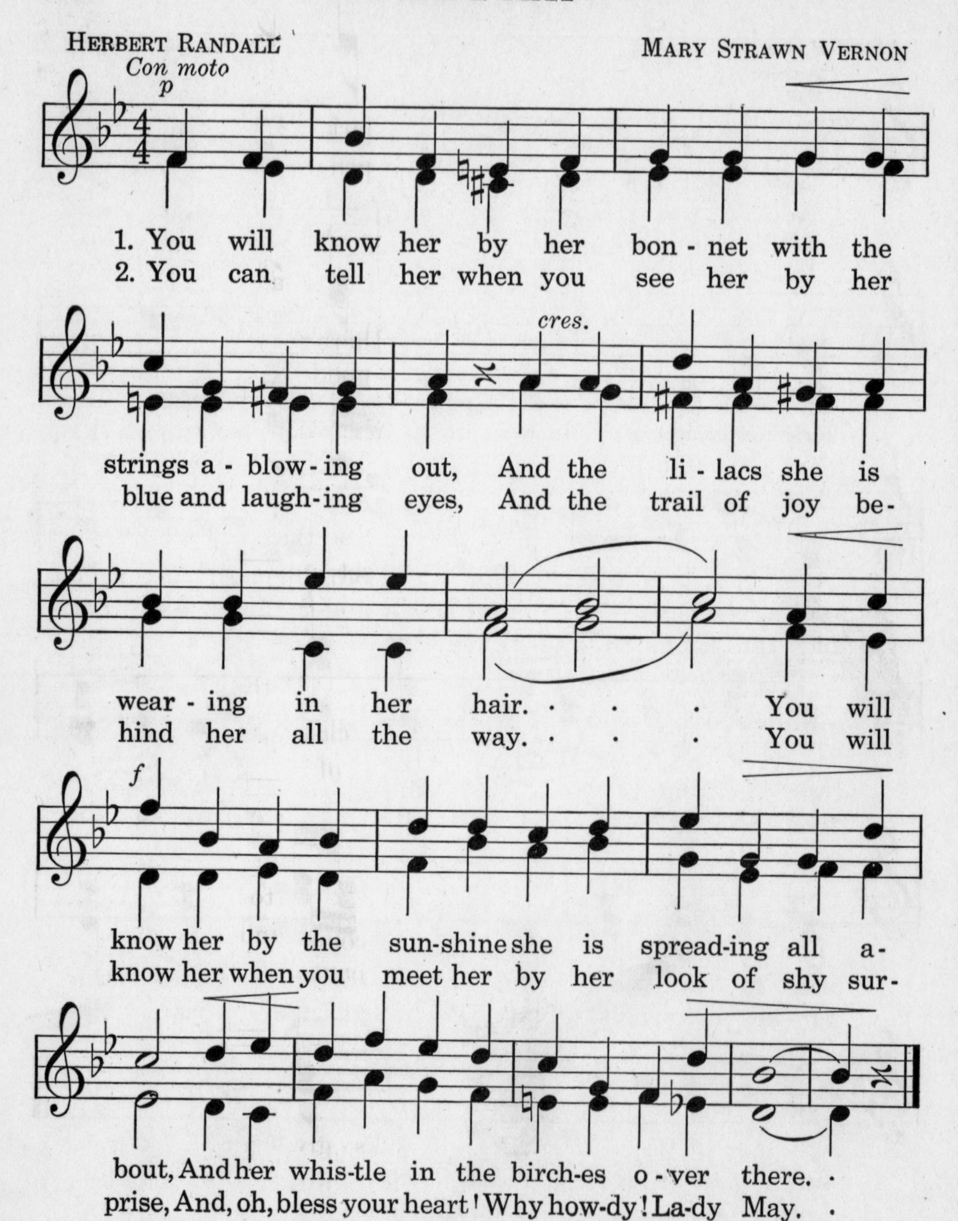

1. You will know her by her bon - net with the
2. You can tell her when you see her by her

strings a - blow - ing out, And the li - lacs she is
blue and laugh - ing eyes, And the trail of joy be-

wear - ing in her hair. · · · You will
hind her all the way. · · · You will

know her by the sun-shine she is spread-ing all a-
know her when you meet her by her look of shy sur-

bout, And her whis-tle in the birch-es o - ver there. ·
prise, And, oh, bless your heart! Why how-dy! La-dy May. ·

WINTER WOODS

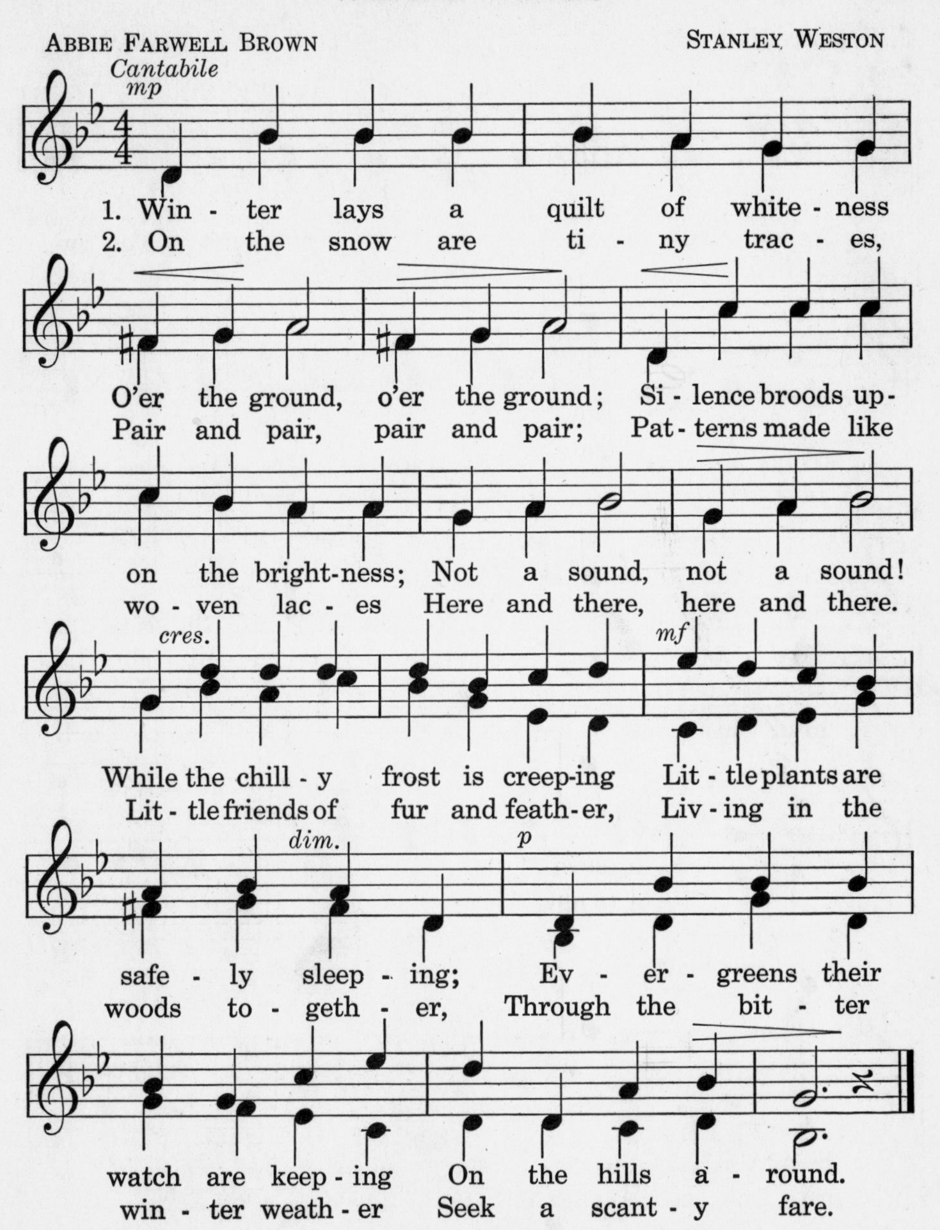

ABBIE FARWELL BROWN

STANLEY WESTON

Cantabile
mp

1. Win - ter lays a quilt of white - ness
2. On the snow are ti - ny trac - es,

O'er the ground, o'er the ground; Si - lence broods up -
Pair and pair, pair and pair; Pat - terns made like

on the bright-ness; Not a sound, not a sound!
wo - ven lac - es Here and there, here and there.

cres. ... *mf*

While the chill - y frost is creep-ing Lit - tle plants are
Lit - tle friends of fur and feath-er, Liv - ing in the

dim. ... *p*

safe - ly sleep - ing; Ev - er - greens their
woods to - geth - er, Through the bit - ter

watch are keep - ing On the hills a - round.
win - ter weath - er Seek a scant - y fare.

M. Louise Baum

Pauline Meyer

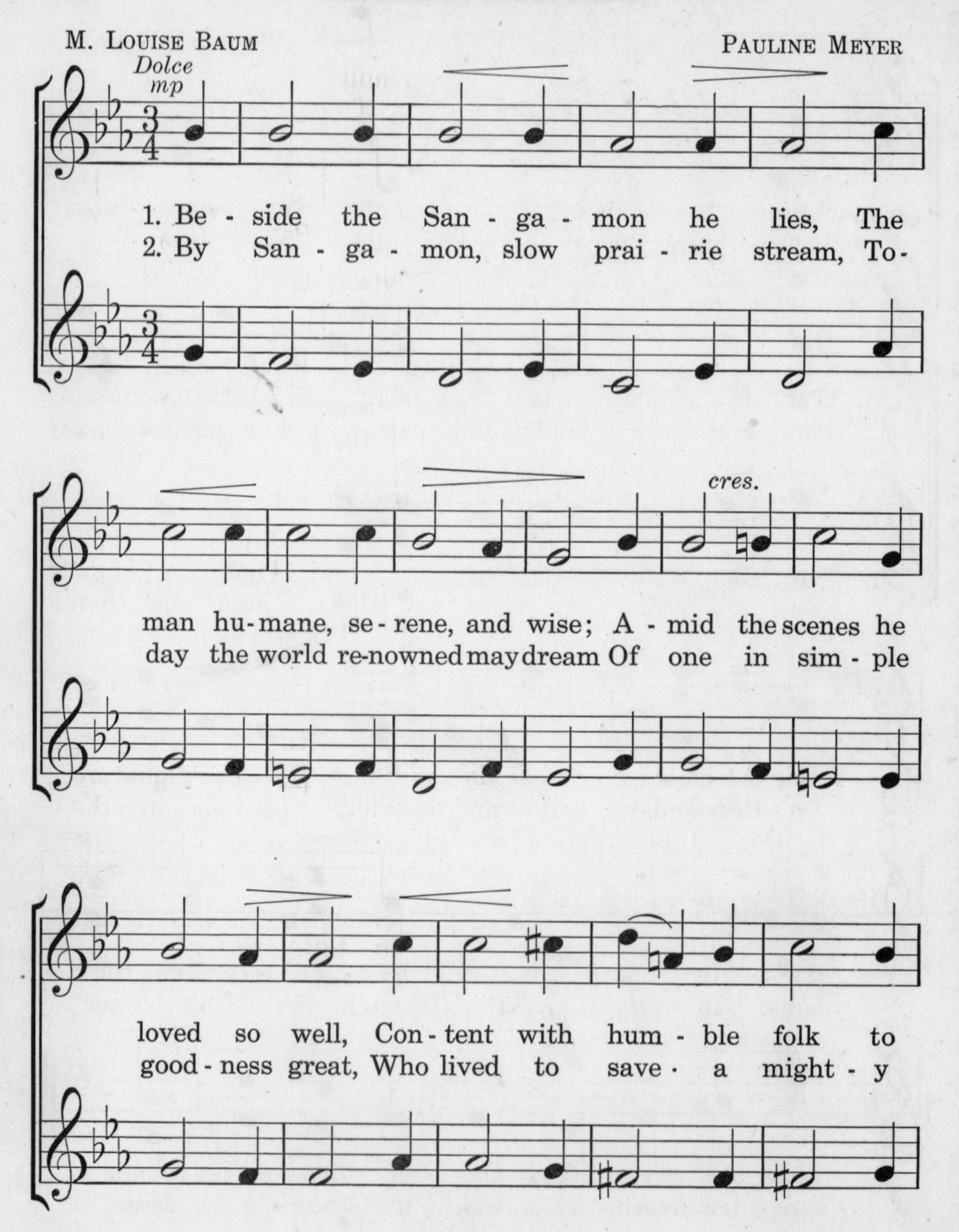

Dolce
mp

1. Be - side the San - ga - mon he lies, The
2. By San - ga - mon, slow prai - rie stream, To-

man hu - mane, se - rene, and wise; A - mid the scenes he
day the world re-nowned may dream Of one in sim - ple

cres.

loved so well, Con - tent with hum - ble folk to
good - ness great, Who lived to save · a might - y

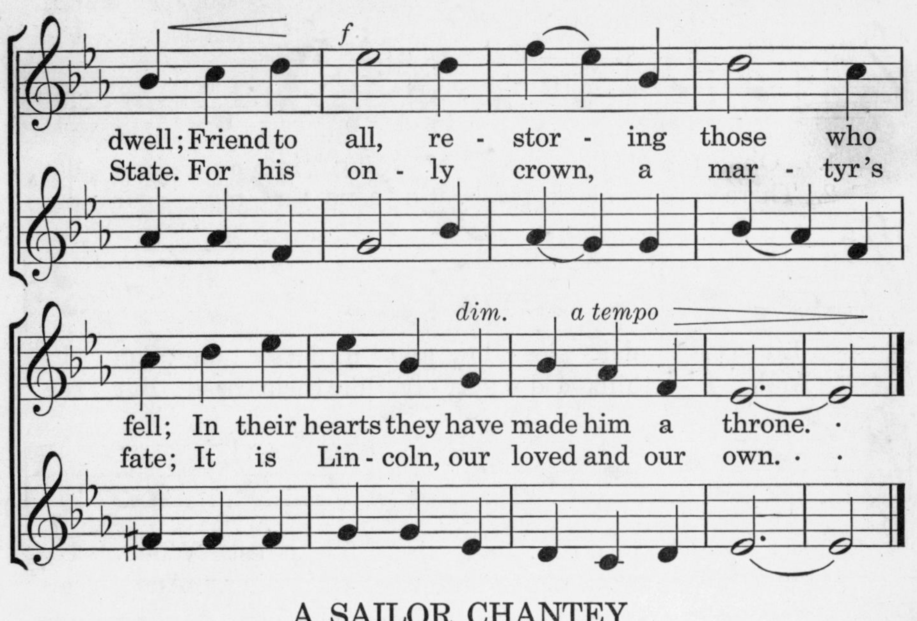

dwell; Friend to all, re - stor - ing those who
State. For his on - ly crown, a mar - tyr's

dim. *a tempo*

fell; In their hearts they have made him a throne.
fate; It is Lin - coln, our loved and our own.

A SAILOR CHANTEY

Robert Brigham

French Folk Tune

Leggiero
mp

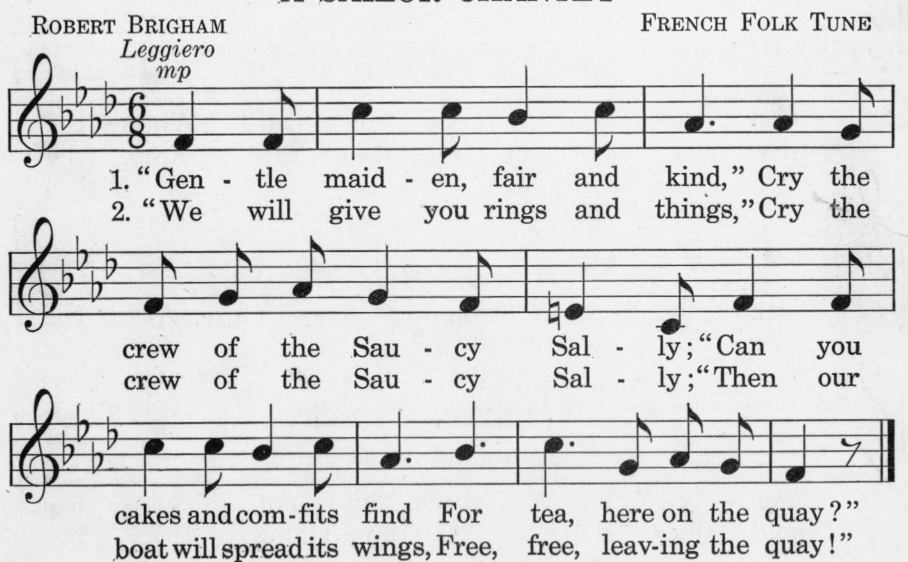

1. "Gen - tle maid - en, fair and kind," Cry the
2. "We will give you rings and things," Cry the

crew of the Sau - cy Sal - ly; "Can you
crew of the Sau - cy Sal - ly; "Then our

cakes and com-fits find For tea, here on the quay?"
boat will spread its wings, Free, free, leav-ing the quay!"

IN MY GARDEN

KATE FORMAN

EDUARDO MARZO

Andante espressivo

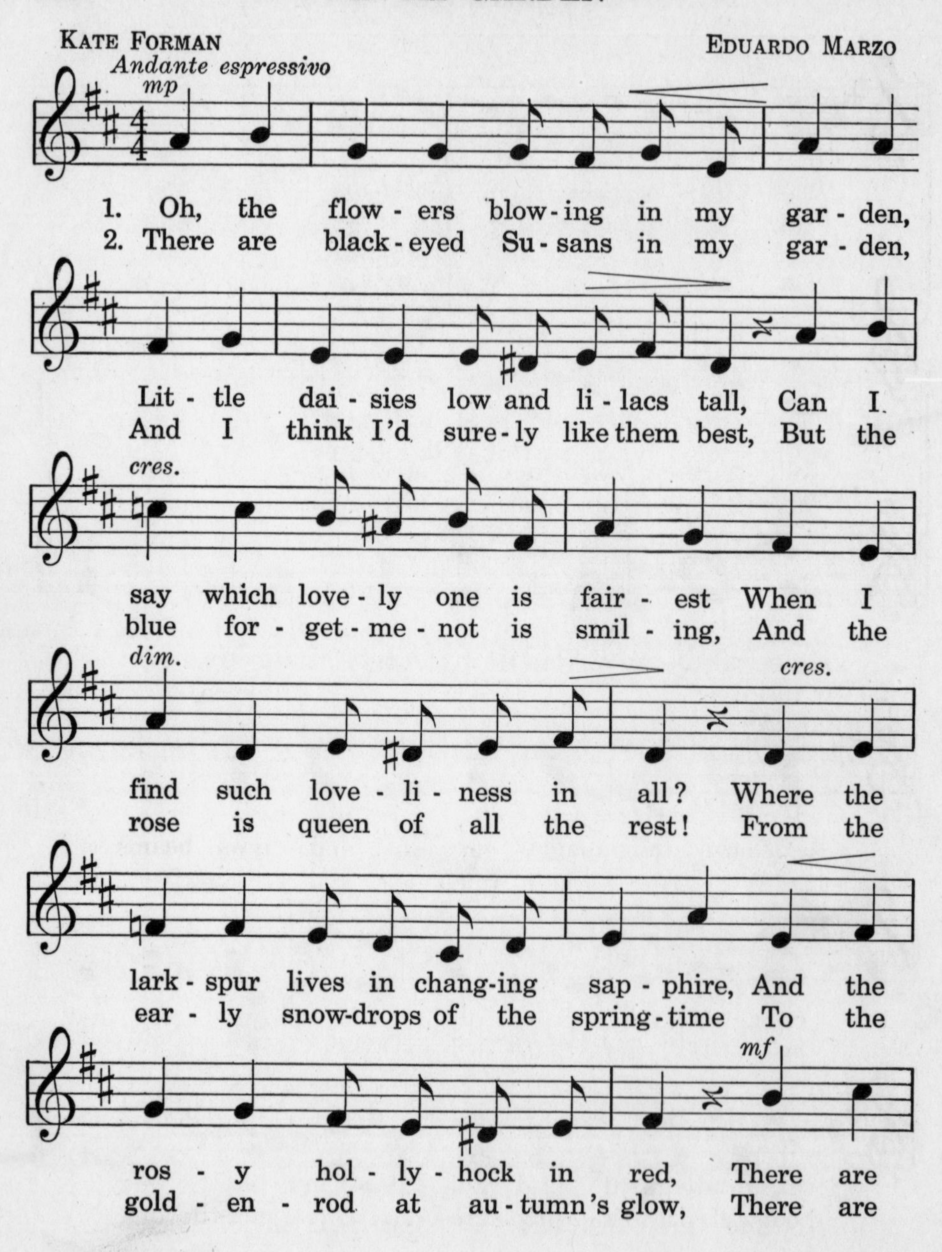

1. Oh, the flow - ers blow-ing in my gar - den,
2. There are black - eyed Su - sans in my gar - den,

Lit - tle dai - sies low and li - lacs tall, Can I
And I think I'd sure - ly like them best, But the

say which love - ly one is fair - est When I
blue for - get - me - not is smil - ing, And the

find such love - li - ness in all? Where the
rose is queen of all the rest! From the

lark - spur lives in chang-ing sap - phire, And the
ear - ly snow-drops of the spring - time To the

ros - y hol - ly - hock in red, There are
gold - en - rod at au - tumn's glow, There are

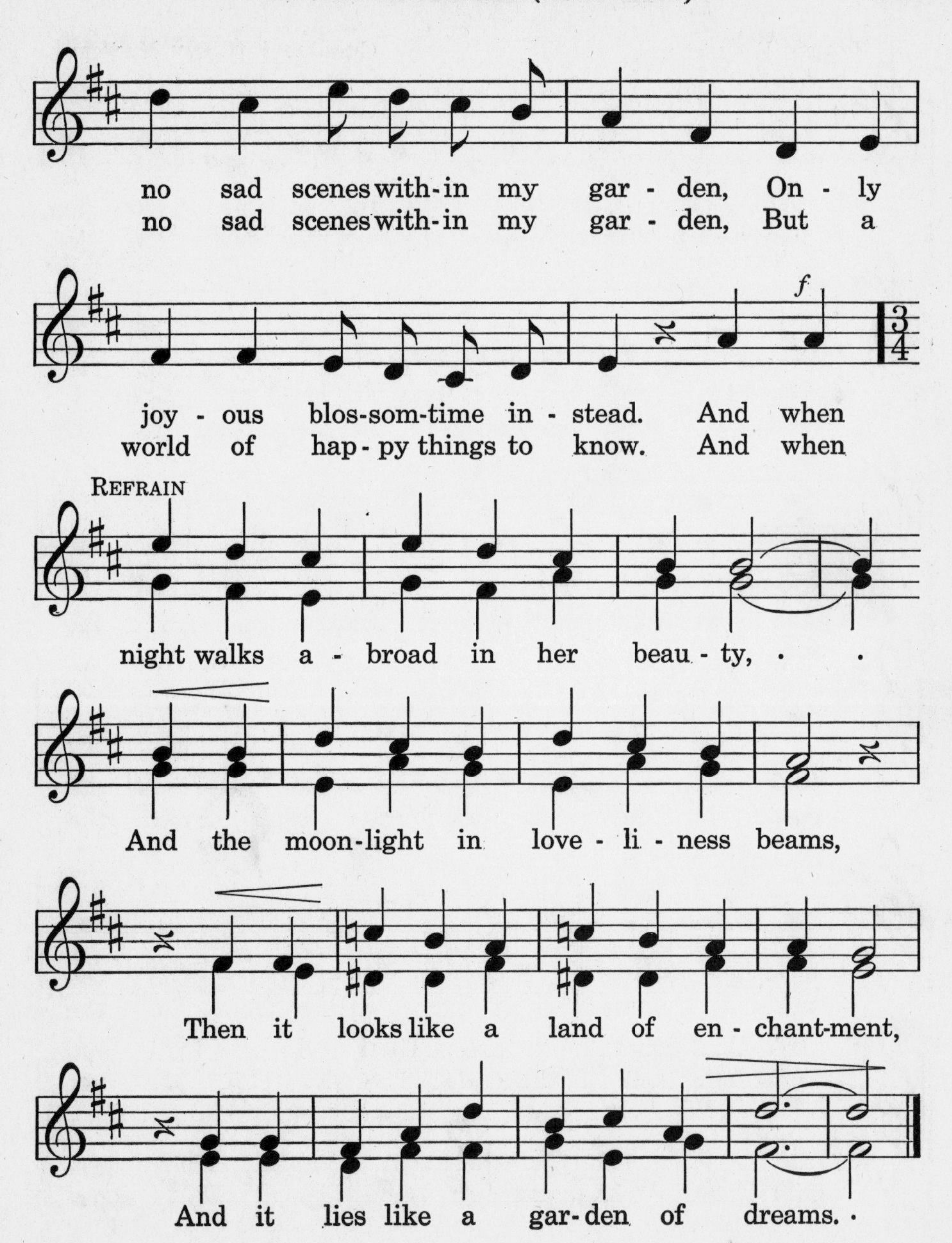

no   sad   scenes with-in   my   gar - den,   On - ly
no   sad   scenes with-in   my   gar - den,   But   a

joy - ous   blos-som-time in - stead.   And   when
world   of   hap - py things to   know.   And   when

REFRAIN

night walks   a - broad   in   her   beau - ty,   .   .

And   the   moon-light   in   love - li - ness   beams,

Then   it   looks like   a   land   of   en - chant-ment,

And   it   lies like   a   gar - den   of   dreams. .

THE ARMIES OF SPRING

M. Louise Baum

Charles Fonteyn Manney

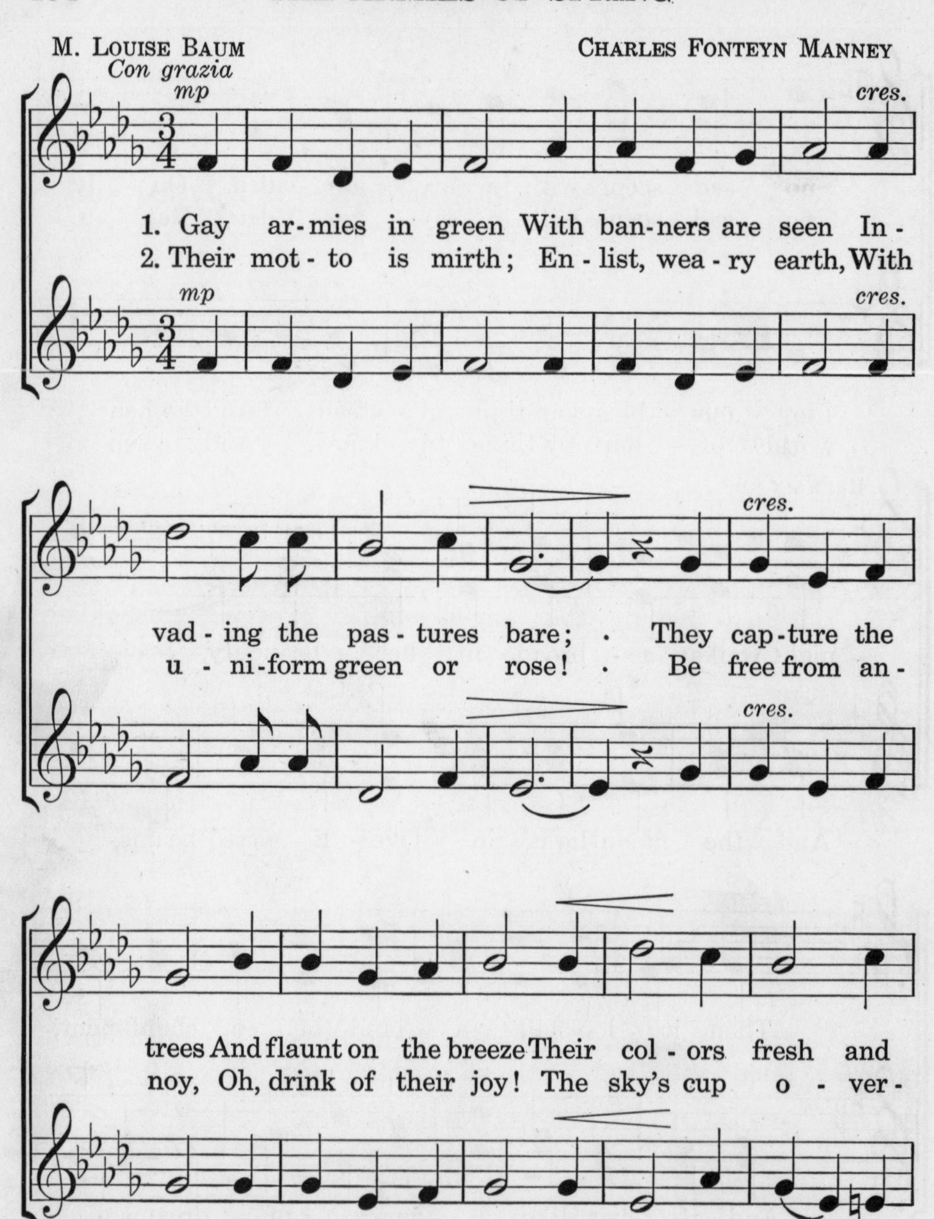

1. Gay ar-mies in green With ban-ners are seen In-
2. Their mot-to is mirth; En-list, wea-ry earth, With

vad-ing the pas-tures bare; . They cap-ture the
u-ni-form green or rose! . Be free from an-

trees And flaunt on the breeze Their col-ors fresh and
noy, Oh, drink of their joy! The sky's cup o-ver-

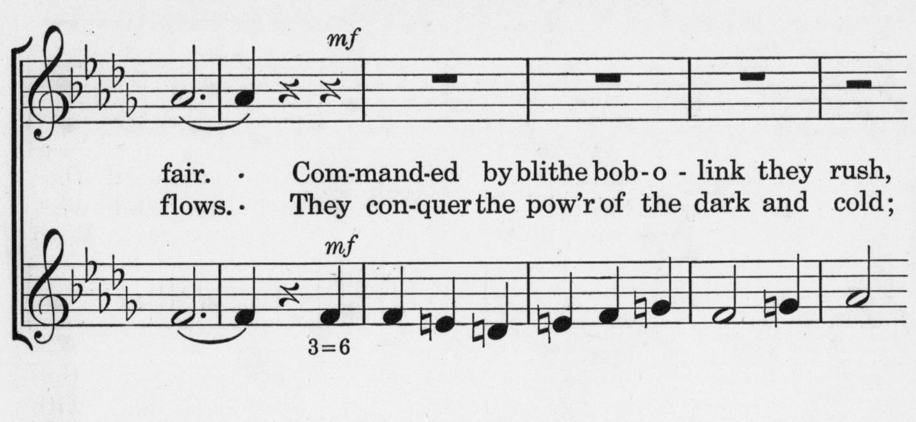

fair.   ·   Com-mand-ed by blithe bob-o-link they rush,
flows.   ·   They con-quer the pow'r of the dark and cold;

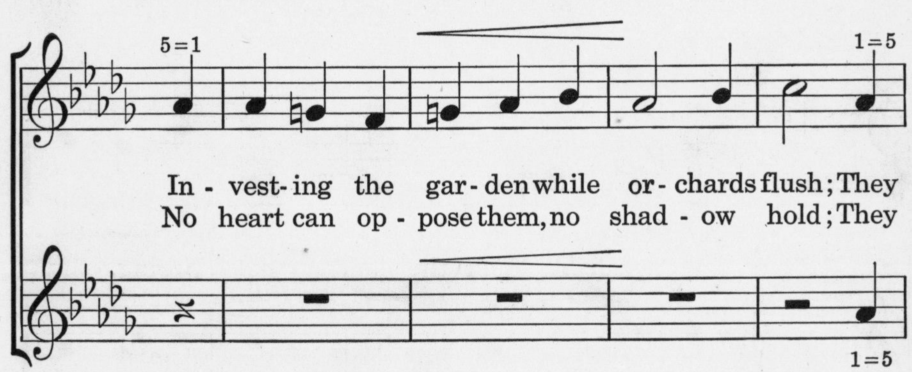

In - vest-ing the gar-den while or-chards flush; They
No heart can op - pose them, no shad - ow hold; They

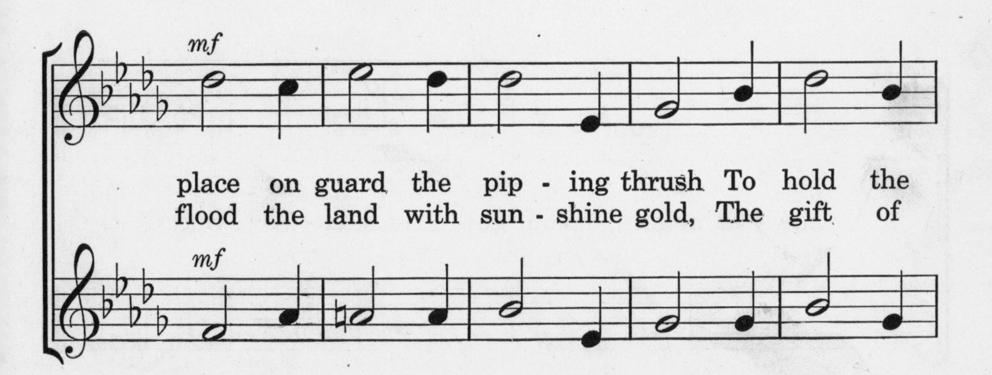

place on guard the pip - ing thrush To hold the
flood the land with sun - shine gold, The gift of

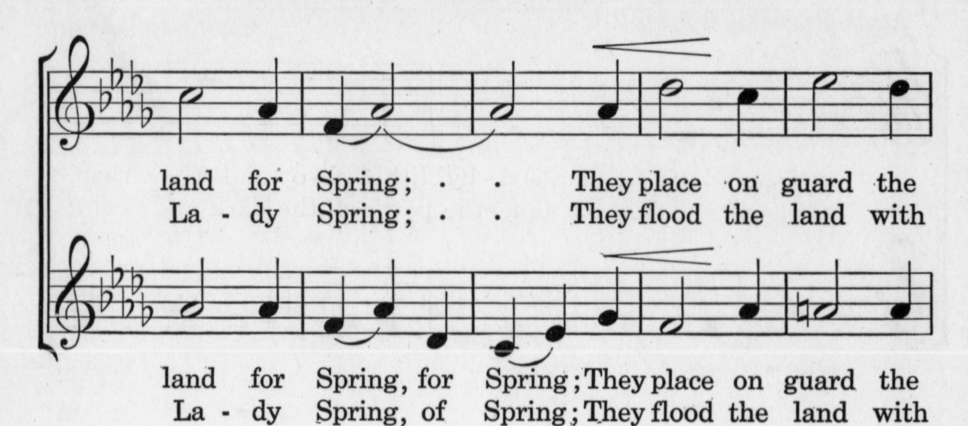

land for Spring; · · They place on guard the
La - dy Spring; · · They flood the land with

land for Spring, for Spring; They place on guard the
La - dy Spring, of Spring; They flood the land with

pip - ing thrush To hold the land for Spring. · ·

sun - shine gold, The gift · of La - dy Spring. · ·

OUR COUNTRY

157

ABBIE FARWELL BROWN

CARRIE BULLARD

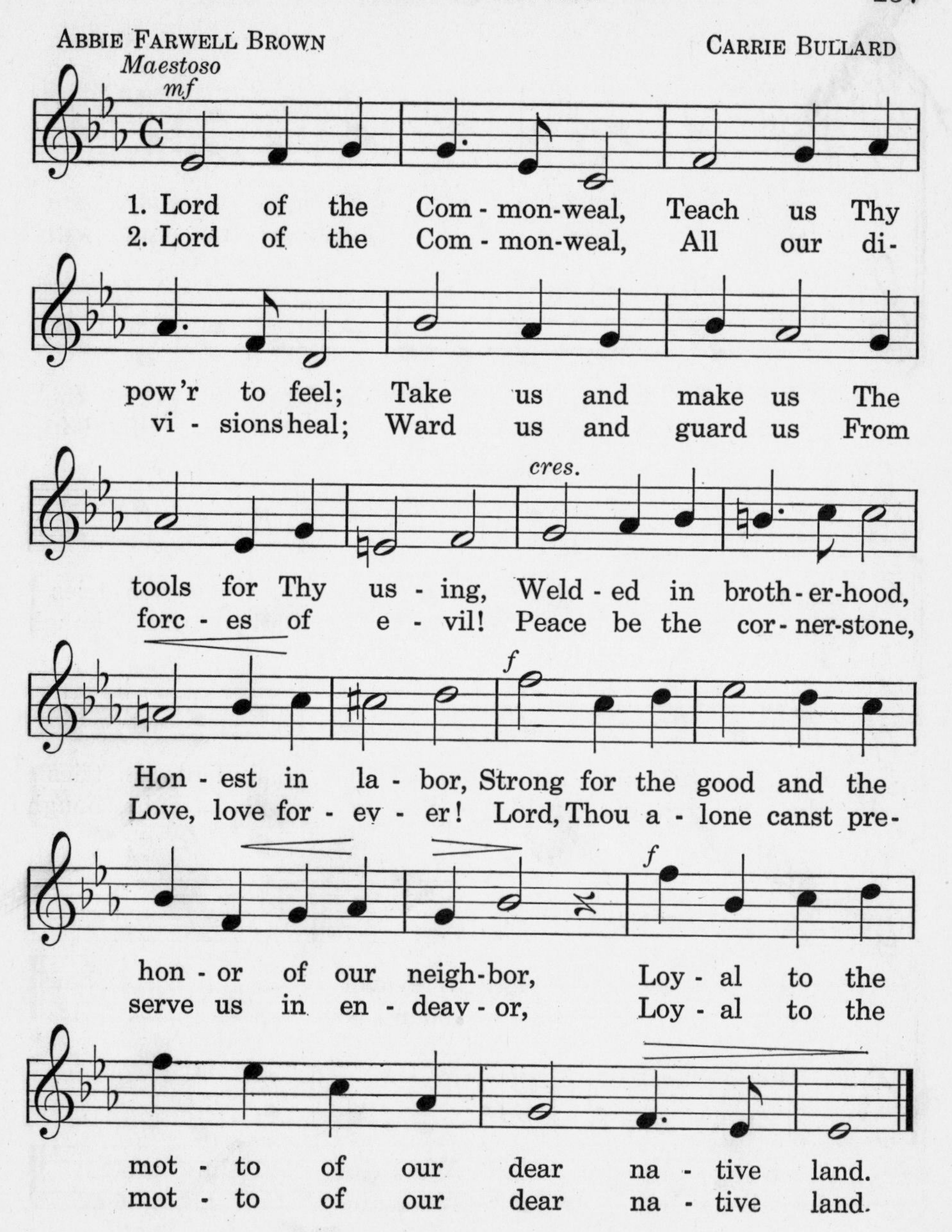

1. Lord of the Com-mon-weal, Teach us Thy
2. Lord of the Com-mon-weal, All our di-

pow'r to feel; Take us and make us The
vi - sions heal; Ward us and guard us From

tools for Thy us - ing, Weld - ed in broth-er-hood,
forc - es of e - vil! Peace be the cor-ner-stone,

Hon - est in la - bor, Strong for the good and the
Love, love for - ev - er! Lord, Thou a - lone canst pre-

hon - or of our neigh-bor, Loy - al to the
serve us in en - deav - or, Loy - al to the

mot - to of our dear na - tive land.
mot - to of our dear na - tive land.

SENTINELS OF NIGHT

ELIZABETH NOXON

LAURETTA V. SWEESY

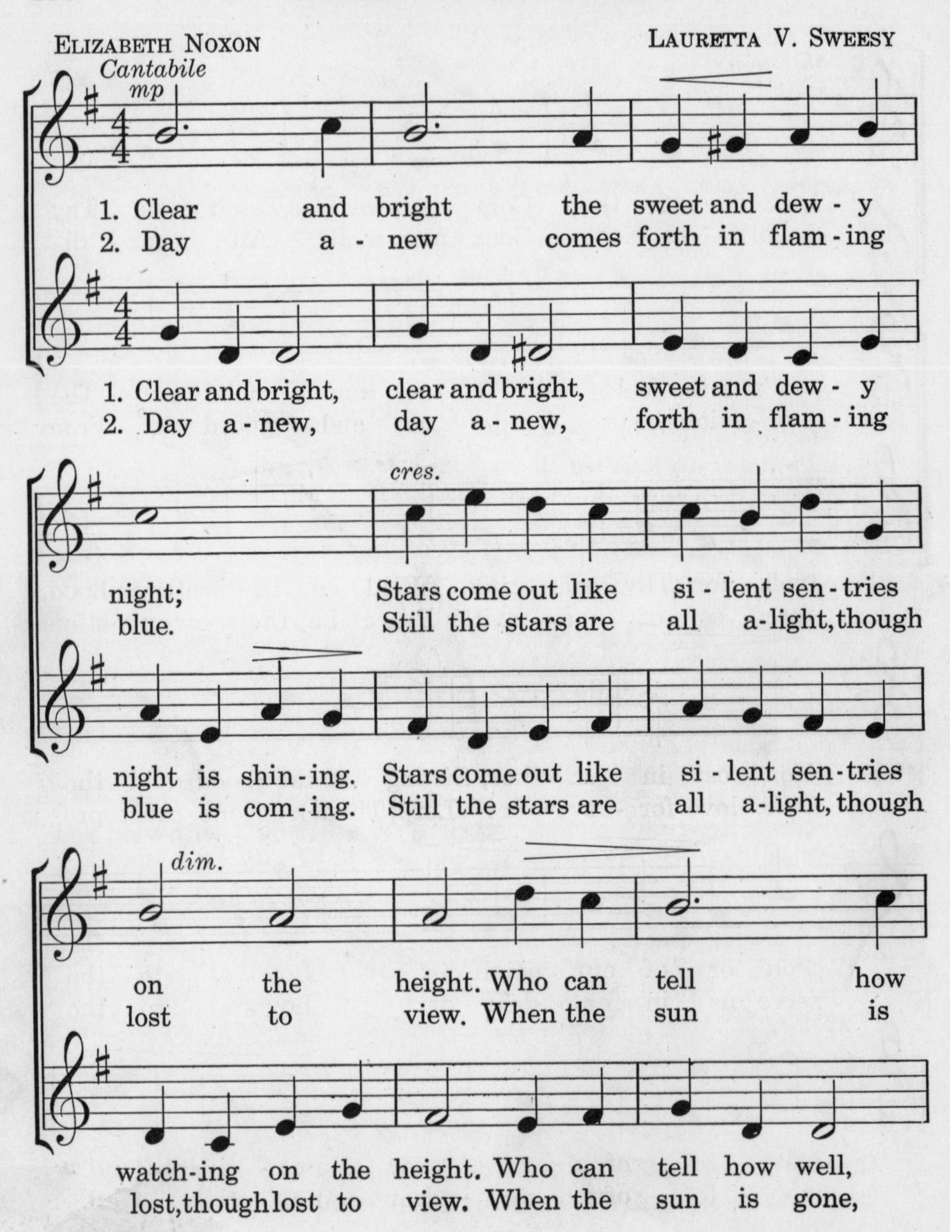

1. Clear and bright the sweet and dew-y night; Stars come out like si-lent sen-tries on the height. Who can tell how

2. Day a-new comes forth in flam-ing blue. Still the stars are all a-light, though lost to view. When the sun is

1. Clear and bright, clear and bright, sweet and dew-y night is shin-ing. Stars come out like si-lent sen-tries watch-ing on the height. Who can tell how well,

2. Day a-new, day a-new, forth in flam-ing blue is com-ing. Still the stars are all a-light, though lost, though lost to view. When the sun is gone,

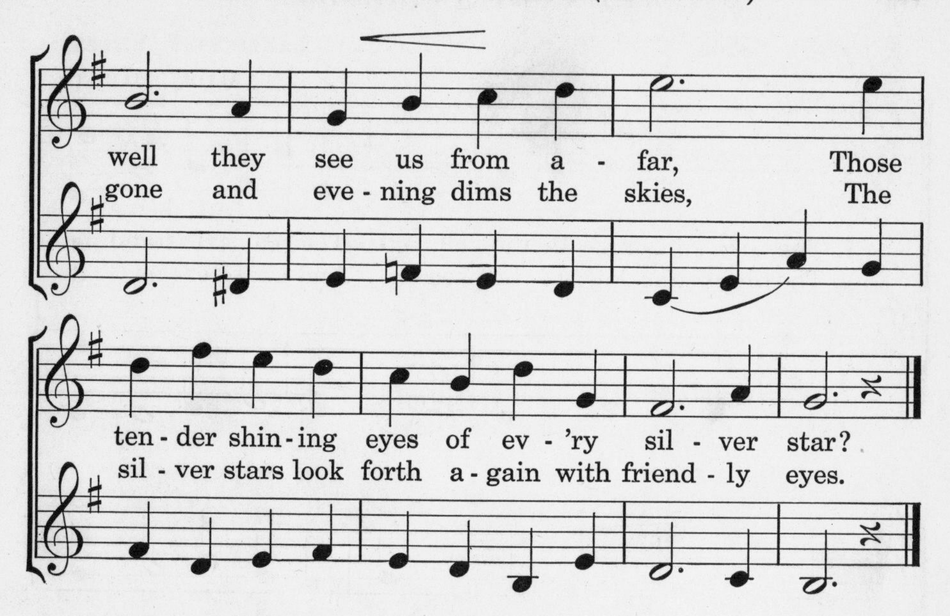

well they see us from a - far, Those
gone and eve - ning dims the skies, The

ten - der shin - ing eyes of ev - 'ry sil - ver star?
sil - ver stars look forth a - gain with friend - ly eyes.

THE HERRING BOATS

English Version by
Margaret Connolly

Norwegian Folk Song

Andante mp

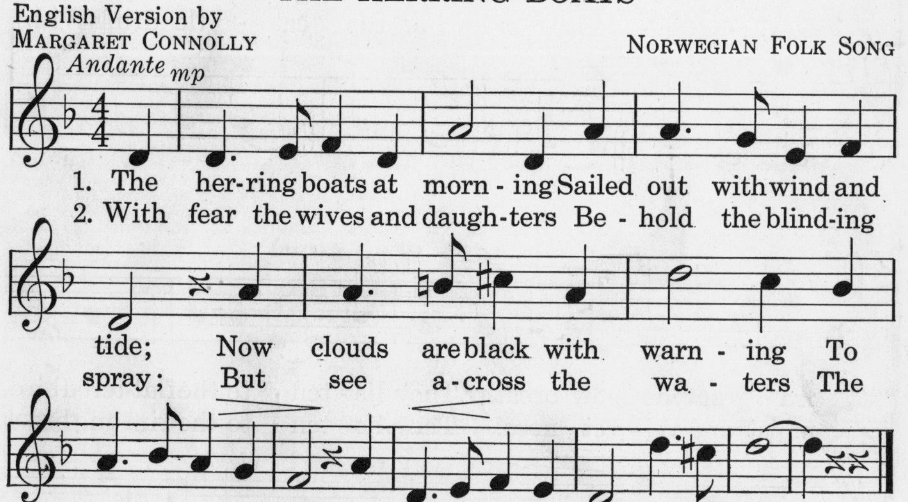

1. The her-ring boats at morn - ing Sailed out with wind and
2. With fear the wives and daugh-ters Be - hold the blind-ing

tide; Now clouds are black with warn - ing To
spray; But see a - cross the wa - ters The

those at home that bide. Oh, can the fish-ing fleet safe-ly ride? ·
bea-con's friend-ly ray! Oh, can my fish-er's boat find the way? ·

THE POET'S FRIENDS

WILLIAM DEAN HOWELLS
Second Stanza by
M. L. BAUM

MABEL DANIELS

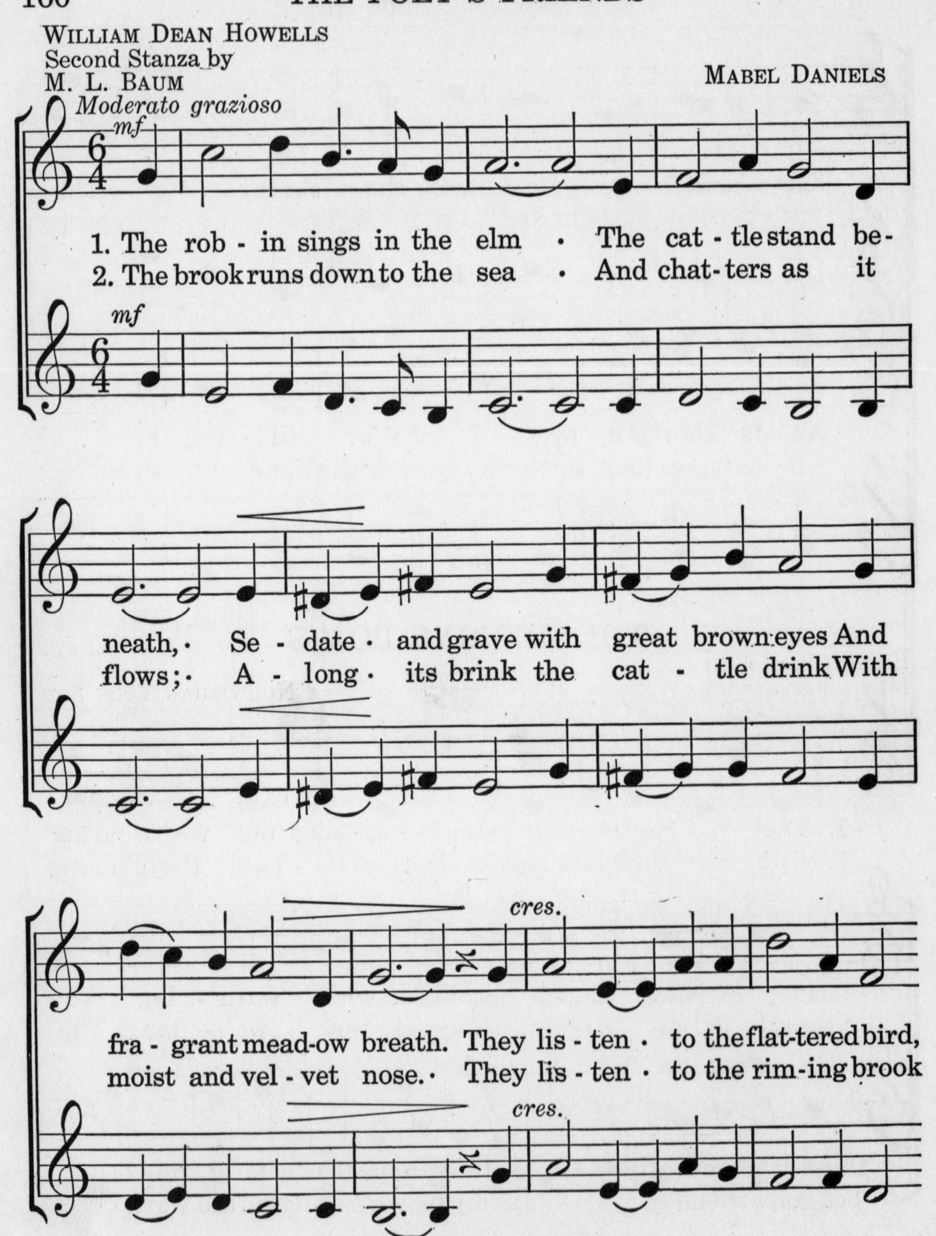

Moderato grazioso

1. The rob - in sings in the elm · The cat - tle stand be-
2. The brook runs down to the sea · And chat - ters as it

neath, · Se - date · and grave with great brown eyes And
flows; · A - long · its brink the cat - tle drink With

cres.

fra - grant mead-ow breath. They lis - ten · to the flat-tered bird,
moist and vel - vet nose. · They lis - ten · to the rim-ing brook

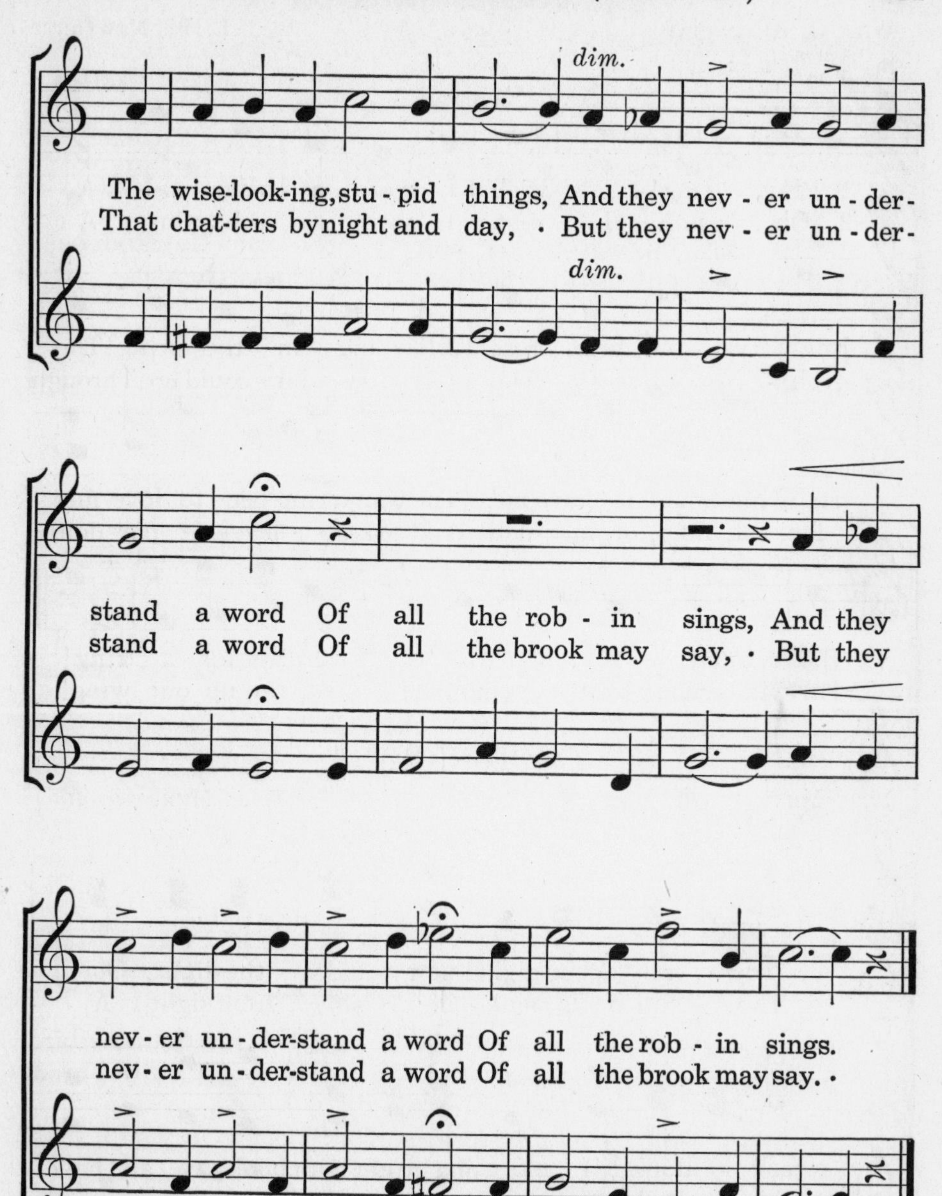

The wise-look-ing, stu-pid things, And they nev-er un-der-
That chat-ters by night and day, · But they nev-er un-der-

stand a word Of all the rob-in sings, And they
stand a word Of all the brook may say, · But they

nev-er un-der-stand a word Of all the rob-in sings.
nev-er un-der-stand a word Of all the brook may say. ·

WISHING

WILLIAM ALLINGHAM

E. W. NEWTON

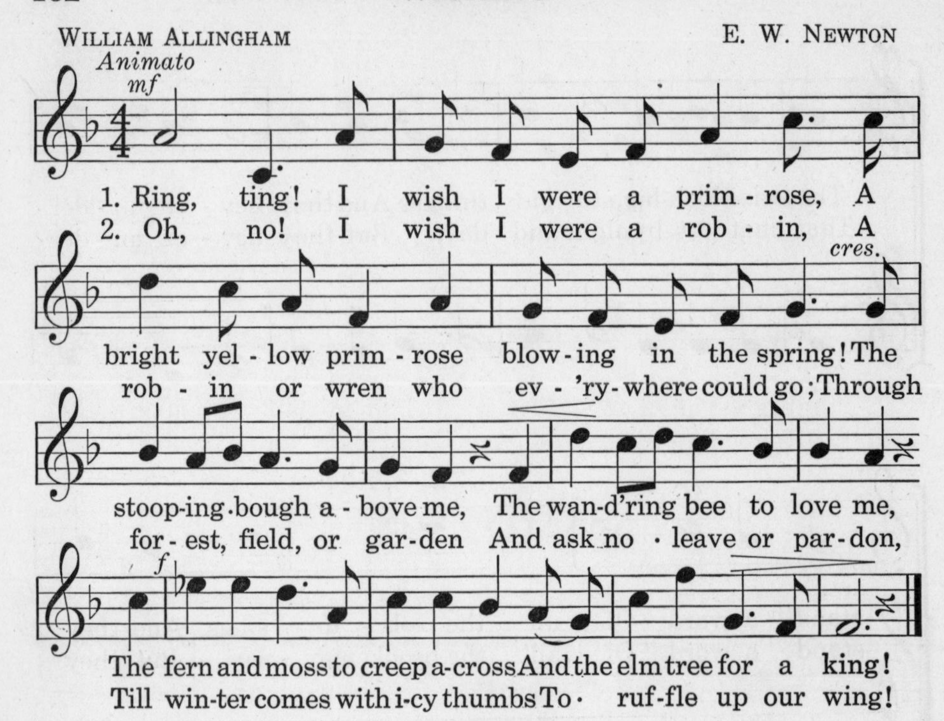

1. Ring, ting! I wish I were a prim - rose, A
2. Oh, no! I wish I were a rob - in, A

bright yel - low prim - rose blow-ing in the spring! The
rob - in or wren who ev - 'ry-where could go; Through

stoop-ing bough a - bove me, The wan-d'ring bee to love me,
for - est, field, or gar-den And ask no leave or par-don,

The fern and moss to creep a-cross And the elm tree for a king!
Till win-ter comes with i-cy thumbs To ruf-fle up our wing!

GOOD NIGHT

ROSE MILES

FELIX MENDELSSOHN

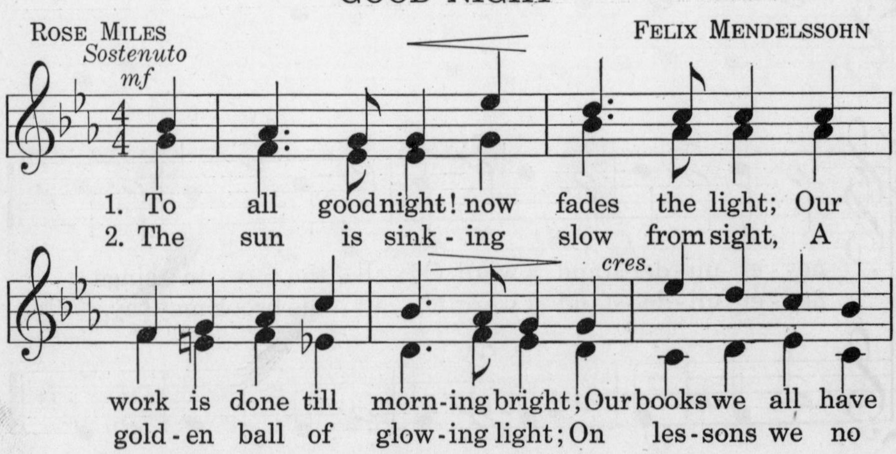

1. To all good night! now fades the light; Our
2. The sun is sink - ing slow from sight, A

work is done till morn-ing bright; Our books we all have
gold - en ball of glow-ing light; On les-sons we no

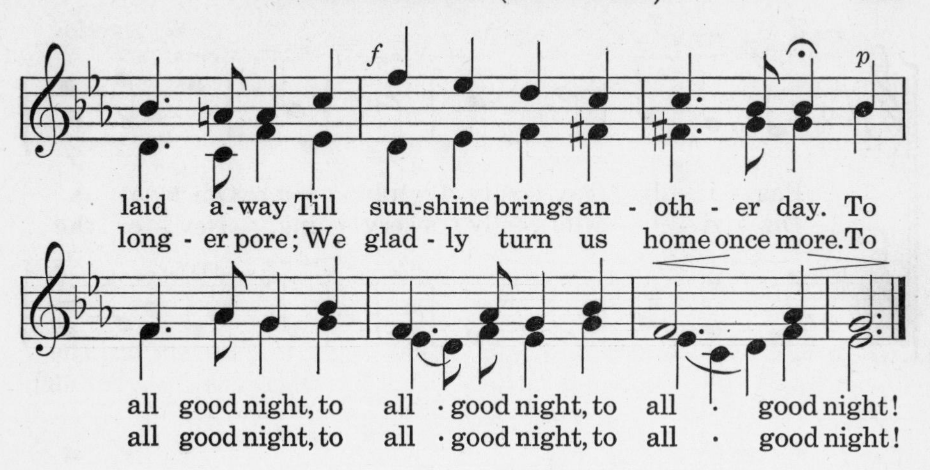

laid a-way Till sun-shine brings an - oth - er day. To
long - er pore; We glad - ly turn us home once more. To

all good night, to all · good night, to all · good night!
all good night, to all · good night, to all · good night!

SKATING SONG

Abbie Farwell Brown

Edna Clark

Con espressione
mp

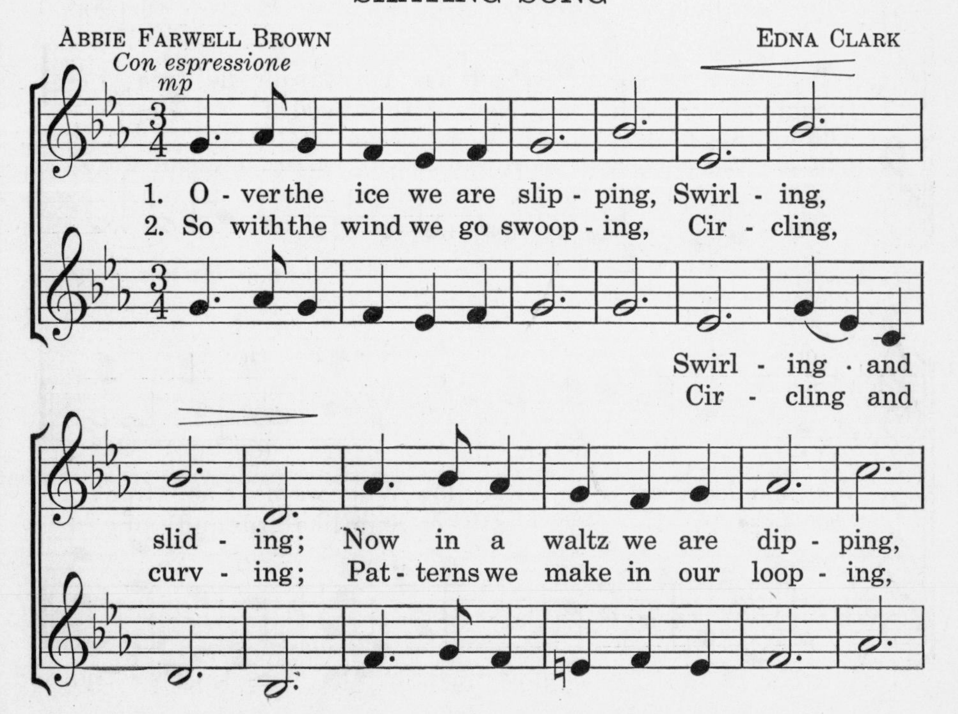

1. O - ver the ice we are slip - ping, Swirl - ing,
2. So with the wind we go swoop - ing, Cir - cling,

Swirl - ing · and
Cir - cling and

slid - ing; Now in a waltz we are dip - ping,
curv - ing; Pat - terns we make in our loop - ing,

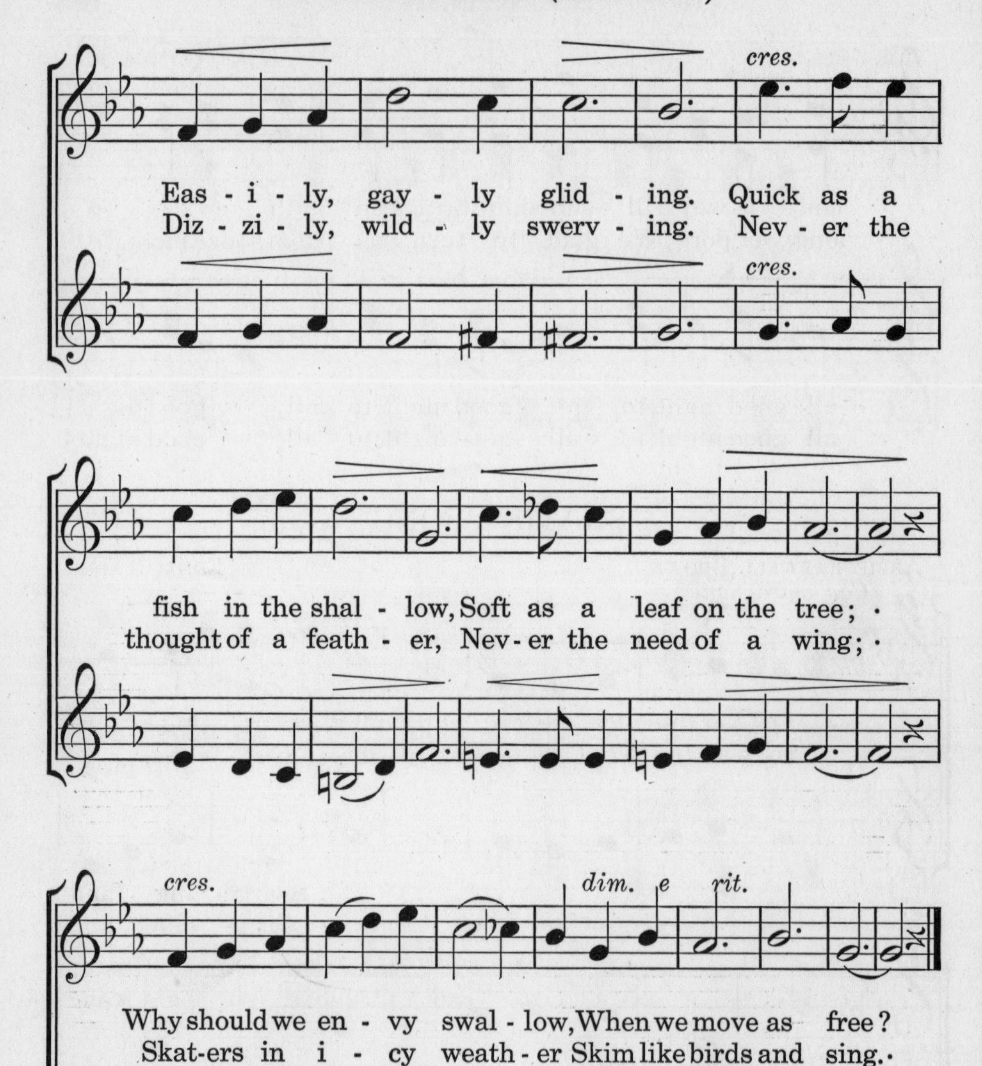

Eas - i - ly, gay - ly glid - ing. Quick as a
Diz - zi - ly, wild - ly swerv - ing. Nev - er the

fish in the shal - low, Soft as a leaf on the tree; ·
thought of a feath - er, Nev - er the need of a wing; ·

Why should we en - vy swal - low, When we move as free?
Skat - ers in i - cy weath - er Skim like birds and sing.·

SNOW MAN

JOHN REED

HARTLEY MOORE

Con spirito

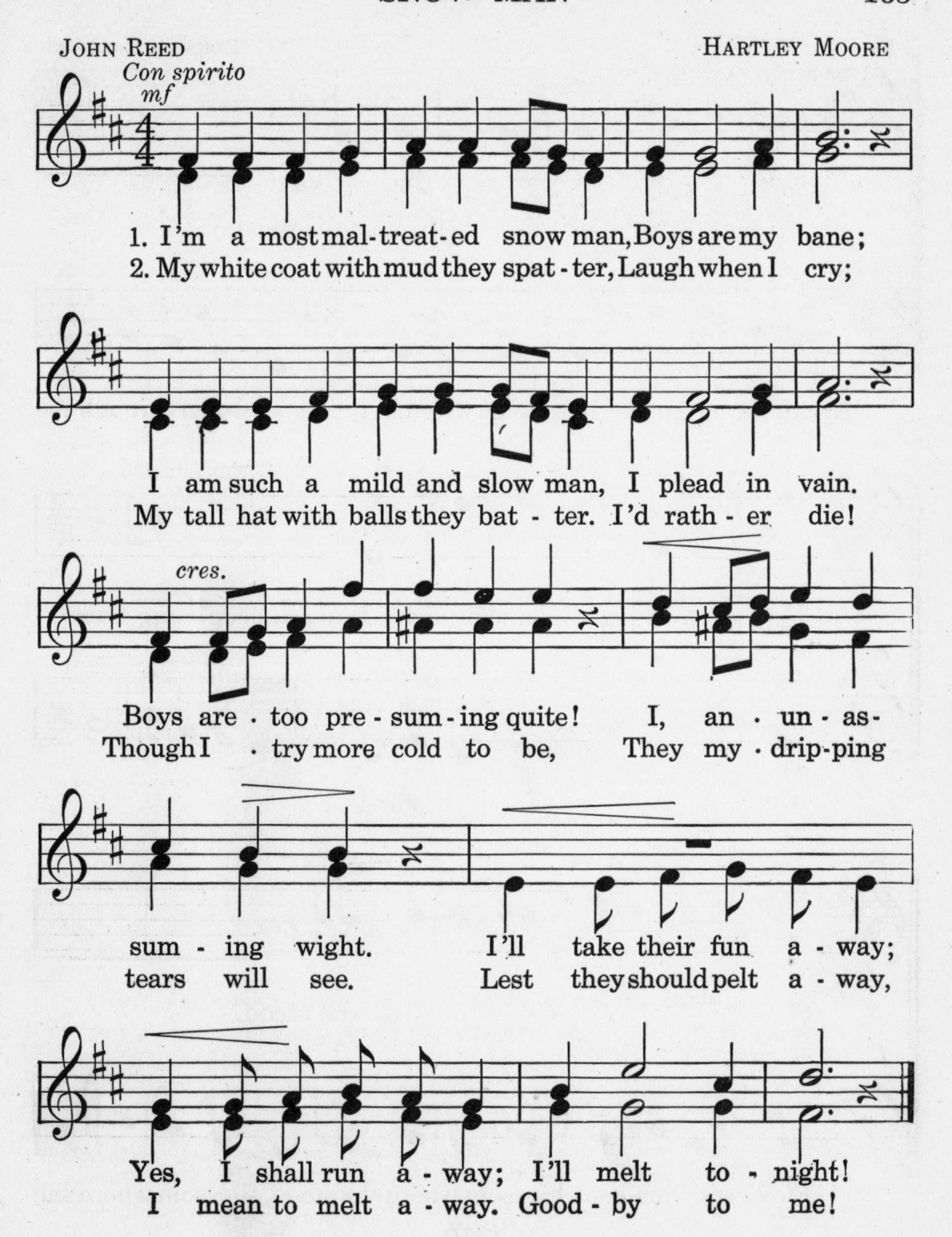

1. I'm a most mal-treat-ed snow man, Boys are my bane;
2. My white coat with mud they spat-ter, Laugh when I cry;

I am such a mild and slow man, I plead in vain.
My tall hat with balls they bat-ter. I'd rath-er die!

Boys are too pre-sum-ing quite! I, an un-as-
Though I try more cold to be, They my drip-ping

sum-ing wight. I'll take their fun a-way;
tears will see. Lest they should pelt a-way,

Yes, I shall run a-way; I'll melt to-night!
I mean to melt a-way. Good-by to me!

Translated

EDUARD LASSEN

Andante cantabile

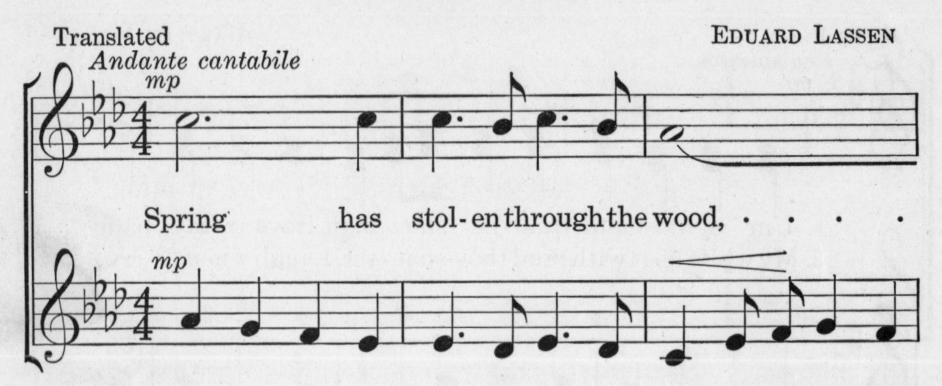

Spring　　　　has　stol- en through the wood, ．　．　．　．

Spring, sweet spring, has stolen through the wood, stolen through the

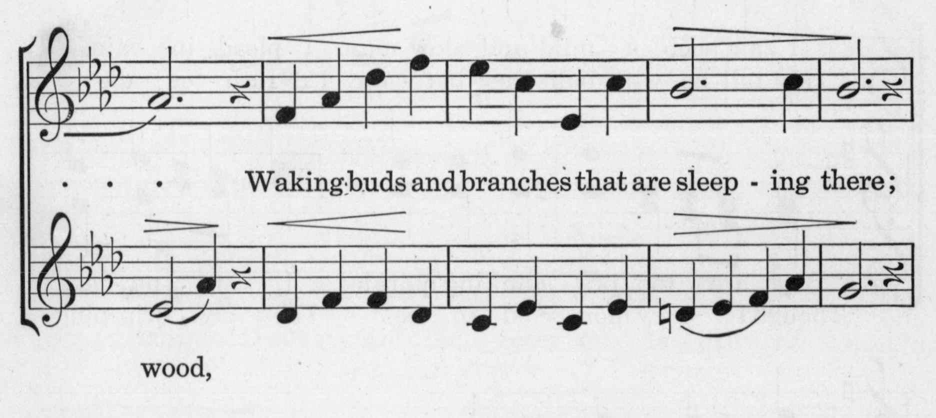

．　．　．　Waking buds and branches that are sleep - ing there;

wood,

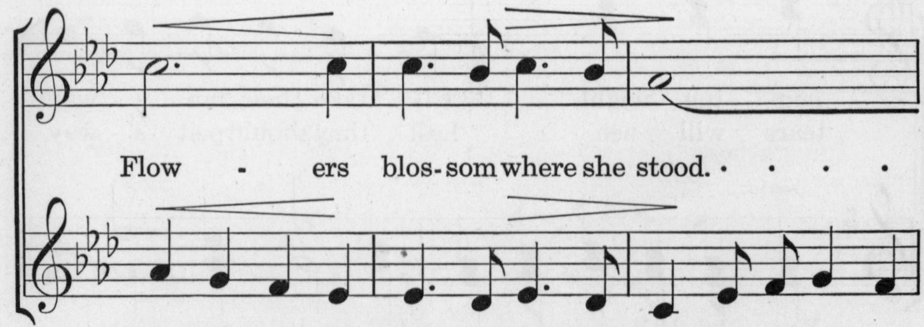

Flow　-　ers　blos- som where she stood. ．　．　．　．

Flow - ers blos- som, blossom where she stood, Blossom where she

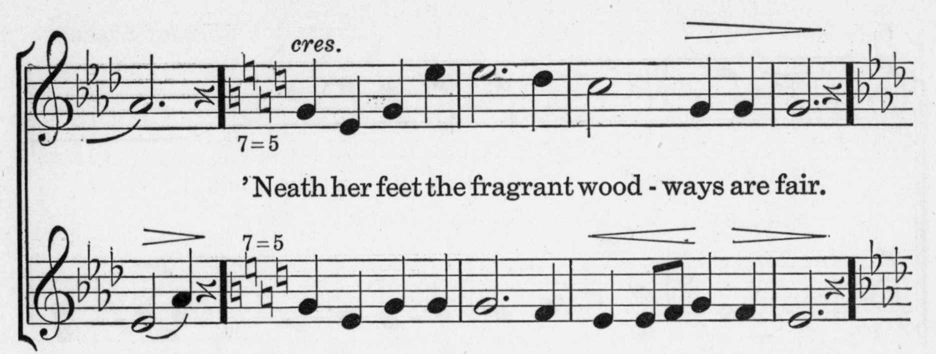

'Neath her feet the fragrant wood - ways are fair.

stood.   'Neath her feet the fragrant woodland ways are fair.

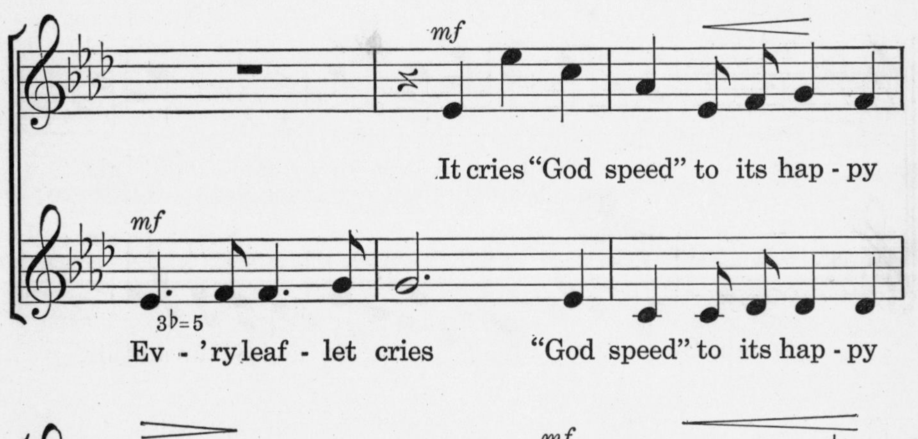

It cries "God speed" to its hap - py

Ev - 'ry leaf - let cries   "God speed" to its hap - py

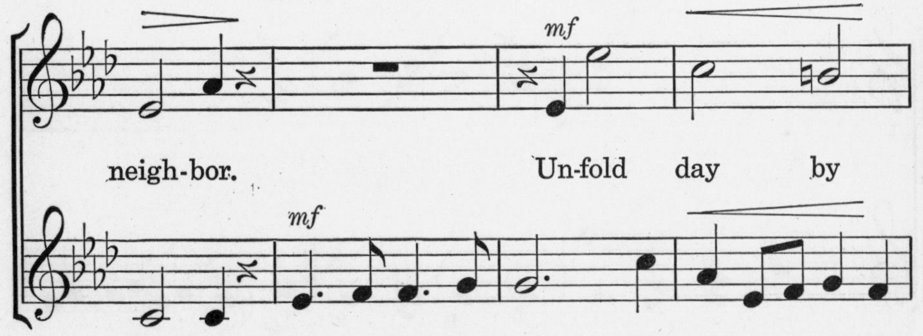

neigh-bor.   Un-fold   day   by

neigh-bor. Love - ly things un-fold   and blos-som day by

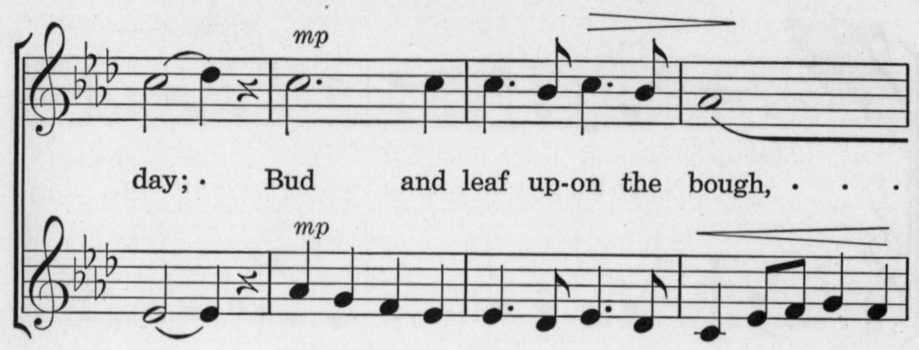

day; · Bud and leaf up-on the bough, · · ·

day; · Bud and lac-y leaf up-on the bough, up - on the

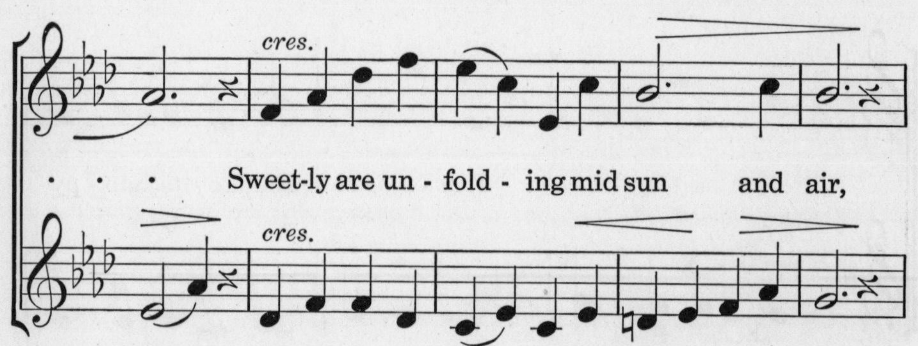

· · · Sweet-ly are un - fold - ing mid sun and air,

bough, Sweet-ly are un - fold - ing mid gen-tle sun and air,

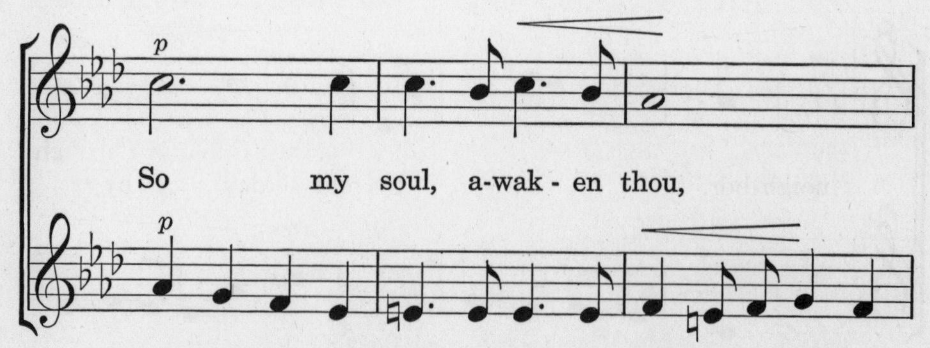

So my soul, a-wak - en thou,

So my soul, a - wake, a-wak - en thou, oh a-wak - en

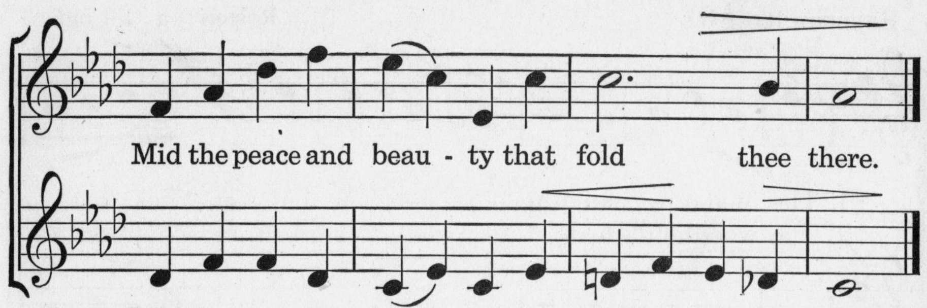

Mid the peace and beau - ty that fold   thee there.

Mid the peace and beau - ty that fold thee soft - ly there.

THE MESSENGER

Allan Brigham   Russian Folk Tune

Con brio
mf

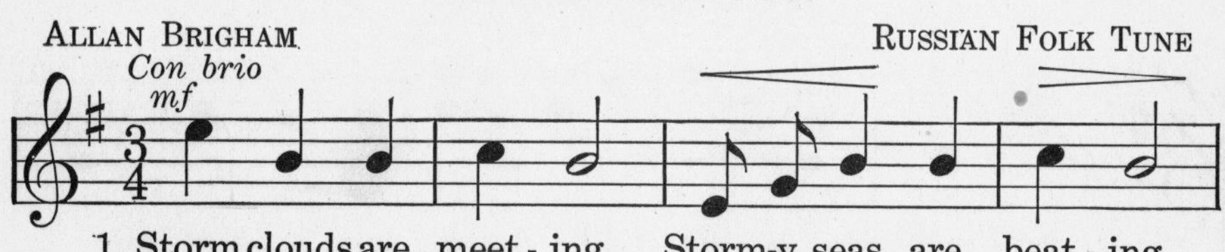

1. Storm clouds are meet - ing,   Storm-y seas are beat - ing,
2. Storm clouds can nev - er   Baf - fle his en - deav - or,

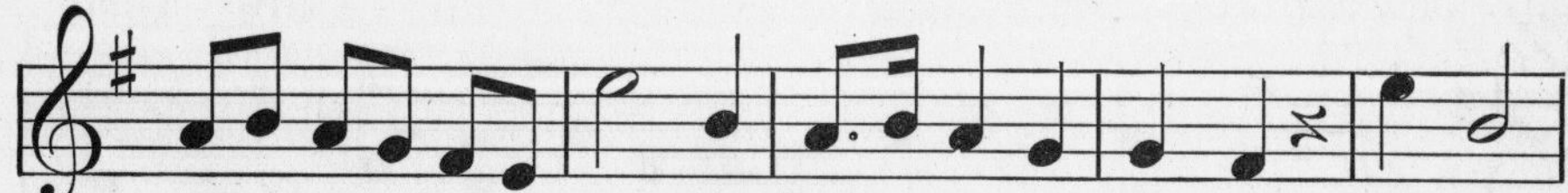

Sea - birds are cry - ing, Landward are fly - ing. Stal-wart,
No - wind can beat him Nor wave defeat him. Strong-willed,

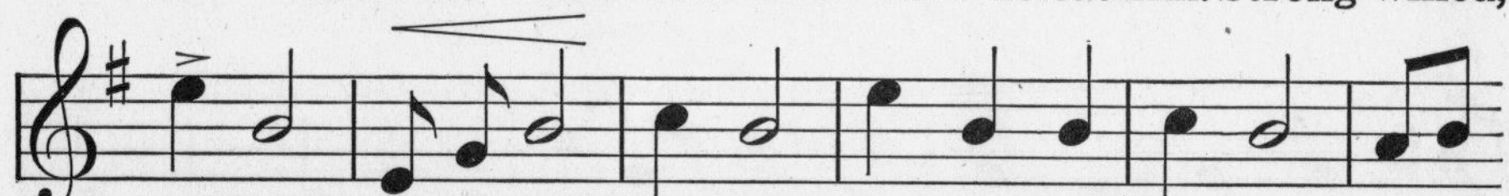

tear-less, See the youth fear-less! Homeward he's tak-ing Through
dar-ing, Sails the youth bear-ing Friend-ship ad - mir - ing, Cour-

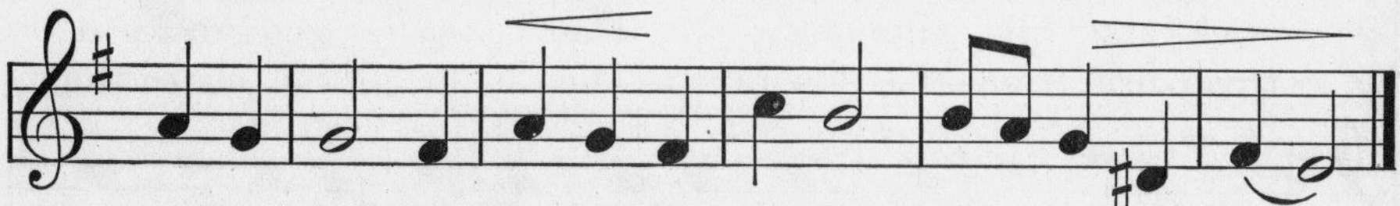

surg-es break-ing, Hope for his peo-ple O - ver the sea. ·
age ne'er tir - ing, Hope for his peo-ple O - ver the sea. ·

SUMMER

Herbert Randall

Rossetter G. Cole

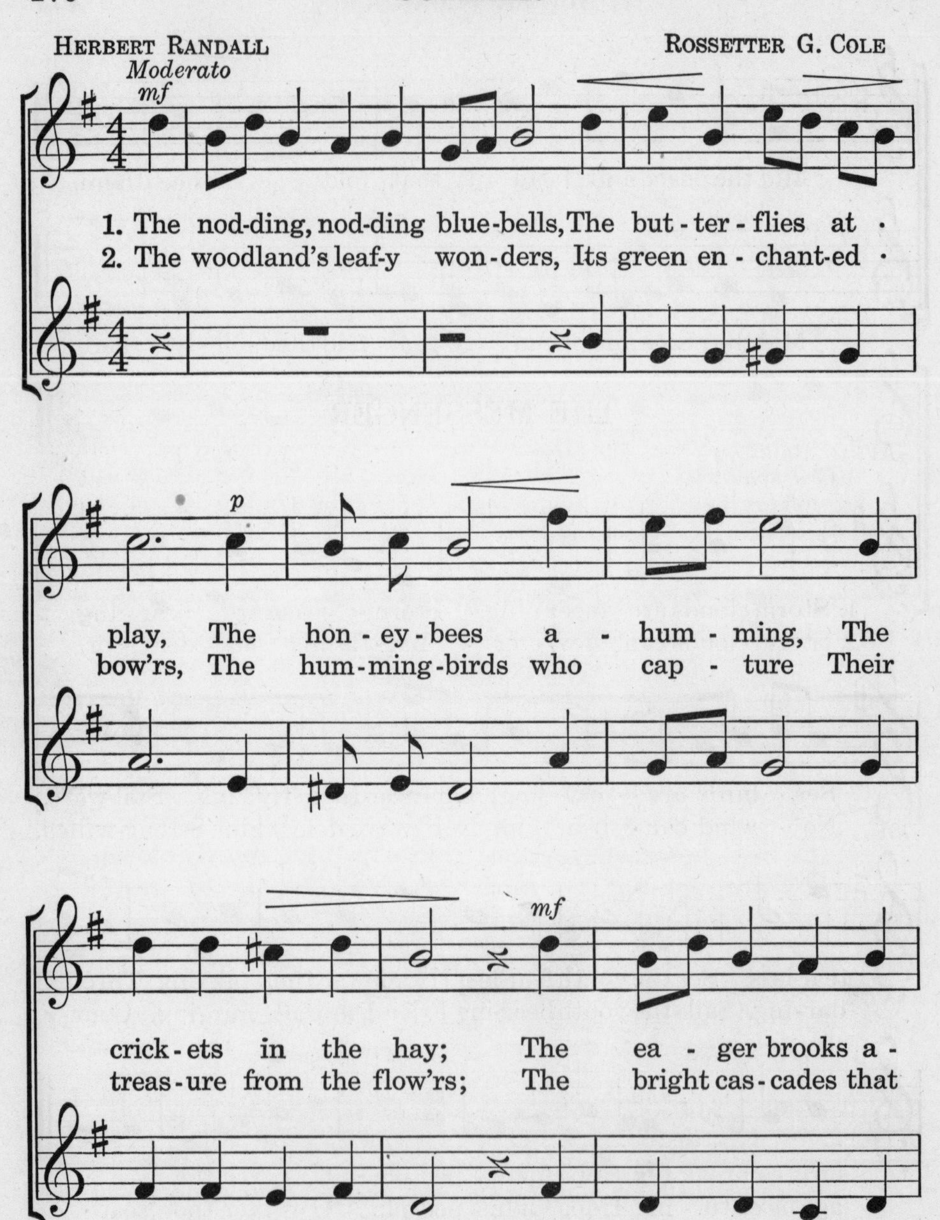

1. The nod-ding, nod-ding blue-bells, The but - ter - flies at ·
2. The woodland's leaf-y won-ders, Its green en - chant-ed ·

play, The hon - ey - bees a - hum - ming, The
bow'rs, The hum-ming-birds who cap - ture Their

crick - ets in the hay; The ea - ger brooks a -
treas - ure from the flow'rs; The bright cas - cades that

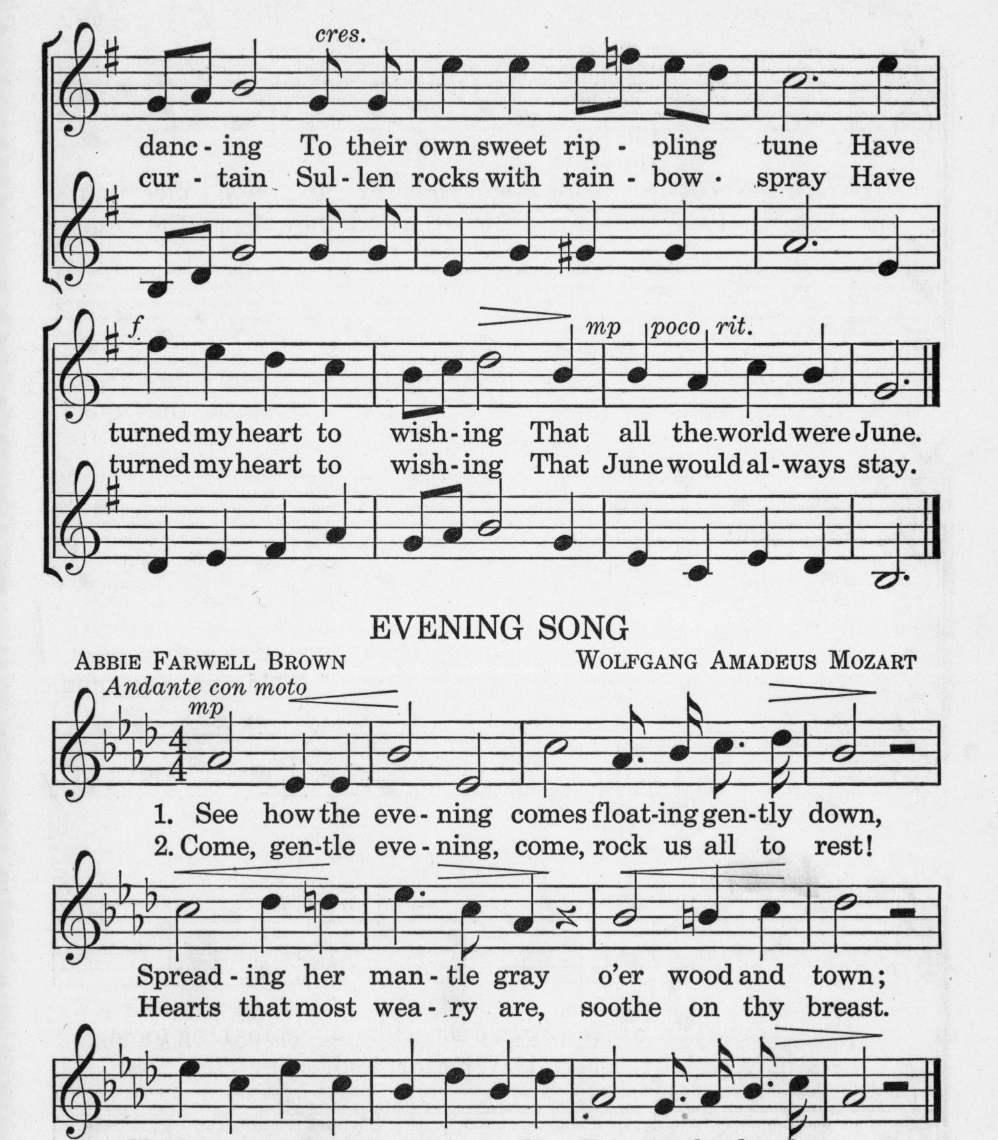

cres.

danc - ing To their own sweet rip - pling   tune   Have
cur - tain Sul - len rocks with rain - bow · spray Have

f.   *mp poco rit.*

turned my heart to   wish - ing That all the world were June.
turned my heart to   wish - ing That June would al - ways stay.

EVENING SONG

ABBIE FARWELL BROWN   WOLFGANG AMADEUS MOZART

Andante con moto
mp

1. See how the eve - ning comes float-ing gen-tly down,
2. Come, gen-tle eve - ning, come, rock us all to   rest!

Spread - ing her man - tle gray   o'er wood and town;
Hearts that most wea - ry are,   soothe on thy breast.

Shades are trail-ing, meadows veiling, Fringing her lovely gown.
Hith-er stealing, bring thy healing, Blown from the rosy west.

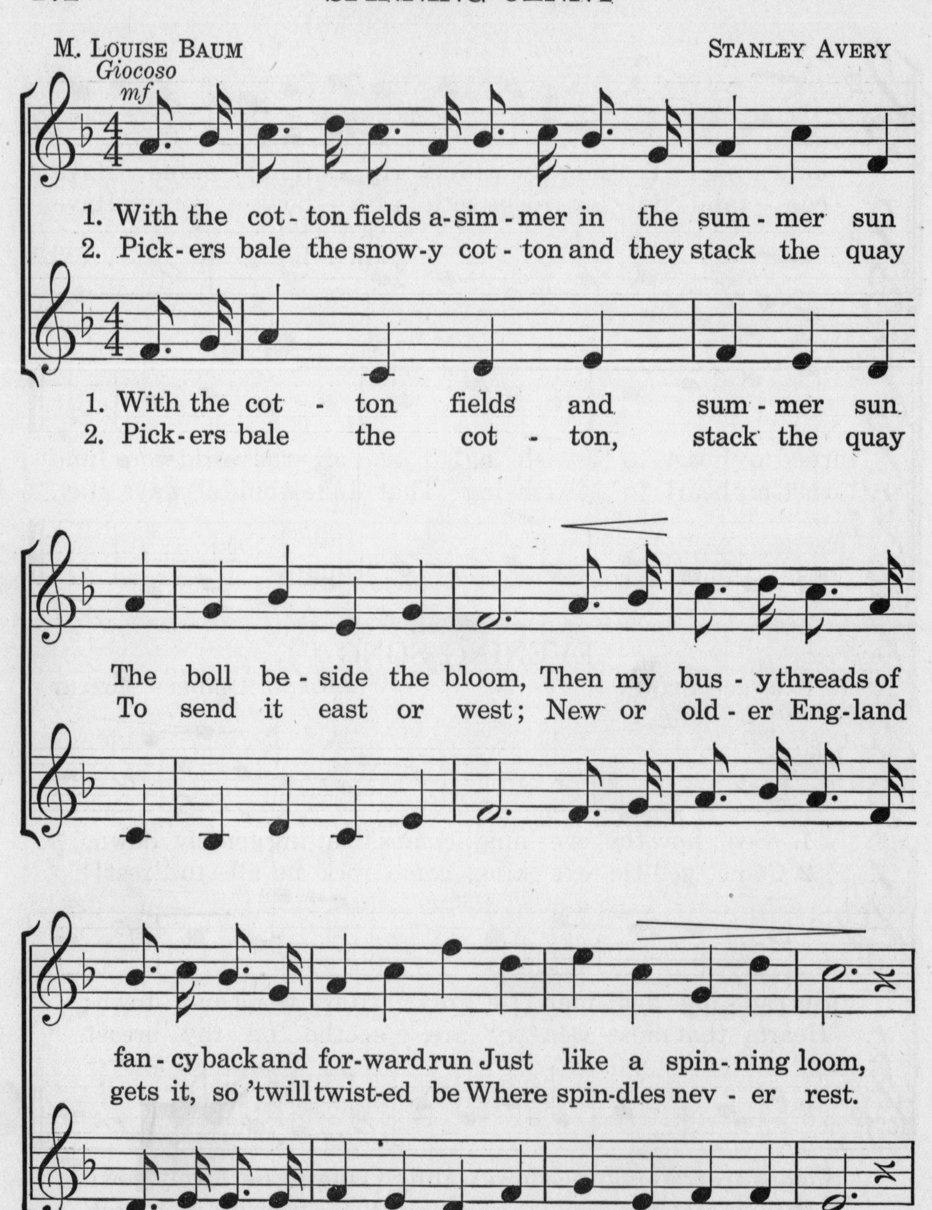

SPINNING JENNY

M. LOUISE BAUM

STANLEY AVERY

Giocoso
mf

1. With the cot - ton fields a-sim - mer in the sum - mer sun
2. Pick - ers bale the snow-y cot - ton and they stack the quay

1. With the cot - ton fields and sum - mer sun
2. Pick - ers bale the cot - ton, stack the quay

The boll be - side the bloom, Then my bus - y threads of
To send it east or west; New or old - er Eng-land

fan - cy back and for-ward run Just like a spin - ning loom,
gets it, so 'twill twist-ed be Where spin-dles nev - er rest.

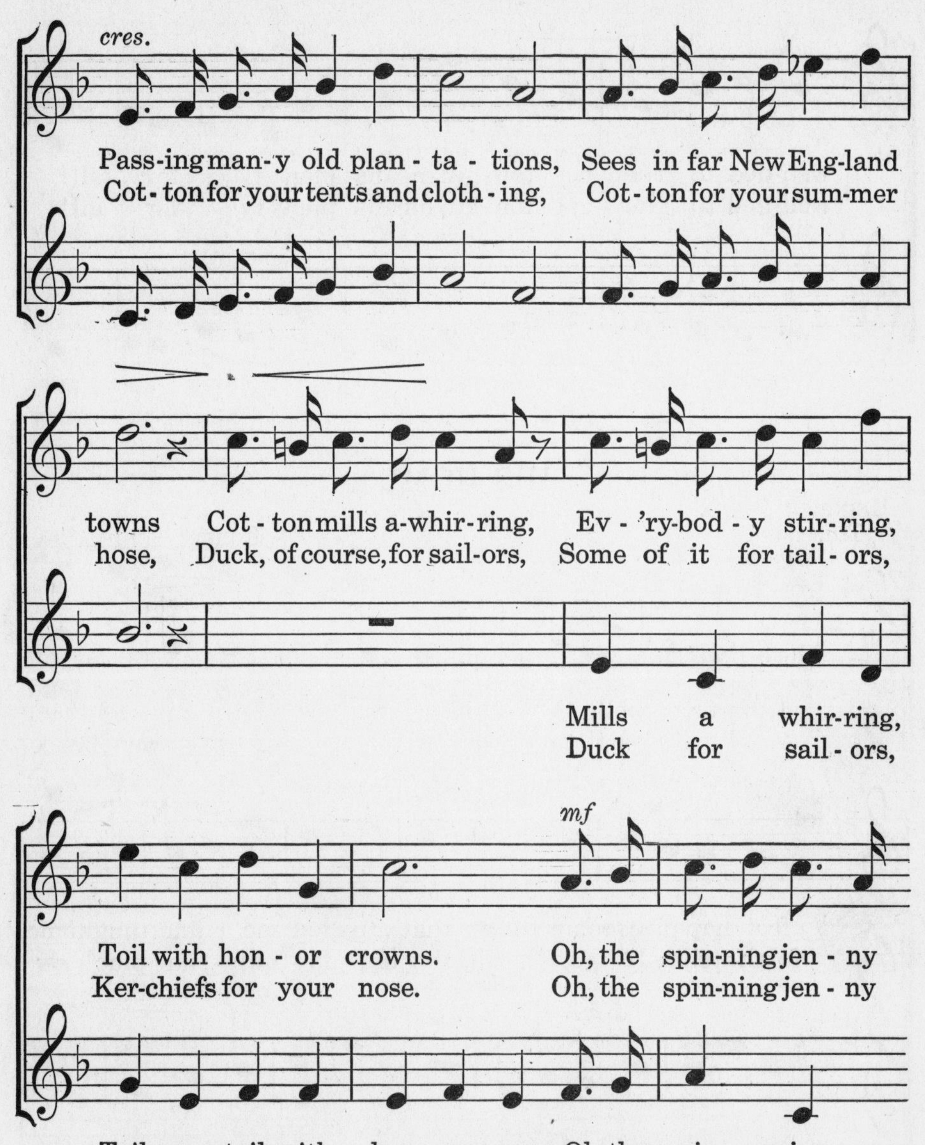

cres.

Pass-ing man-y old plan - ta - tions, Sees in far New Eng-land
Cot - ton for your tents and cloth - ing, Cot - ton for your sum-mer

towns Cot - ton mills a-whir-ring, Ev - 'ry-bod - y stir-ring,
hose, Duck, of course, for sail-ors, Some of it for tail-ors,

Mills a whir-ring,
Duck for sail - ors,

mf

Toil with hon - or crowns. Oh, the spin-ning jen - ny
Ker-chiefs for your nose. Oh, the spin-ning jen - ny

Toil, yes toil with hon - or crowns. Oh, the spin - ning
Kerchiefs, ker-chiefs for your nose. Oh, the spin - ning

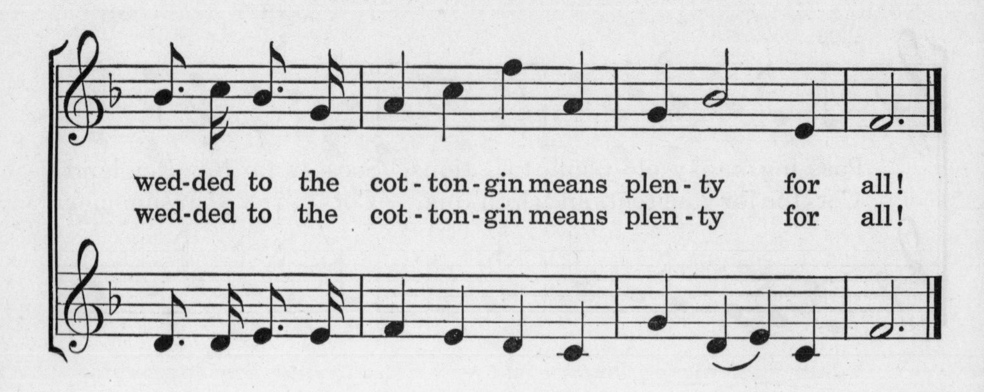

wed-ded to the cot-ton-gin means plen-ty for all!
wed-ded to the cot-ton-gin means plen-ty for all!

HIS HOME

Heinrich Heine
Translated

Robert Schumann

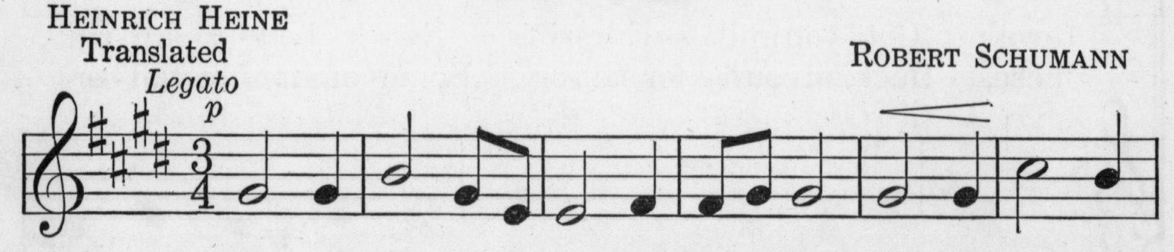

1. Fare you well, O · qui - et by - ways, Paths my wand'ring
2. I de-part to · dwell mid stran-gers, Oth-er ways, hence-

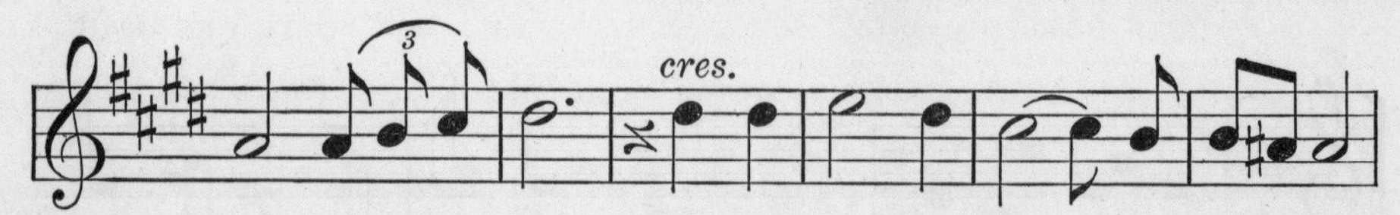

feet hap-pi-ly roam, Town that cra-dled me and taught me,
forth wea-ri-ly go, Ah, the old fa - mil - iar plac - es,

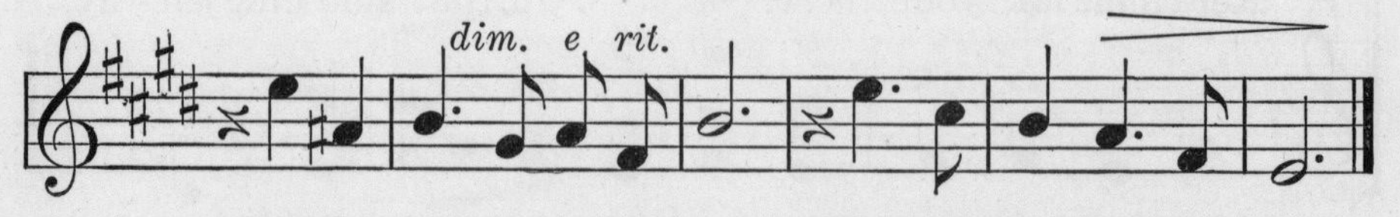

Fare you well, be-lov-ed home, Fare you well, fare you well.
Fare you well, I loved you so. Fare you well, fare you well.

Norman MacLeod

Arthur S. Sullivan

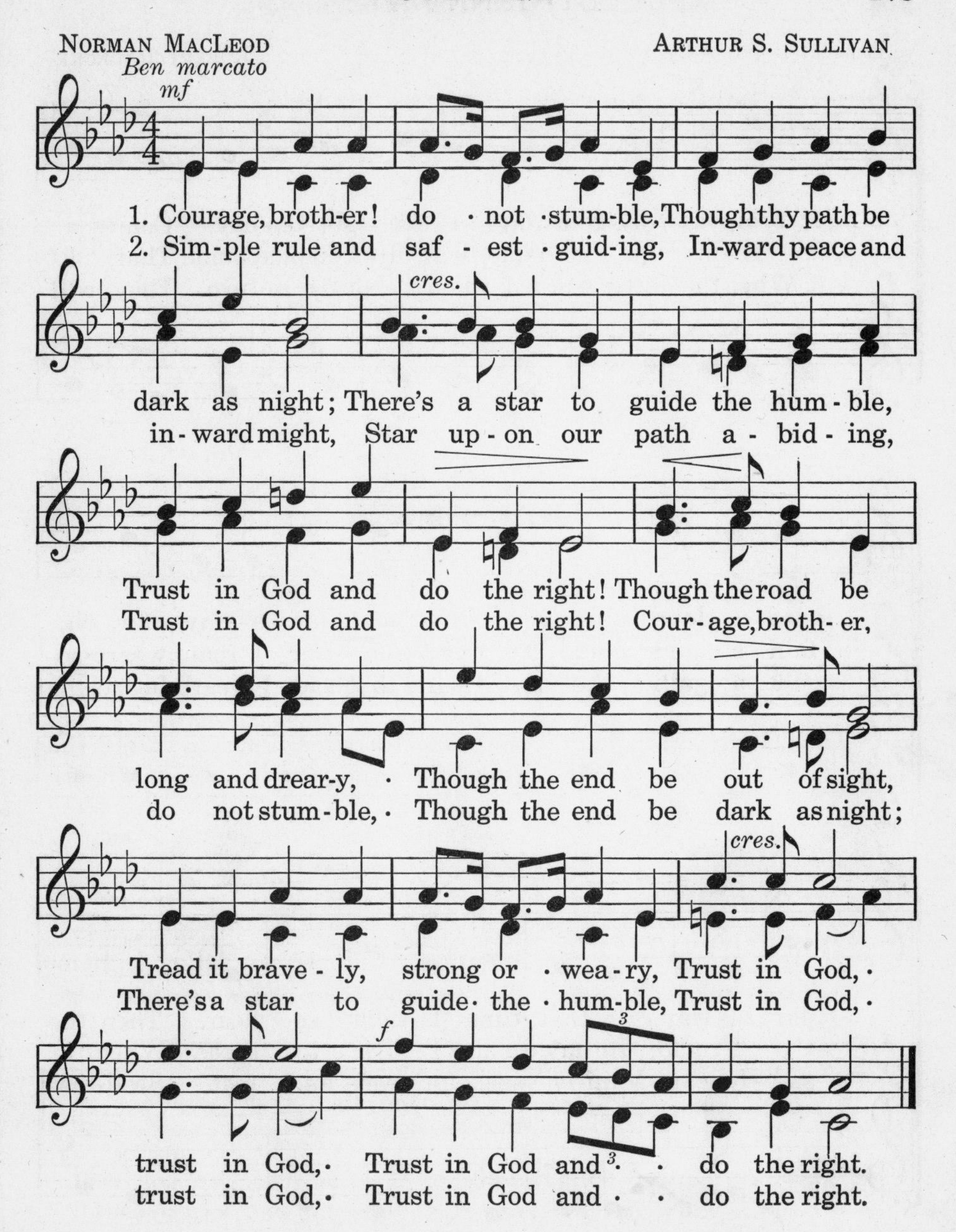

1. Courage, broth-er! do not stum-ble, Though thy path be
dark as night; There's a star to guide the hum-ble,
Trust in God and do the right! Though the road be
long and drear-y, · Though the end be out of sight,
Tread it brave-ly, strong or · wea-ry, Trust in God, ·
trust in God, · Trust in God and · · do the right.

2. Sim-ple rule and saf-est guid-ing, In-ward peace and
in-ward might, Star up-on our path a-bid-ing,
Trust in God and do the right! Cour-age, broth-er,
do not stum-ble, · Though the end be dark as night;
There's a star to guide· the · hum-ble, Trust in God, ·
trust in God, · Trust in God and · · do the right.

BY-GONE DAYS

Translated and Adapted

ROBERT RADECKE

Andante semplice

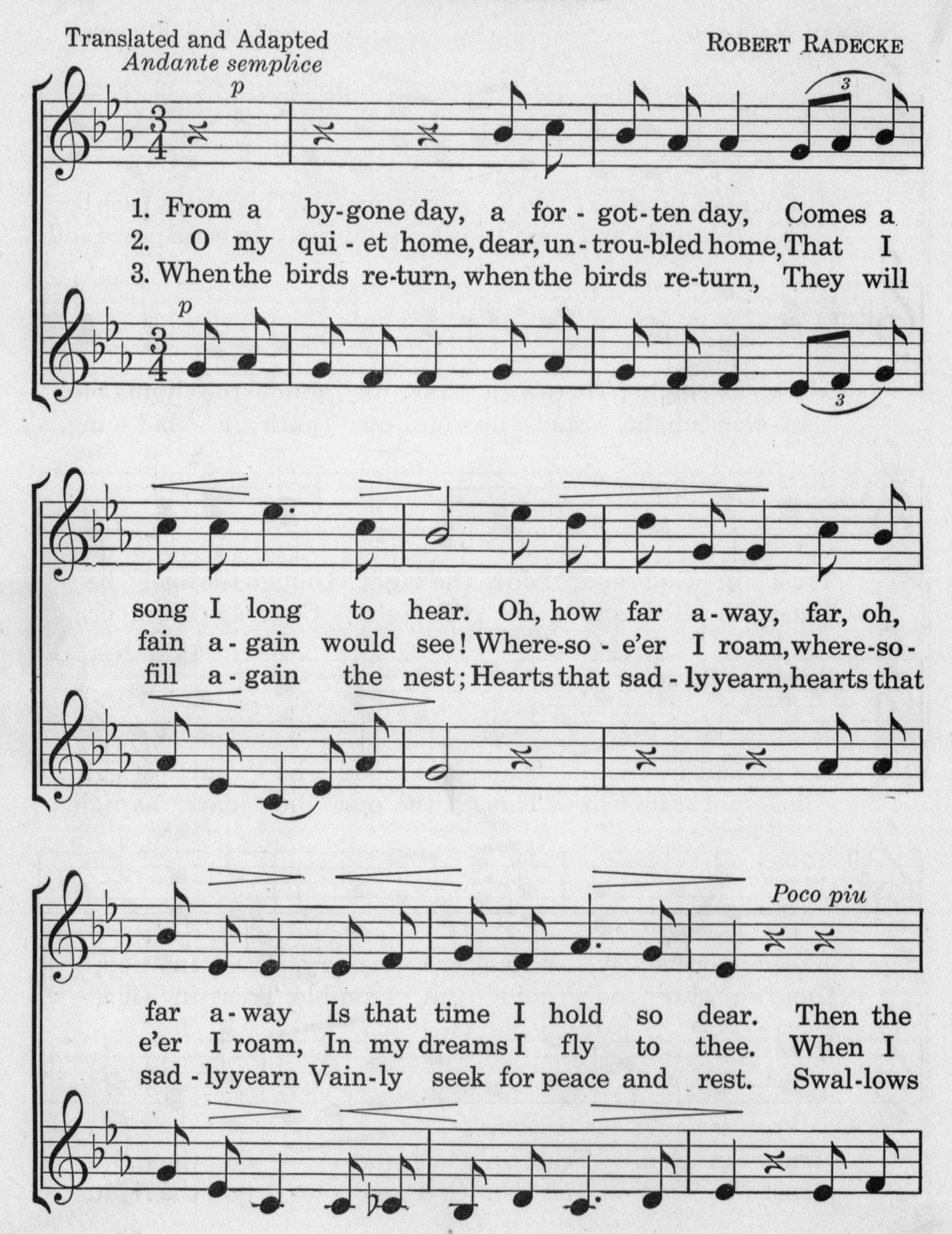

1. From a   by-gone day, a for-got-ten day,   Comes a
2. O my   qui-et home, dear, un-trou-bled home, That   I
3. When the birds re-turn, when the birds re-turn, They will

song I long   to hear. Oh, how far a-way, far, oh,
fain a-gain   would see! Where-so-e'er I roam, where-so-
fill a-gain   the nest; Hearts that sad-ly yearn, hearts that

far a-way Is that time I hold so   dear. Then the
e'er I roam, In my dreams I fly   to   thee. When I
sad-ly yearn Vain-ly seek for peace and rest. Swal-lows

Poco piu

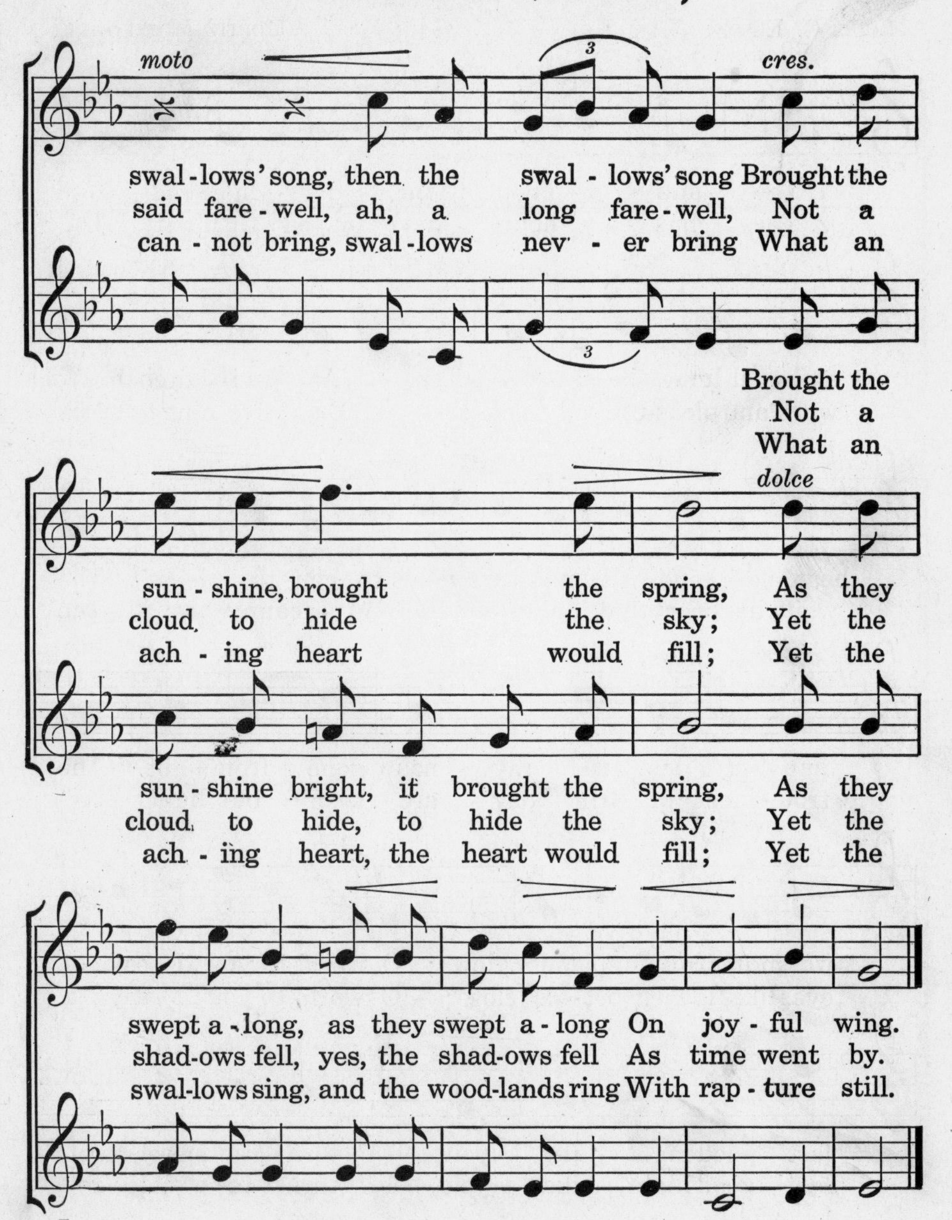

moto *cres.*

swal-lows' song, then the   swal-lows' song Brought the
said fare-well, ah, a   long fare-well, Not a
can-not bring, swal-lows   nev-er bring What an

Brought the
Not a
What an

dolce

sun-shine, brought   the   spring,   As   they
cloud to hide   the   sky;   Yet   the
ach-ing heart   would   fill;   Yet   the

sun-shine bright, it brought the   spring,   As   they
cloud to hide, to hide the   sky;   Yet   the
ach-ing heart, the heart would   fill;   Yet   the

swept a-long, as they swept a-long On joy-ful wing.
shad-ows fell, yes, the shad-ows fell As time went by.
swal-lows sing, and the wood-lands ring With rap-ture still.

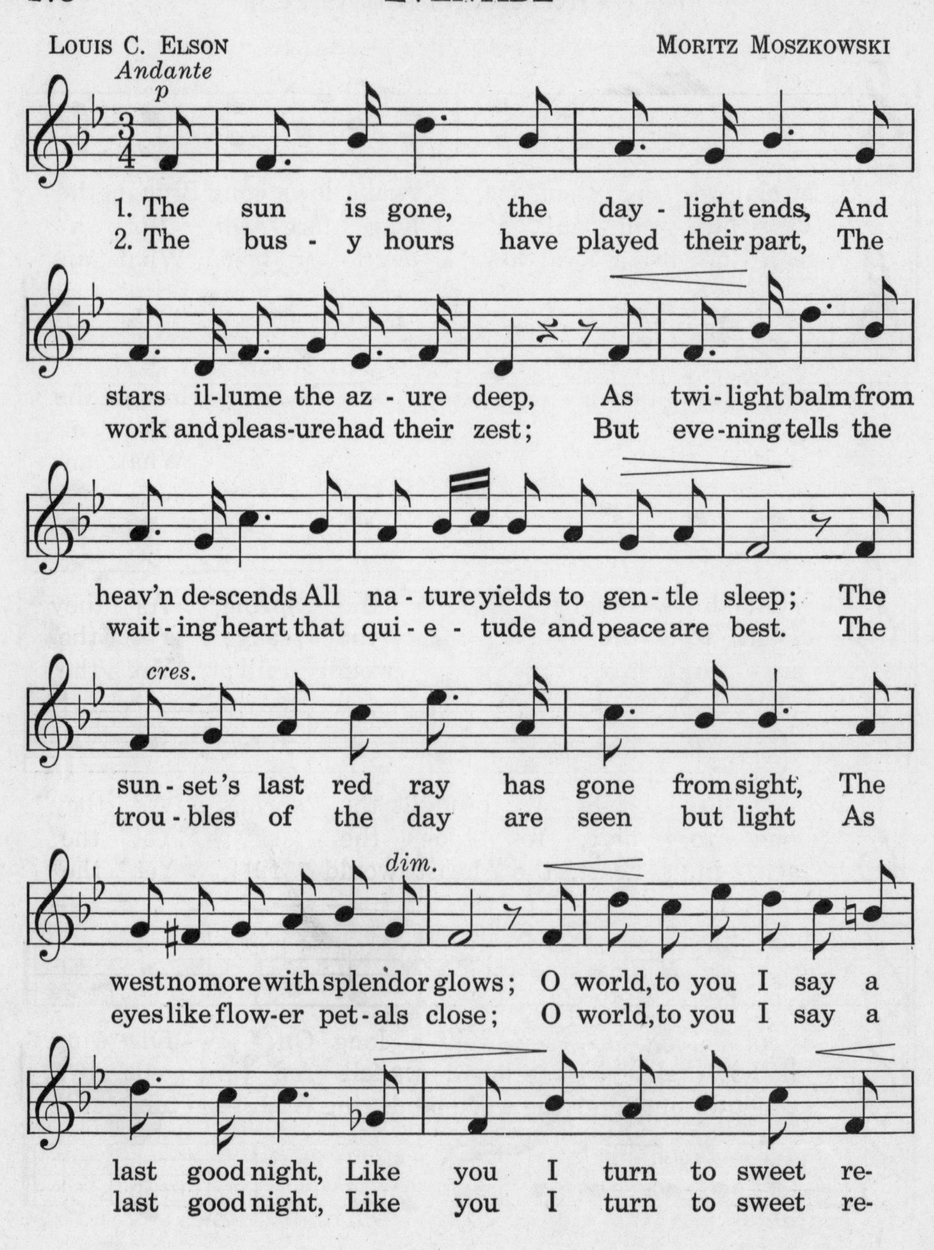

LOUIS C. ELSON

MORITZ MOSZKOWSKI

Andante
p

1. The sun is gone, the day-light ends, And
2. The bus-y hours have played their part, The

stars il-lume the az-ure deep, As twi-light balm from
work and pleas-ure had their zest; But eve-ning tells the

heav'n de-scends All na-ture yields to gen-tle sleep; The
wait-ing heart that qui-e-tude and peace are best. The

cres.

sun-set's last red ray has gone from sight, The
trou-bles of the day are seen but light As

dim.

west no more with splendor glows; O world, to you I say a
eyes like flow-er pet-als close; O world, to you I say a

last good night, Like you I turn to sweet re-
last good night, Like you I turn to sweet re-

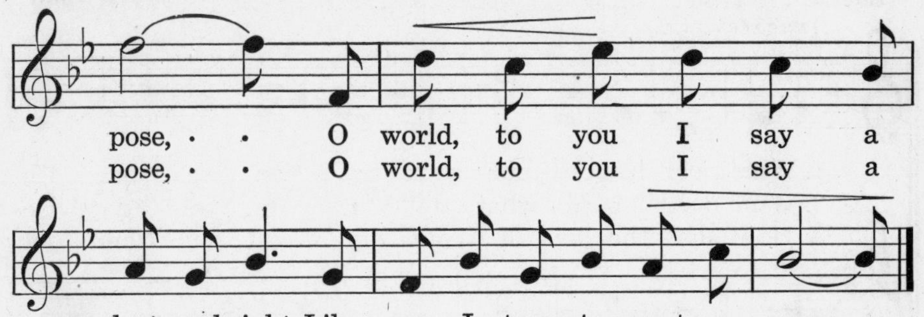

pose, · · O world, to you I say a
pose, · · O world, to you I say a

last good night, Like you I turn to sweet re - pose. ·
last good night, Like you I turn to sweet re - pose. ·

SNAPSHOTS

Agnes Ross

Olive Woodman

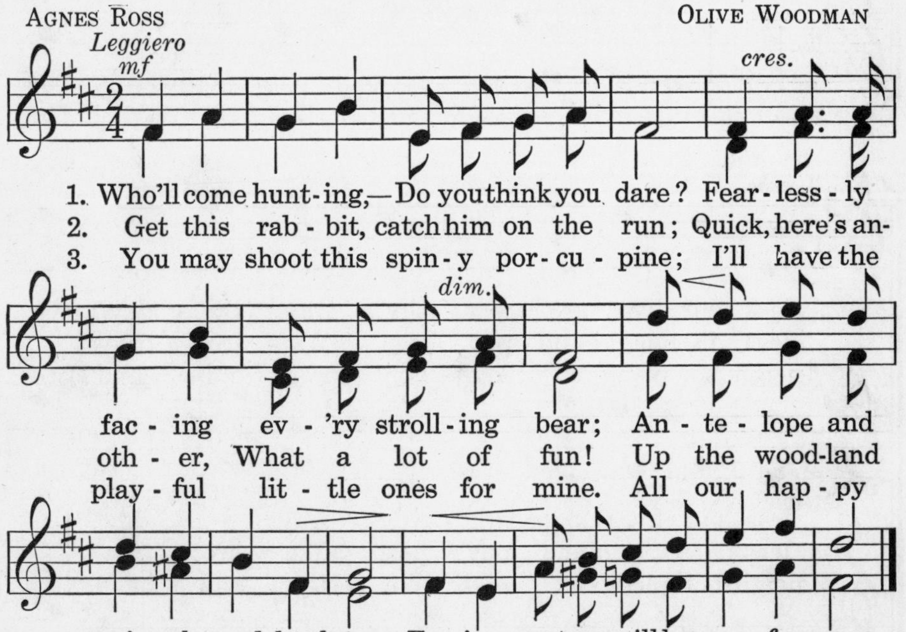

1. Who'll come hunt-ing,—Do you think you dare? Fear - less - ly
2. Get this rab - bit, catch him on the run; Quick, here's an-
3. You may shoot this spin - y por - cu - pine; I'll have the

fac - ing ev - 'ry stroll - ing bear; An - te - lope and
oth - er, What a lot of fun! Up the wood-land
play - ful lit - tle ones for mine. All our hap - py

squir-rel, woodchuck too; Ev - 'ry creature will be game for you.
shad - y there's a fox; Take him with you in your ko - dak box.
snapshots, you'll a-gree, Leave the woodland creatures gay and free.

ALLEGIANCE

LOUISE STICKNEY

FAY WILSON

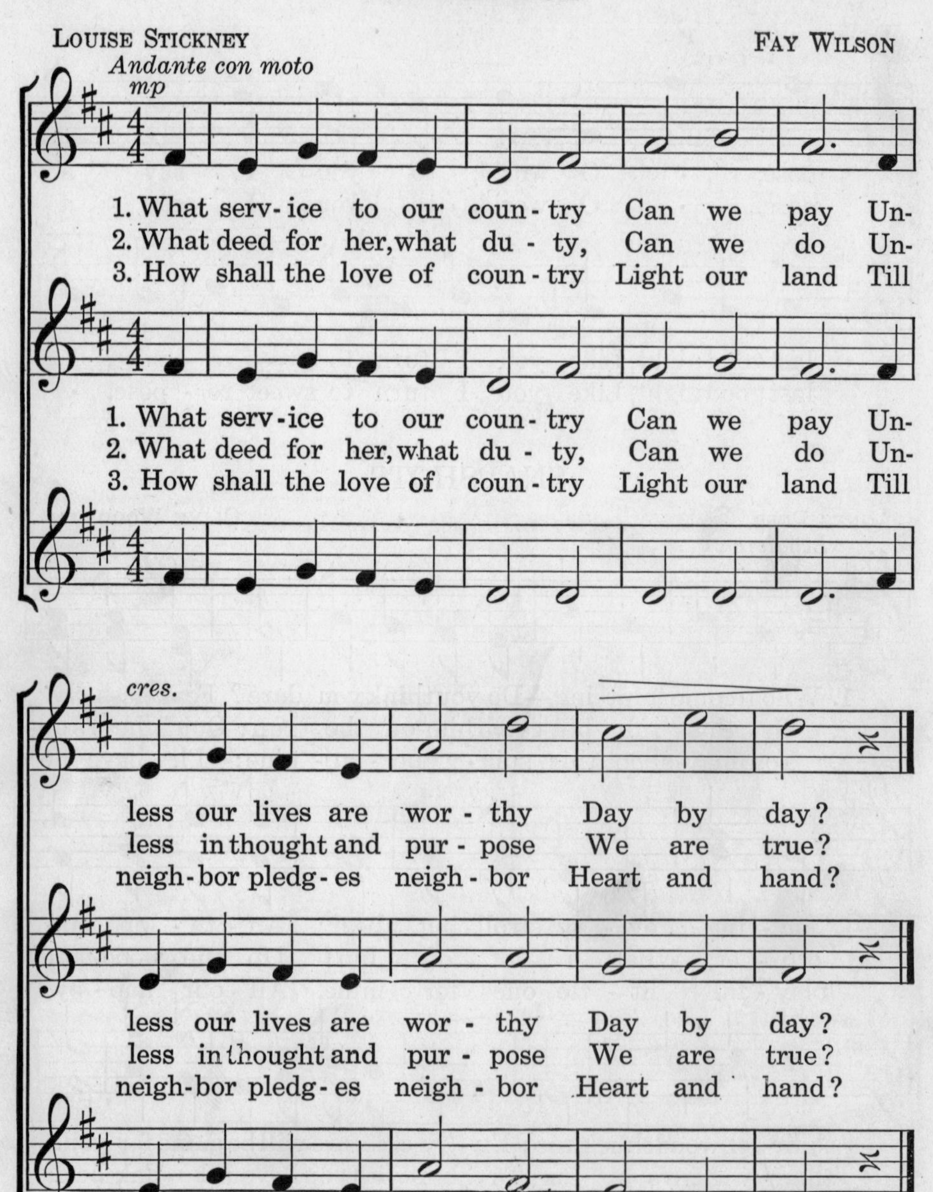

Andante con moto

mp

1. What serv-ice to our coun-try Can we pay Un-
2. What deed for her, what du-ty, Can we do Un-
3. How shall the love of coun-try Light our land Till

1. What serv-ice to our coun-try Can we pay Un-
2. What deed for her, what du-ty, Can we do Un-
3. How shall the love of coun-try Light our land Till

cres.

less our lives are wor-thy Day by day?
less in thought and pur-pose We are true?
neigh-bor pledg-es neigh-bor Heart and hand?

less our lives are wor-thy Day by day?
less in thought and pur-pose We are true?
neigh-bor pledg-es neigh-bor Heart and hand?

Denis A. McCarthy   Laura Streeter

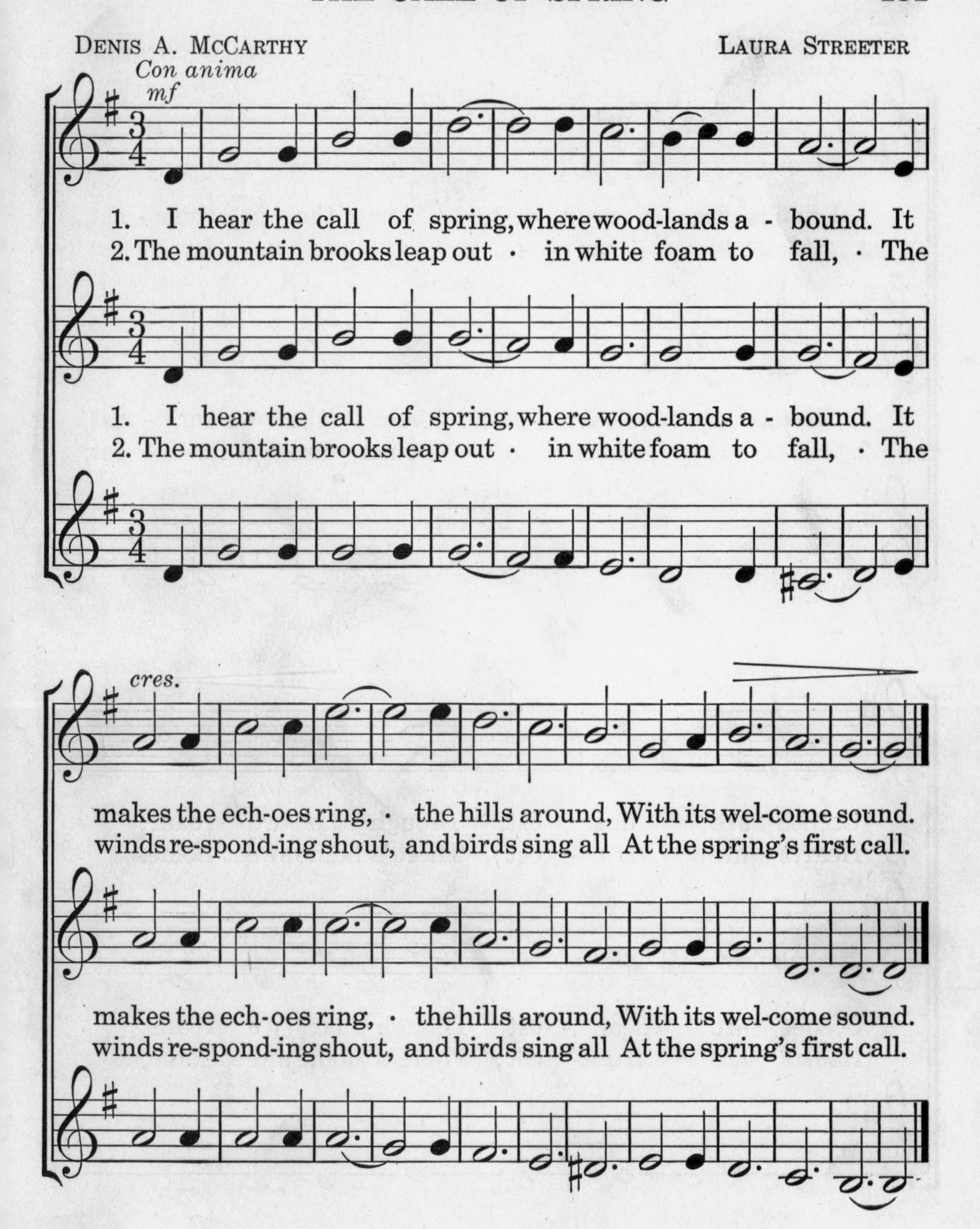

1. I hear the call of spring, where wood-lands a - bound. It
2. The mountain brooks leap out · in white foam to fall, · The

1. I hear the call of spring, where wood-lands a - bound. It
2. The mountain brooks leap out · in white foam to fall, · The

makes the ech-oes ring, · the hills around, With its wel-come sound.
winds re-spond-ing shout, and birds sing all At the spring's first call.

makes the ech-oes ring, · the hills around, With its wel-come sound.
winds re-spond-ing shout, and birds sing all At the spring's first call.

NIXON WATERMAN   HELEN CALL

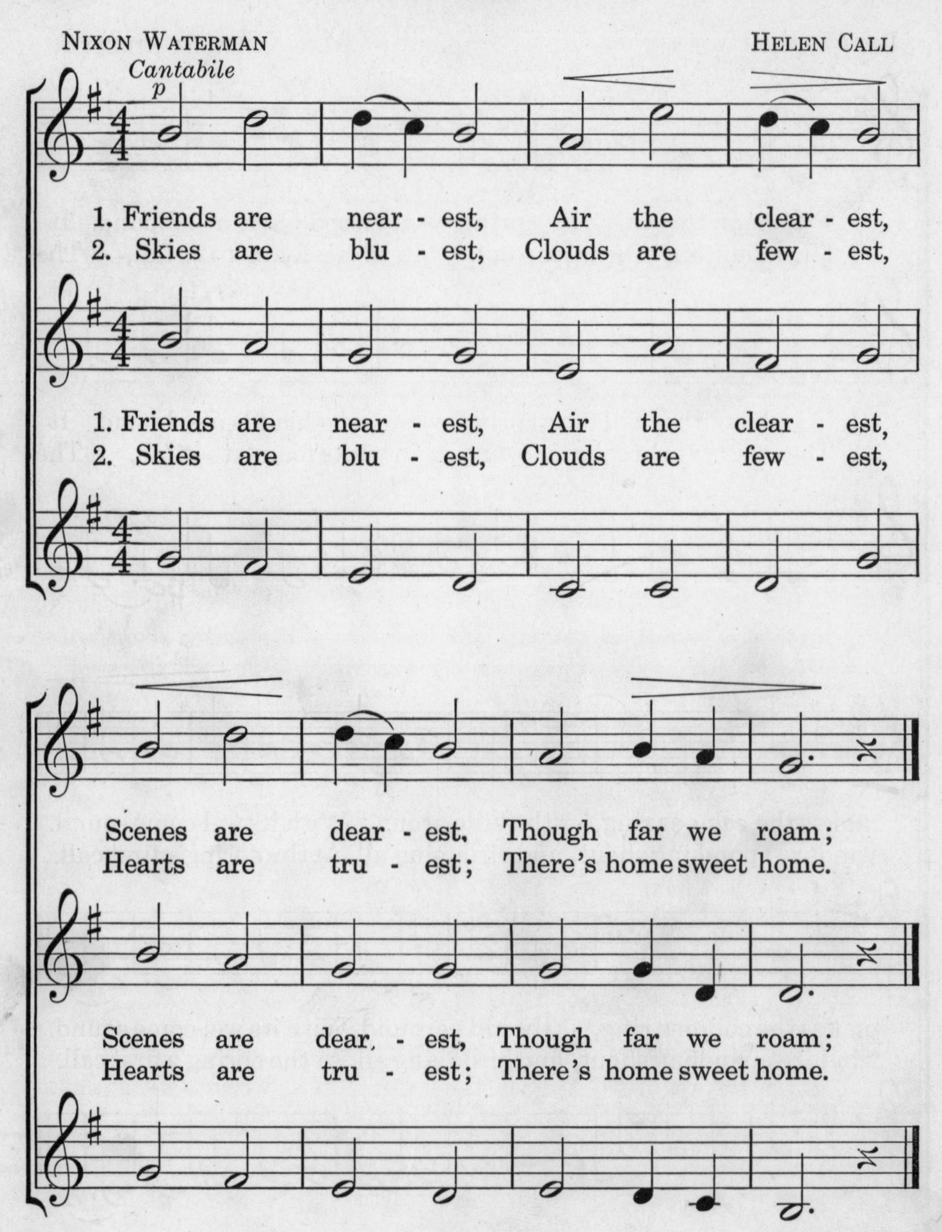

1. Friends are near - est, Air the clear - est,
2. Skies are blu - est, Clouds are few - est,

1. Friends are near - est, Air the clear - est,
2. Skies are blu - est, Clouds are few - est,

Scenes are dear - est, Though far we roam;
Hearts are tru - est; There's home sweet home.

Scenes are dear - est, Though far we roam;
Hearts are tru - est; There's home sweet home.

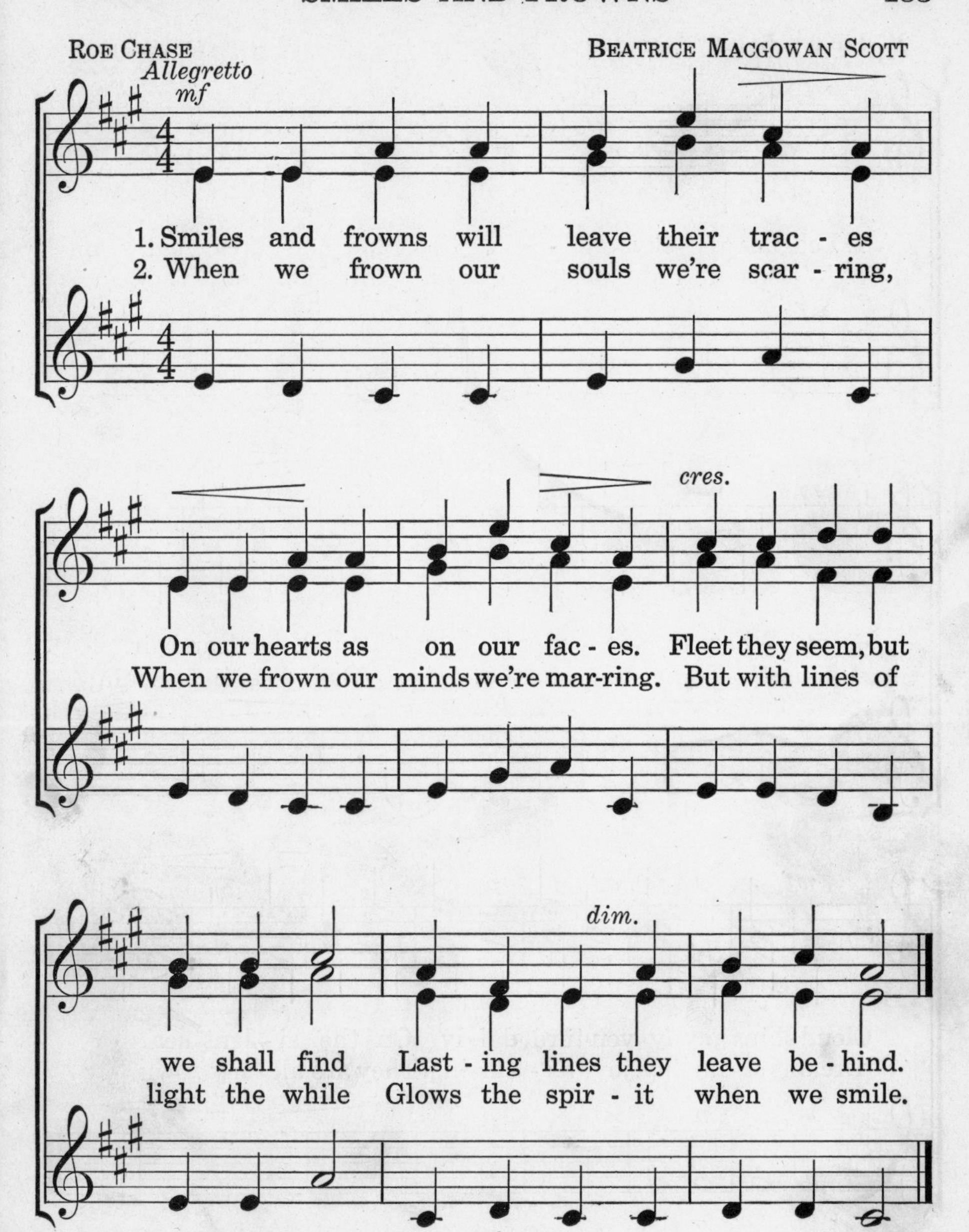

1. Smiles and frowns will leave their trac - es
2. When we frown our souls we're scar - ring,

On our hearts as on our fac - es. Fleet they seem, but
When we frown our minds we're mar - ring. But with lines of

we shall find Last - ing lines they leave be - hind.
light the while Glows the spir - it when we smile.

CASTLES IN SPAIN

M. LOUISE BAUM

RALPH L. BALDWIN

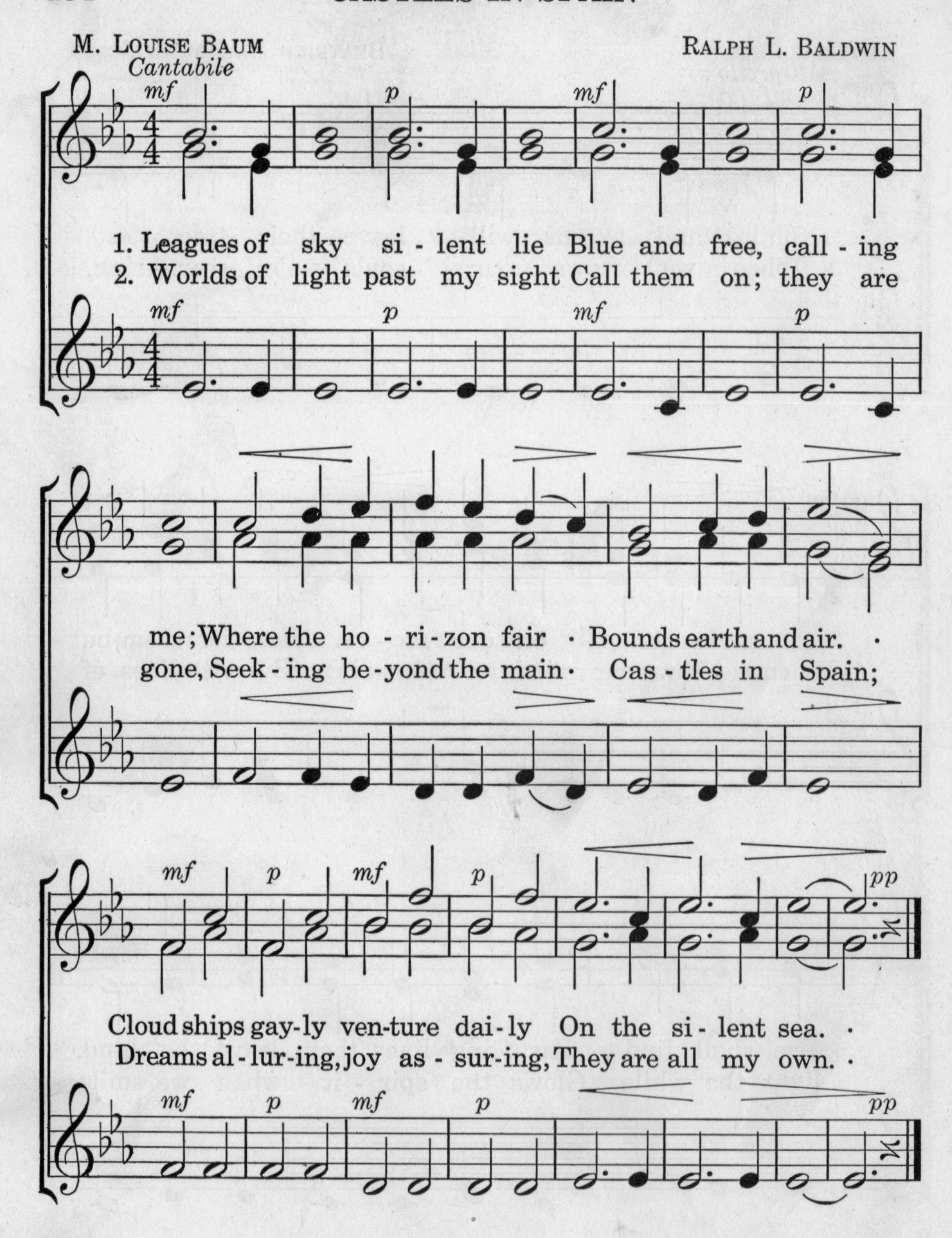

1. Leagues of sky si - lent lie Blue and free, call - ing
2. Worlds of light past my sight Call them on; they are

me; Where the ho - ri - zon fair · Bounds earth and air. ·
gone, Seek - ing be - yond the main · Cas - tles in Spain;

Cloud ships gay - ly ven - ture dai - ly On the si - lent sea. ·
Dreams al - lur - ing, joy as - sur - ing, They are all my own. ·

LEONARD BACON

JOHN HATTON

Maestoso

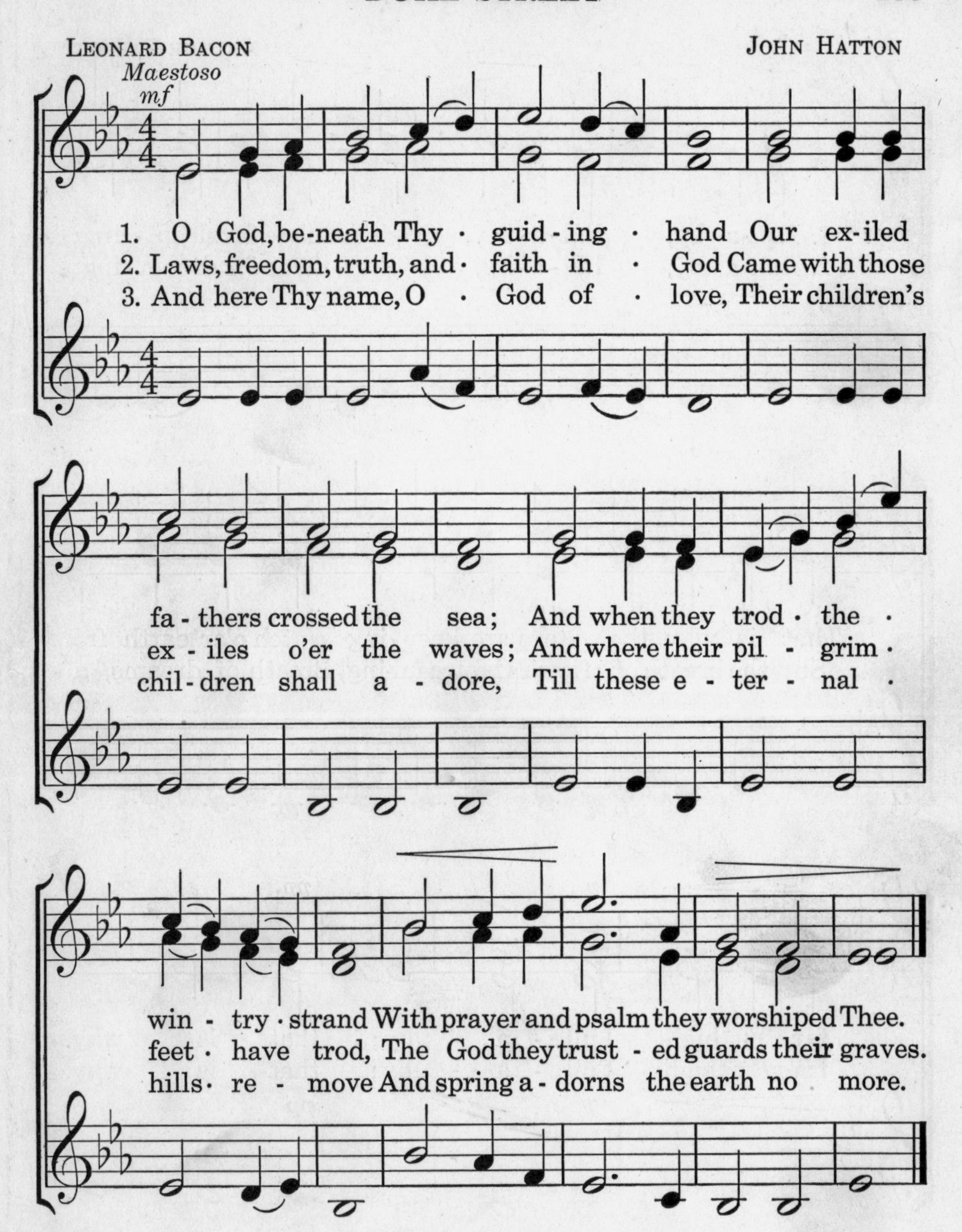

1. O God, be-neath Thy · guid - ing · hand Our ex-iled
2. Laws, freedom, truth, and · faith in · God Came with those
3. And here Thy name, O · God of · love, Their children's

fa - thers crossed the sea; And when they trod · the ·
ex - iles o'er the waves; And where their pil - grim ·
chil - dren shall a - dore, Till these e - ter - nal ·

win - try · strand With prayer and psalm they worshiped Thee.
feet · have trod, The God they trust - ed guards their graves.
hills · re - move And spring a - dorns the earth no · more.

NIGHTFALL

MARY STANHOPE · ARTHUR TARGETT

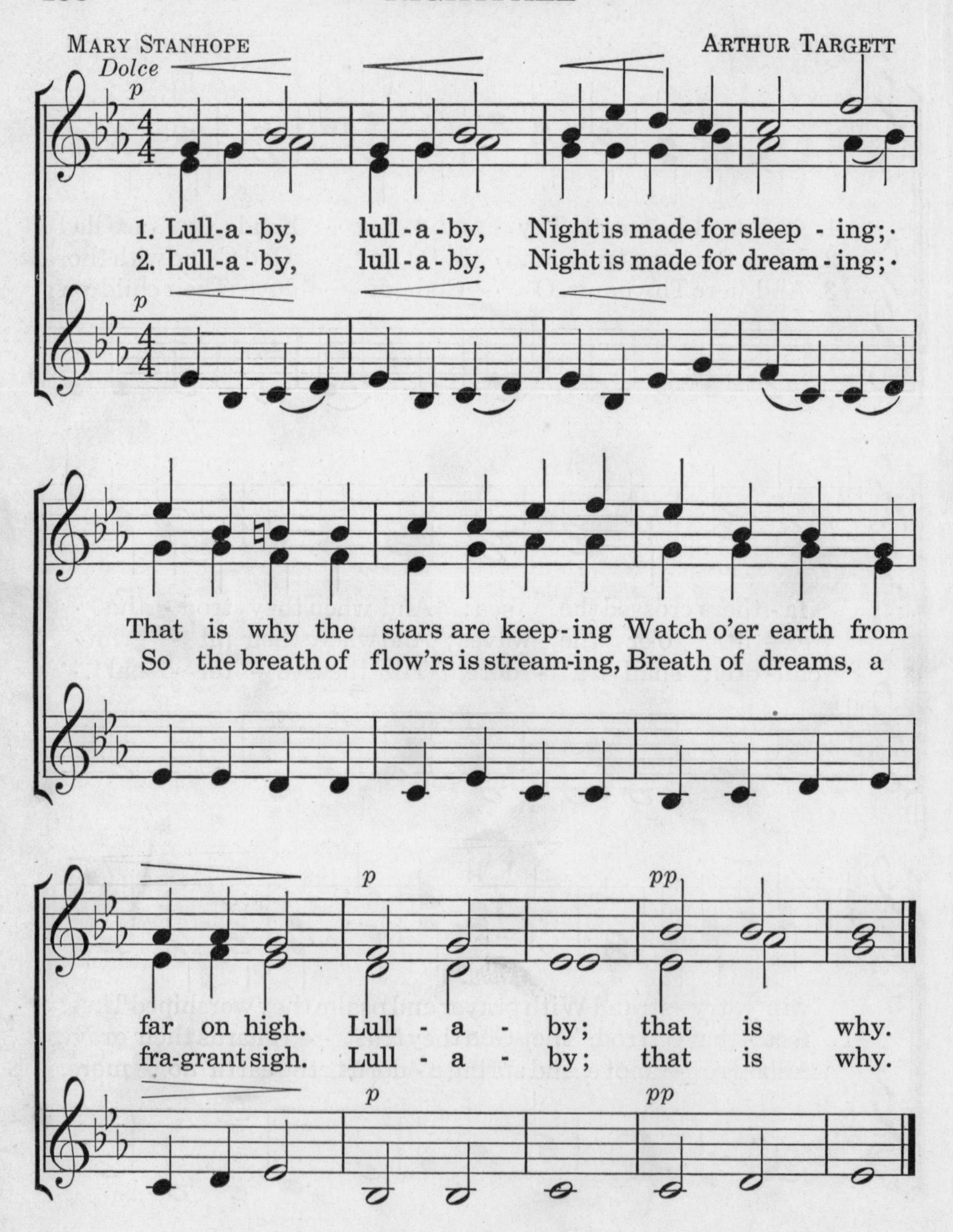

1. Lull-a-by, lull-a-by, Night is made for sleep-ing;·
2. Lull-a-by, lull-a-by, Night is made for dream-ing;·

That is why the stars are keep-ing Watch o'er earth from
So the breath of flow'rs is stream-ing, Breath of dreams, a

far on high. Lull - a - by; that is why.
fra-grant sigh. Lull - a - by; that is why.

ABOVE THE HILL

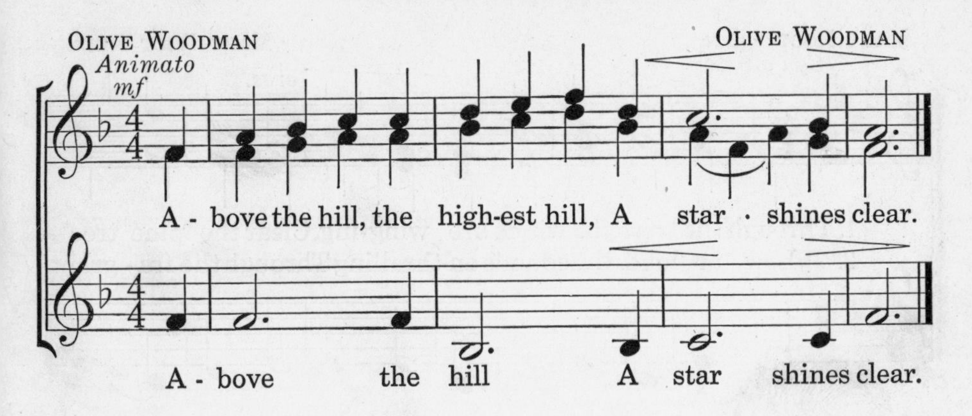

A - bove the hill, the high-est hill, A star shines clear.

A - bove the hill A star shines clear.

NIGHT WATCHERS

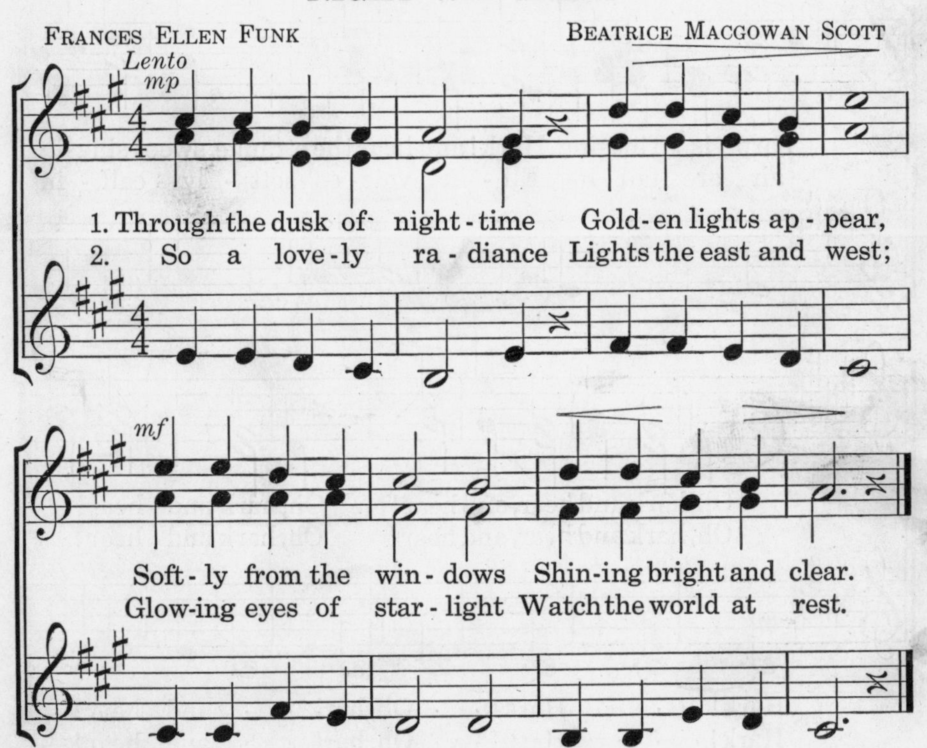

1. Through the dusk of night-time Gold-en lights ap - pear,
2. So a love-ly ra - diance Lights the east and west;

Soft - ly from the win - dows Shin-ing bright and clear.
Glow-ing eyes of star - light Watch the world at rest.

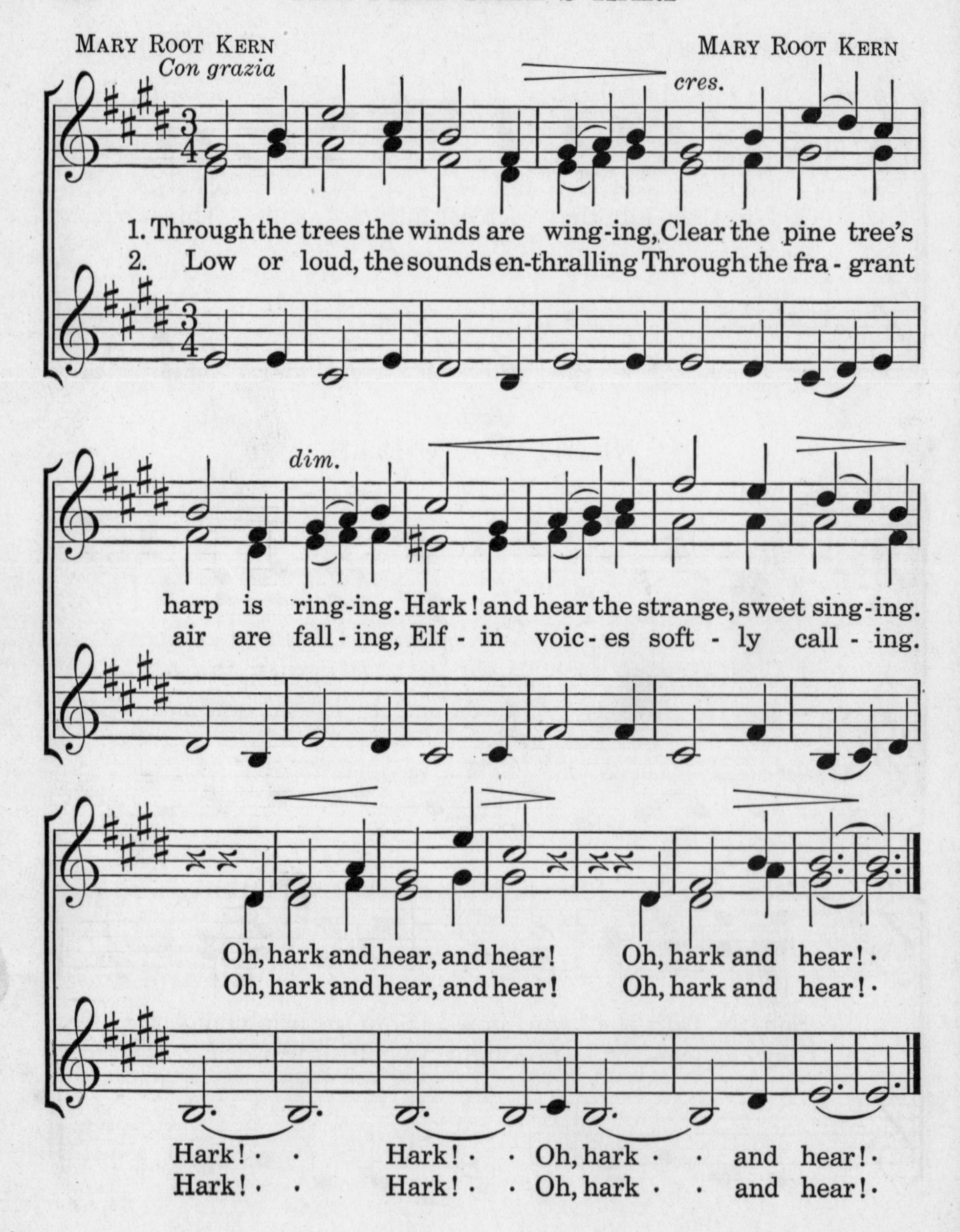

MARY ROOT KERN

MARY ROOT KERN

Con grazia

cres.

1. Through the trees the winds are wing-ing, Clear the pine tree's
2. Low or loud, the sounds en-thralling Through the fra - grant

dim.

harp is ring-ing. Hark! and hear the strange, sweet sing-ing.
air are fall - ing, Elf - in voic - es soft - ly call - ing.

Oh, hark and hear, and hear! Oh, hark and hear! ·
Oh, hark and hear, and hear! Oh, hark and hear! ·

Hark! · · Hark! · · Oh, hark · · and hear! ·
Hark! · · Hark! · · Oh, hark · · and hear! ·

A MEMORY

DENIS A. McCARTHY

E. W. NEWTON

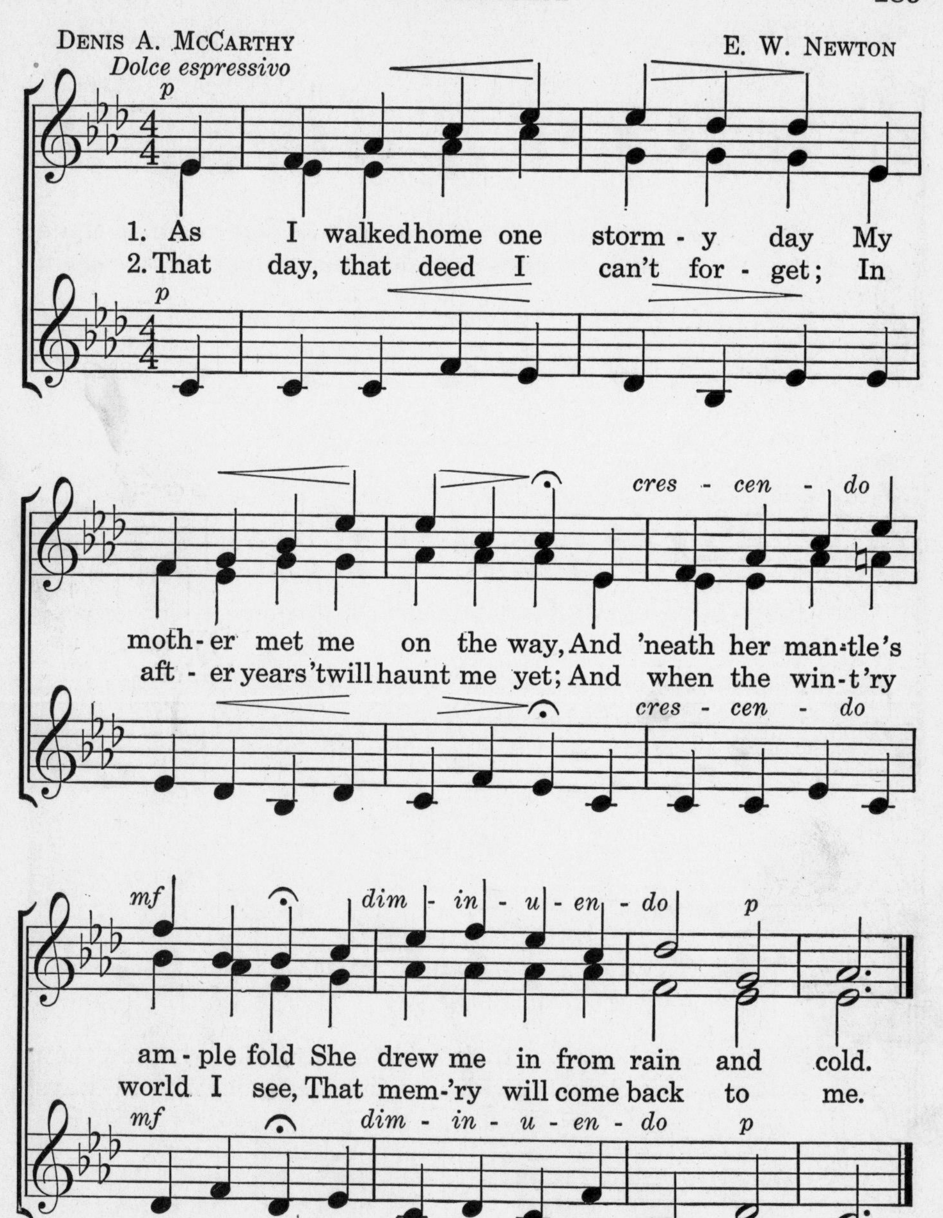

1. As I walked home one storm-y day My
2. That day, that deed I can't for-get; In

cres - cen - do

moth-er met me on the way, And 'neath her man-tle's
aft-er years 'twill haunt me yet; And when the win-t'ry

cres - cen - do

dim-in-u-en-do

am-ple fold She drew me in from rain and cold.
world I see, That mem-'ry will come back to me.

dim-in-u-en-do

HOMEWARD

Robert Brigham

Stanley Avery

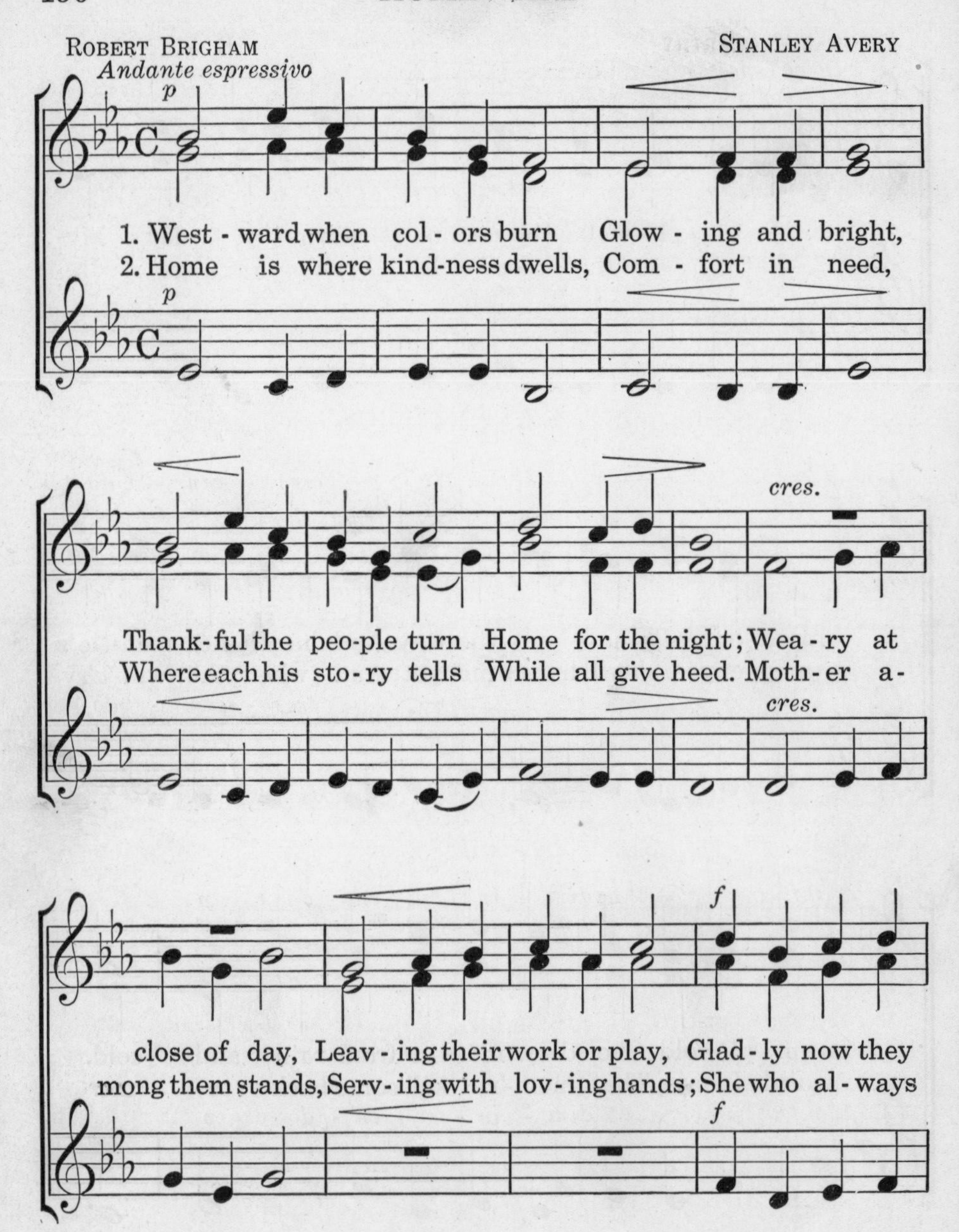

Andante espressivo

1. West - ward when col - ors burn Glow - ing and bright,
2. Home is where kind-ness dwells, Com - fort in need,

Thank-ful the peo-ple turn Home for the night; Wea - ry at
Where each his sto - ry tells While all give heed. Moth - er a-

cres.

close of day, Leav - ing their work or play, Glad - ly now they
mong them stands, Serv - ing with lov - ing hands; She who al - ways

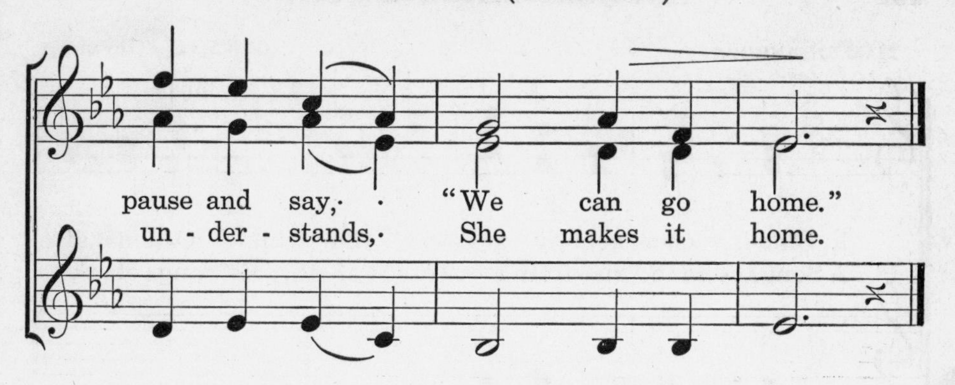

pause and say,· · "We can go home."
un - der - stands,· She makes it home.

ST. VALENTINE'S

Louise Stickney

Mary Eloise Crane

Allegro
mf

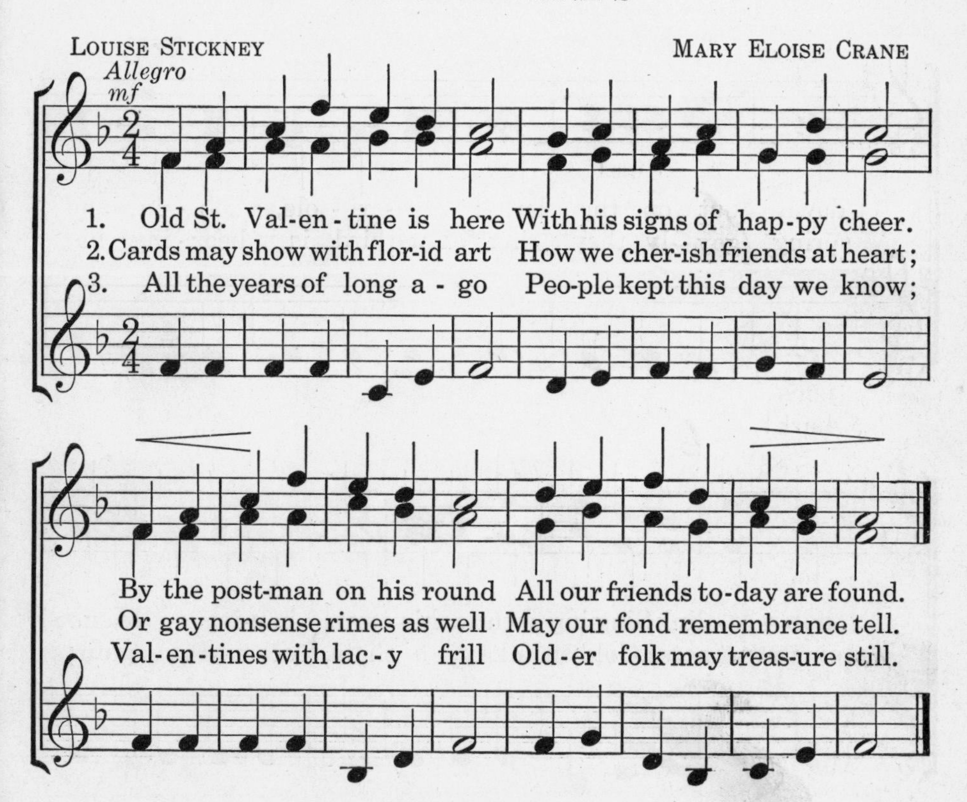

1. Old St. Val-en-tine is here With his signs of hap-py cheer.
2. Cards may show with flor-id art How we cher-ish friends at heart;
3. All the years of long a - go Peo-ple kept this day we know;

By the post-man on his round All our friends to-day are found.
Or gay nonsense rimes as well May our fond remembrance tell.
Val - en-tines with lac - y frill Old - er folk may treas-ure still.

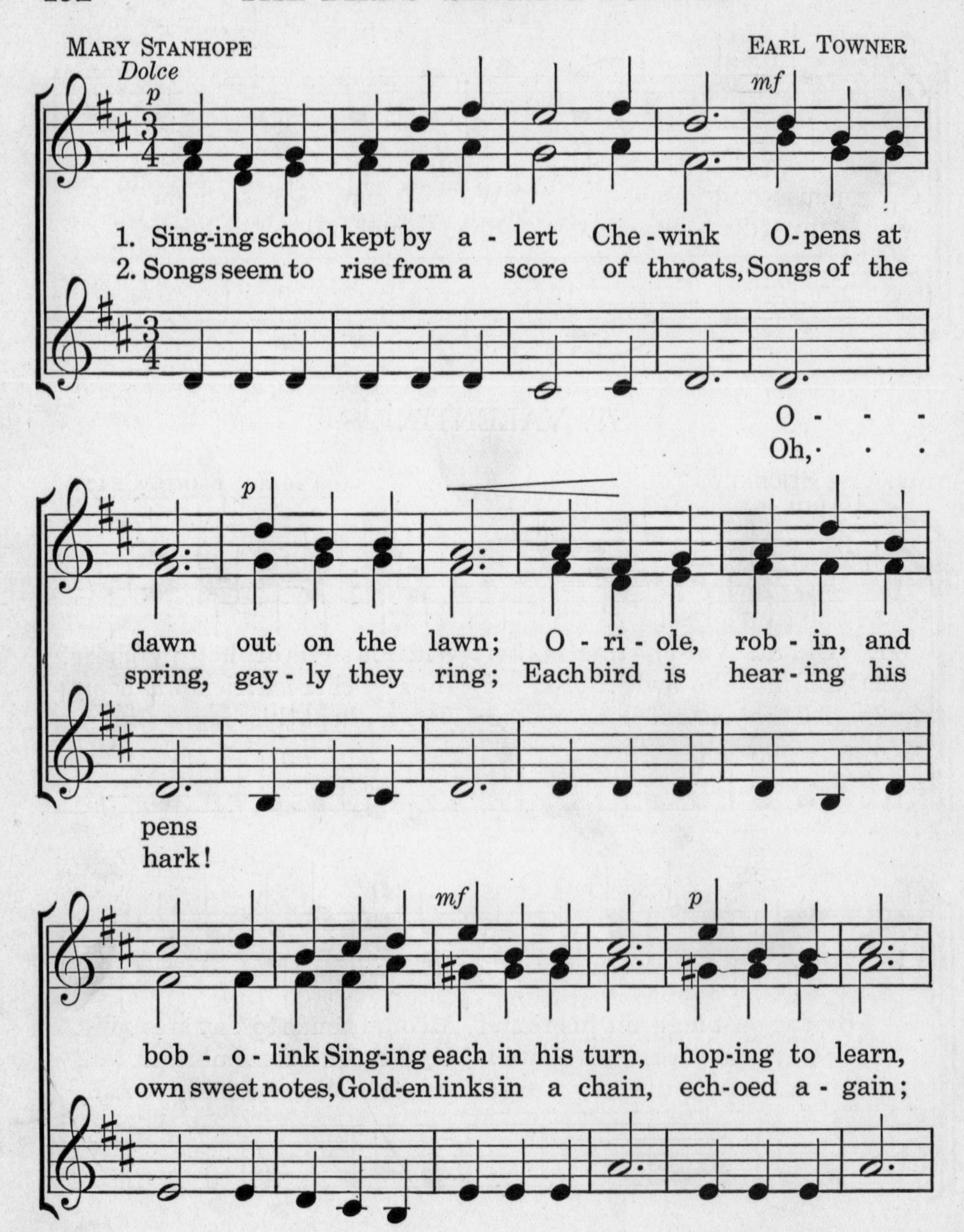

MARY STANHOPE

EARL TOWNER

Dolce

1. Sing-ing school kept by a - lert Che - wink O - pens at
2. Songs seem to rise from a score of throats, Songs of the

O - - -
Oh, · · ·

dawn out on the lawn; O - ri - ole, rob - in, and
spring, gay - ly they ring; Each bird is hear - ing his

pens
hark!

bob - o - link Sing-ing each in his turn, hop-ing to learn,
own sweet notes, Gold-en links in a chain, ech-oed a - gain;

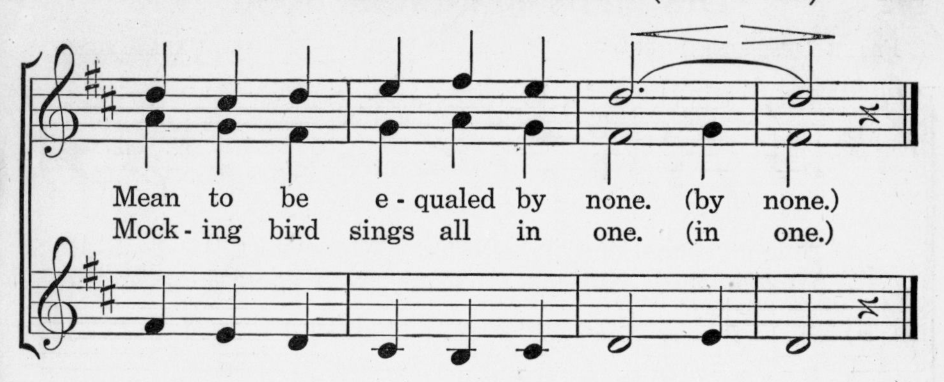

Mean to be e - qualed by none. (by none.)
Mock - ing bird sings all in one. (in one.)

CLOUDS AT SUNSET

DENIS A. MCCARTHY   RUTH MCCONN SPENCER

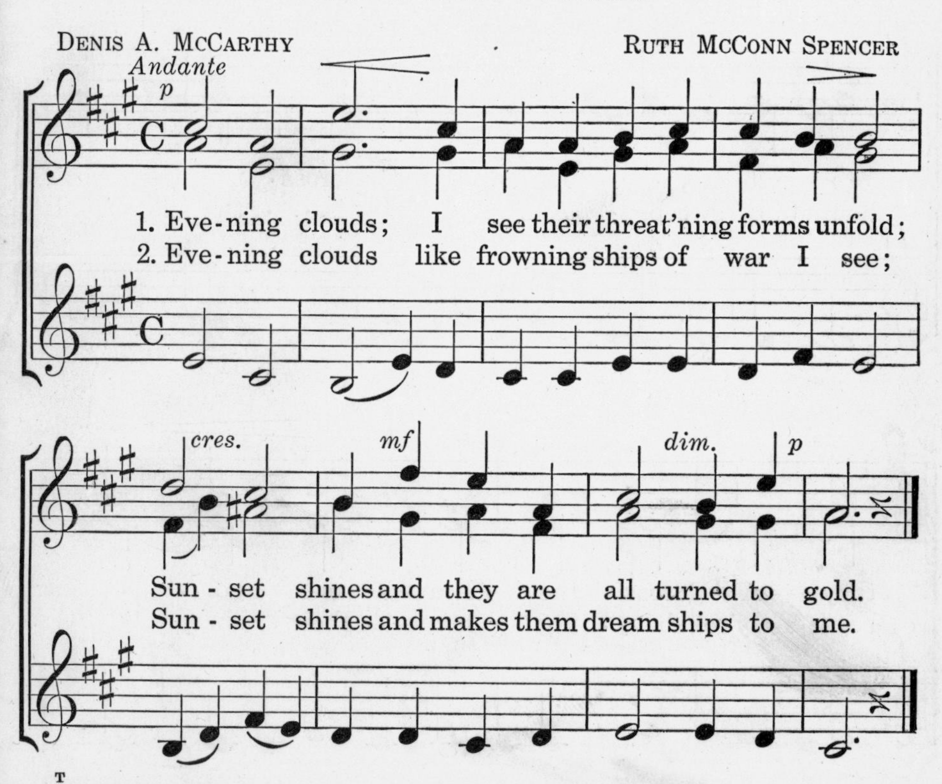

1. Eve-ning clouds; I see their threat'ning forms unfold;
2. Eve-ning clouds like frowning ships of war I see;

Sun - set shines and they are all turned to gold.
Sun - set shines and makes them dream ships to me.

T

CLOUDS

FRANK DEMPSTER SHERMAN

CARL ENGEL

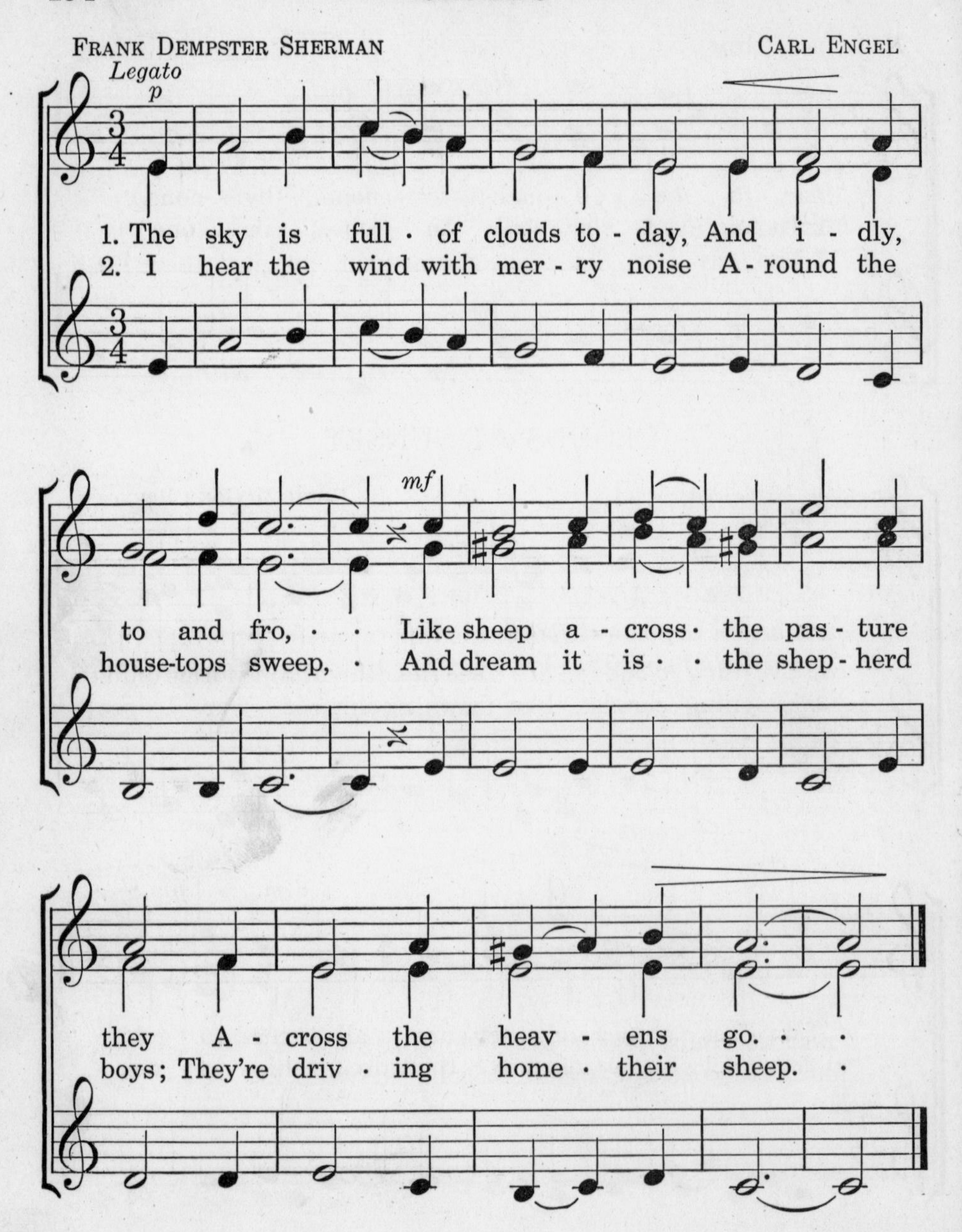

1. The sky is full · of clouds to - day, And i - dly,
2. I hear the wind with mer - ry noise A - round the

to and fro, · · Like sheep a - cross · the pas - ture
house-tops sweep, · And dream it is · · the shep - herd

they A - cross the heav - ens go. · ·
boys; They're driv · ing home · their sheep. ·

A SONG OF SILENCE

M. Louise Baum

W. Otto Miessner

Con grazia

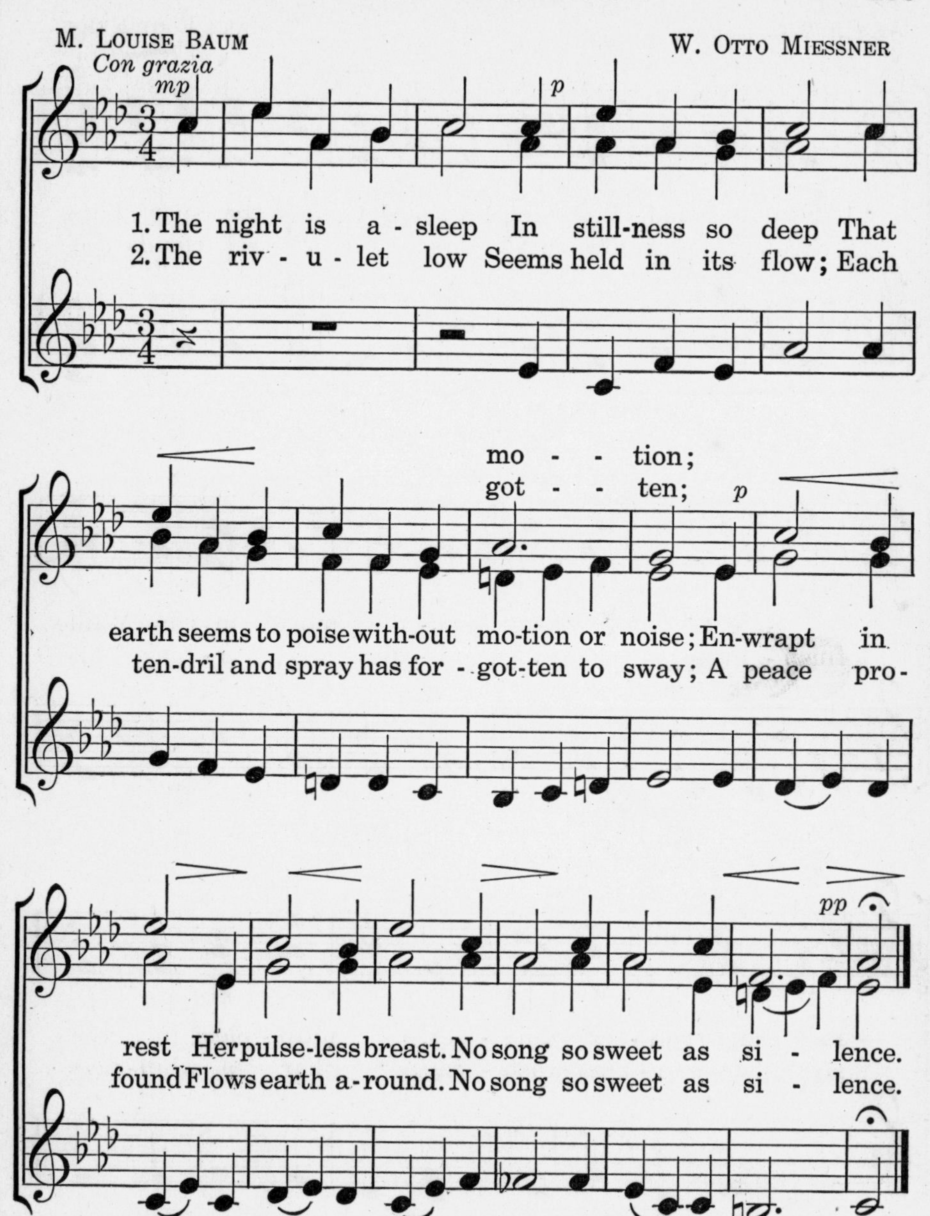

1. The night is a-sleep In still-ness so deep That
2. The riv-u-let low Seems held in its flow; Each

mo - - tion;
got - - ten;

earth seems to poise with-out mo-tion or noise; En-wrapt in
ten-dril and spray has for-got-ten to sway; A peace pro-

rest Her pulse-less breast. No song so sweet as si - lence.
found Flows earth a-round. No song so sweet as si - lence.

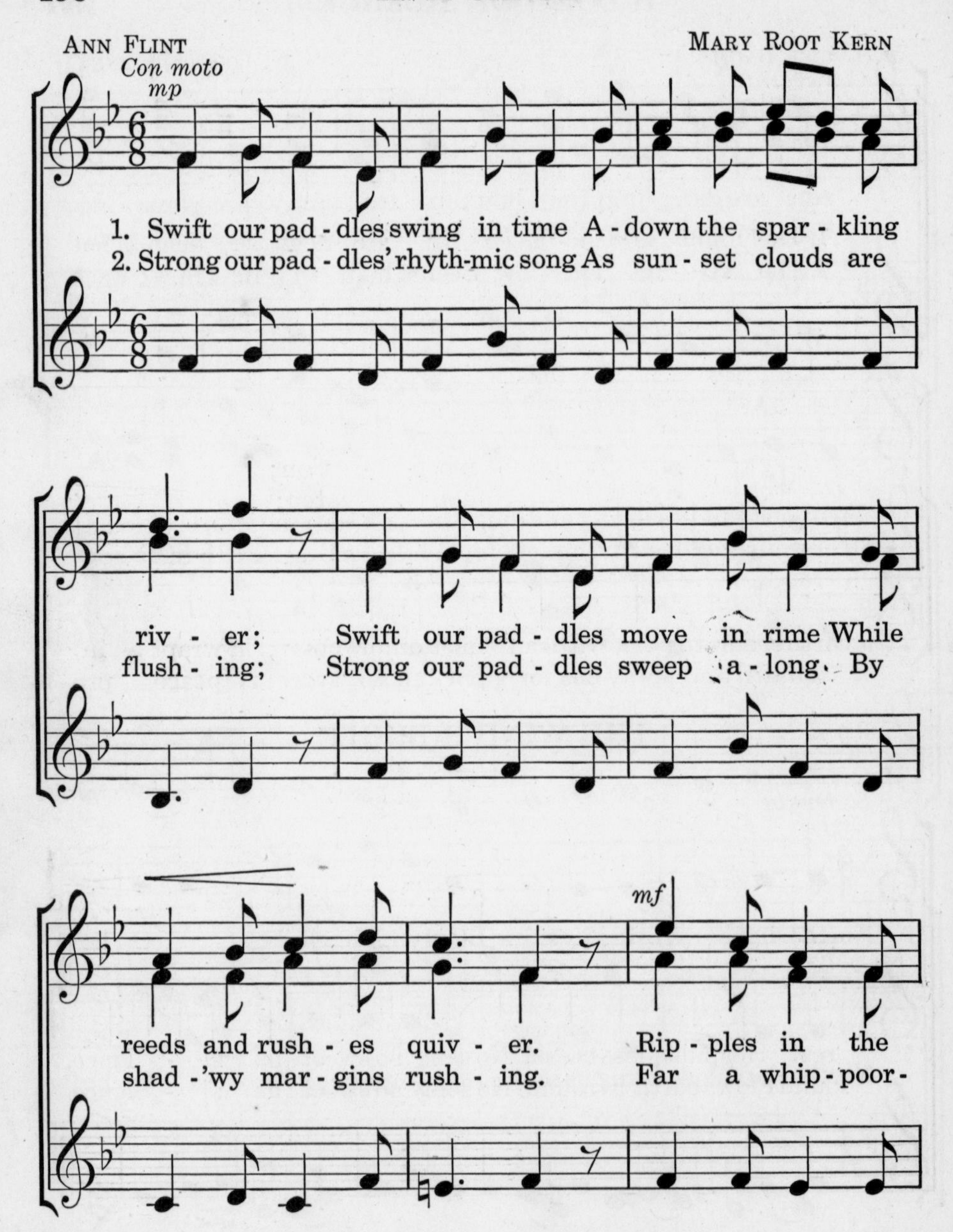

ANN FLINT

Con moto

MARY ROOT KERN

1. Swift our pad - dles swing in time A - down the spar - kling
2. Strong our pad - dles' rhyth-mic song As sun - set clouds are

riv - er;   Swift our pad - dles move in rime While
flush - ing;   Strong our pad - dles sweep a - long. By

reeds and rush - es quiv - er.   Rip - ples in the
shad - 'wy mar - gins rush - ing.   Far a whip-poor-

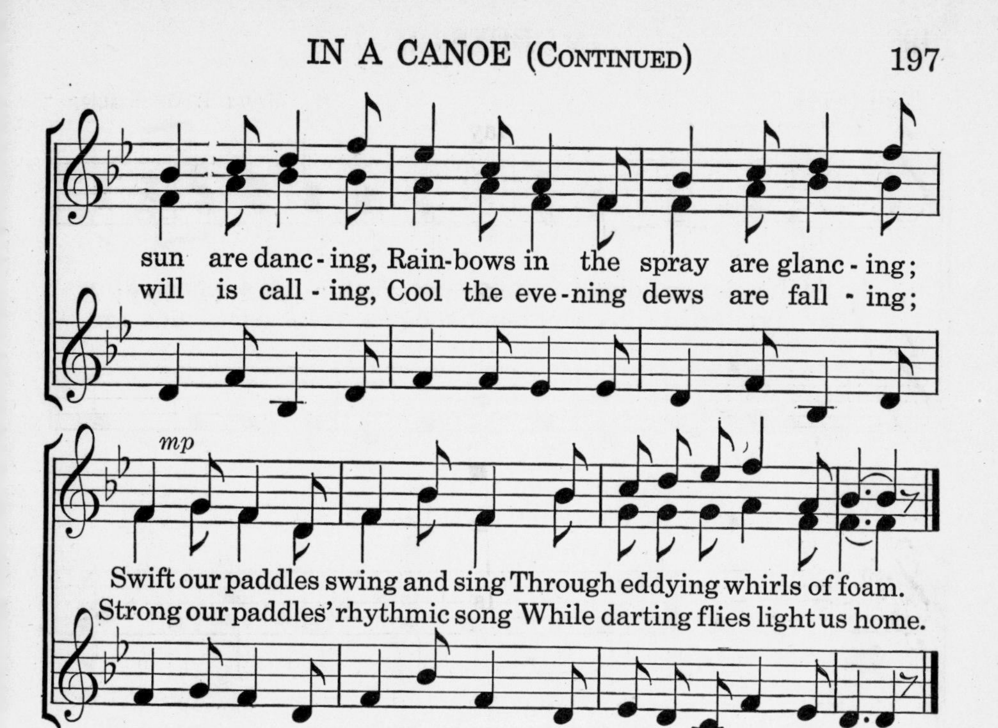

sun are danc-ing, Rain-bows in the spray are glanc-ing;
will is call-ing, Cool the eve-ning dews are fall-ing;

Swift our paddles swing and sing Through eddying whirls of foam.
Strong our paddles' rhythmic song While darting flies light us home.

THE WIND'S BUGLE

Helen Call

Helen Call

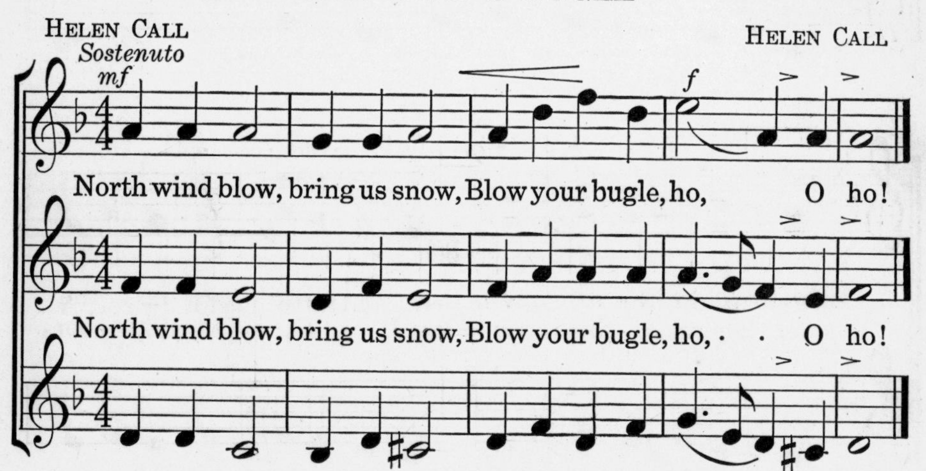

North wind blow, bring us snow, Blow your bugle, ho, O ho!

North wind blow, bring us snow, Blow your bugle, ho, O ho!

BEES

TRADITIONAL
Animato

OLIVE WOODMAN

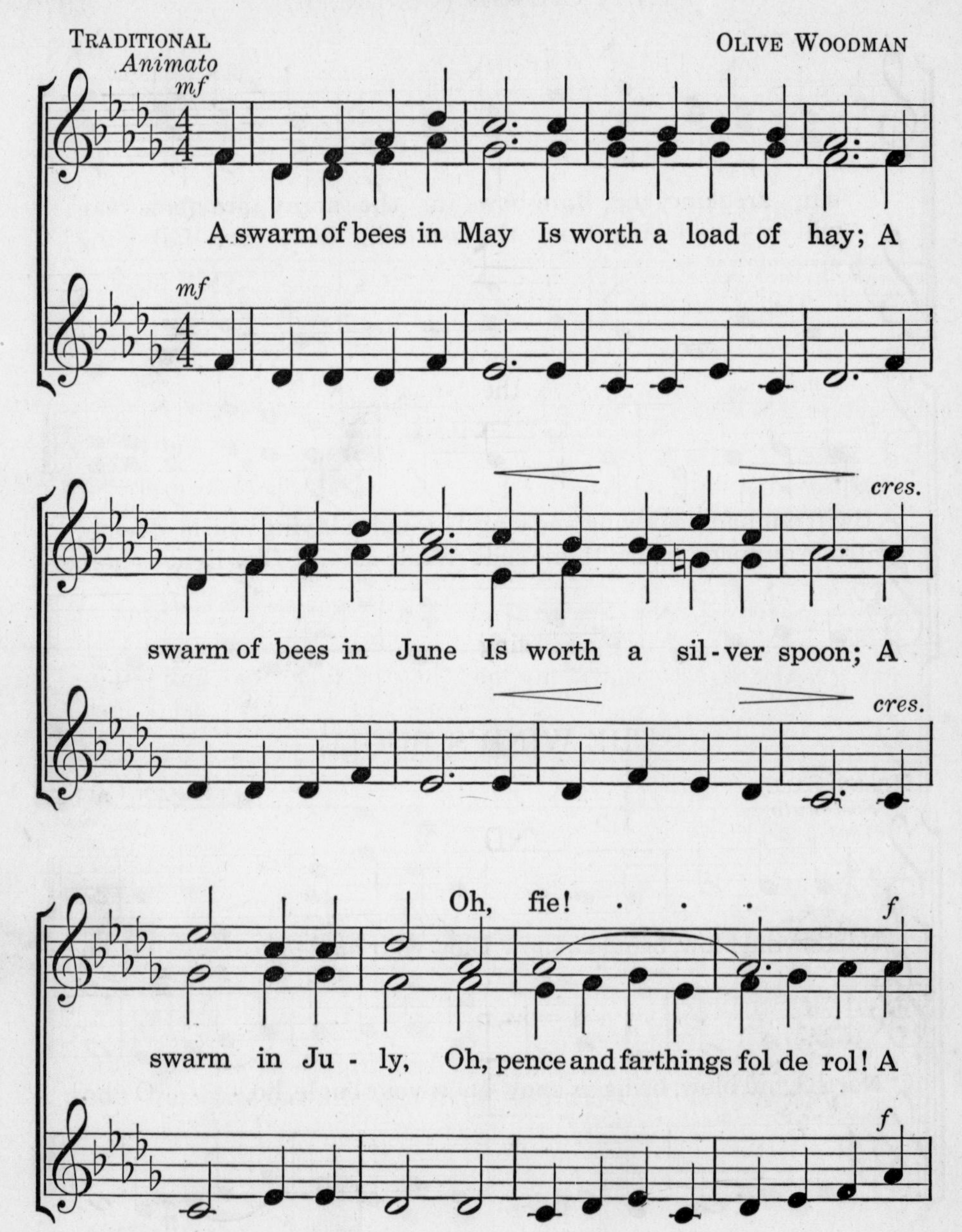

A swarm of bees in May Is worth a load of hay; A

swarm of bees in June Is worth a sil - ver spoon; A

cres.

Oh, fie!

swarm in Ju - ly, Oh, pence and farthings fol de rol! A

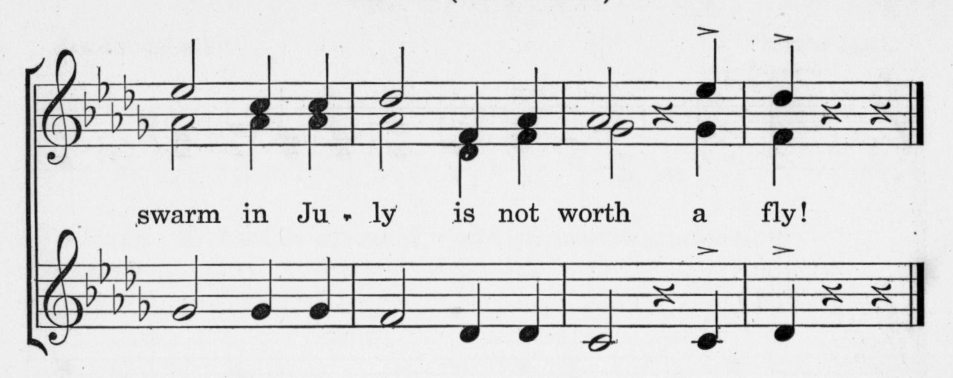

swarm in Ju - ly   is not worth   a   fly!

HUMOR

Nixon Waterman

Evelyn Sprague

Andante espressivo

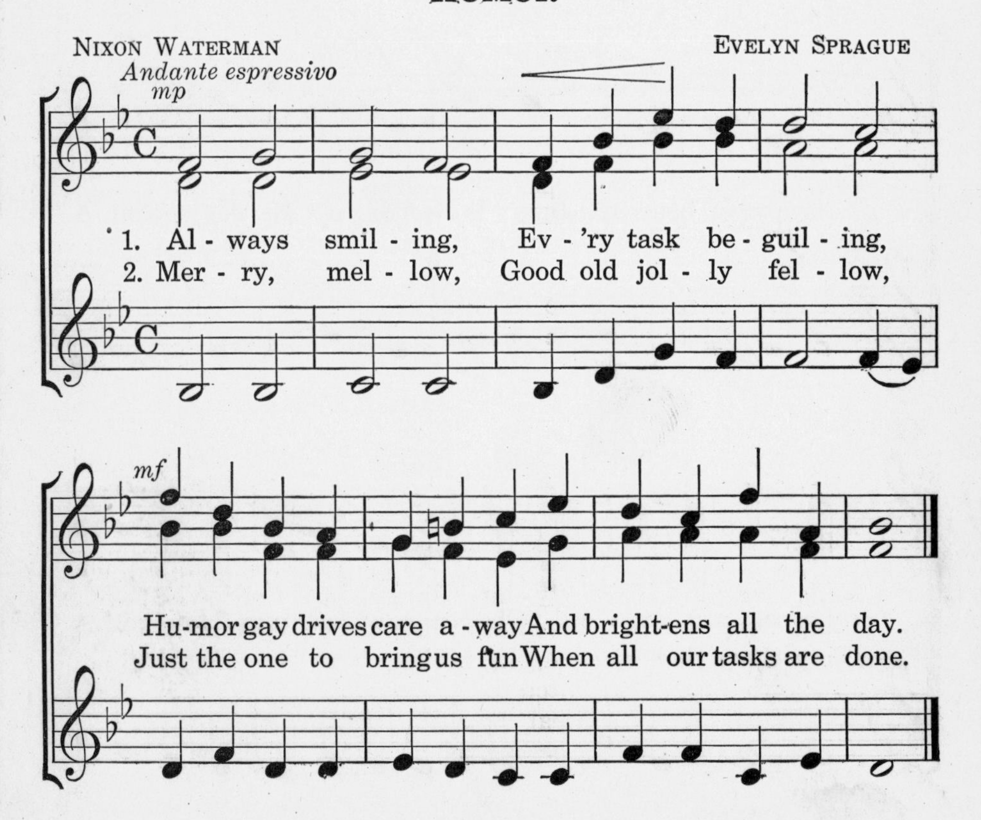

1. Al - ways   smil - ing,   Ev - 'ry task be - guil - ing,
2. Mer - ry,   mel - low,   Good old jol - ly fel - low,

Hu-mor gay drives care a - way And bright-ens all   the   day.
Just the one to   bring us fun When all   our tasks are   done.

CLING, CLANG, CLING

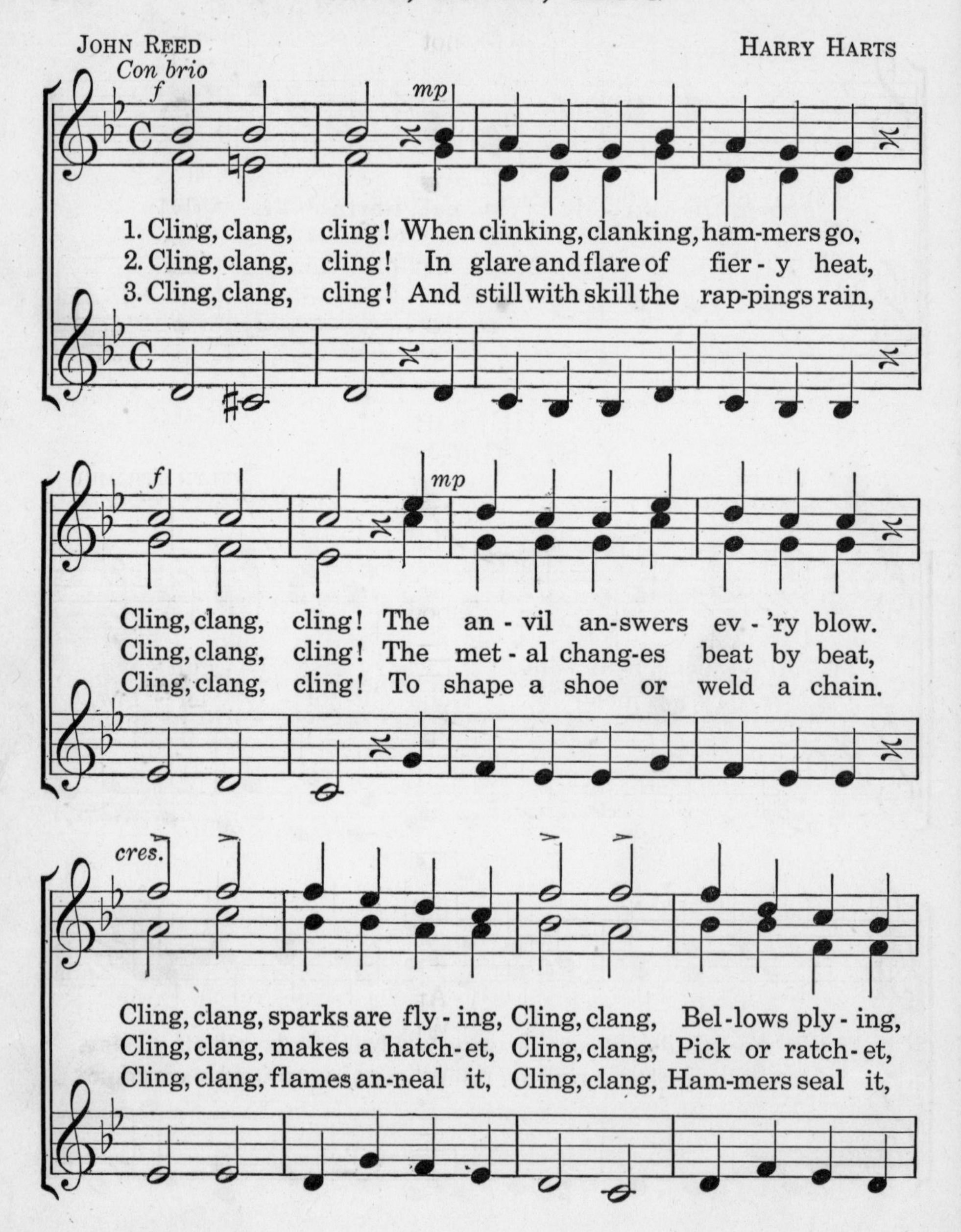

JOHN REED
HARRY HARTS

Con brio

1. Cling, clang, cling! When clinking, clanking, ham-mers go,
2. Cling, clang, cling! In glare and flare of fier - y heat,
3. Cling, clang, cling! And still with skill the rap-pings rain,

Cling, clang, cling! The an - vil an-swers ev - 'ry blow.
Cling, clang, cling! The met - al chang-es beat by beat,
Cling, clang, cling! To shape a shoe or weld a chain.

Cling, clang, sparks are fly - ing, Cling, clang, Bel-lows ply - ing,
Cling, clang, makes a hatch-et, Cling, clang, Pick or ratch-et,
Cling, clang, flames an-neal it, Cling, clang, Ham-mers seal it,

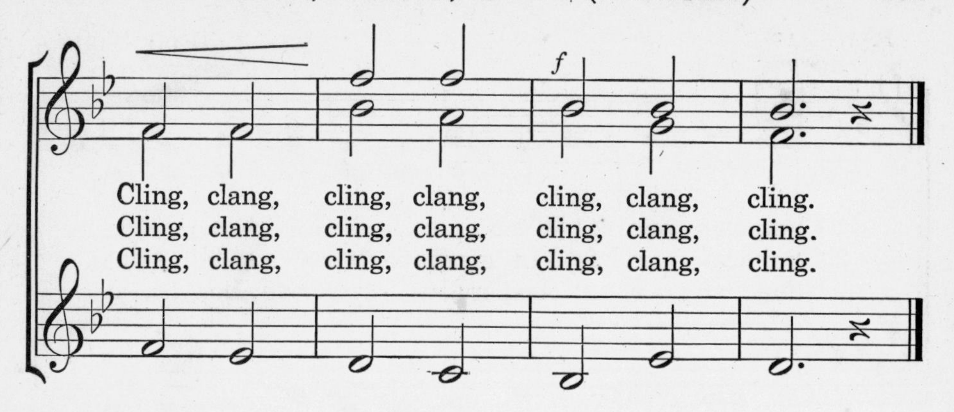

Cling, clang, cling, clang, cling, clang, cling.
Cling, clang, cling, clang, cling, clang, cling.
Cling, clang, cling, clang, cling, clang, cling.

STARLIGHT

T. H. MacCrady

Ruth McConn Spencer

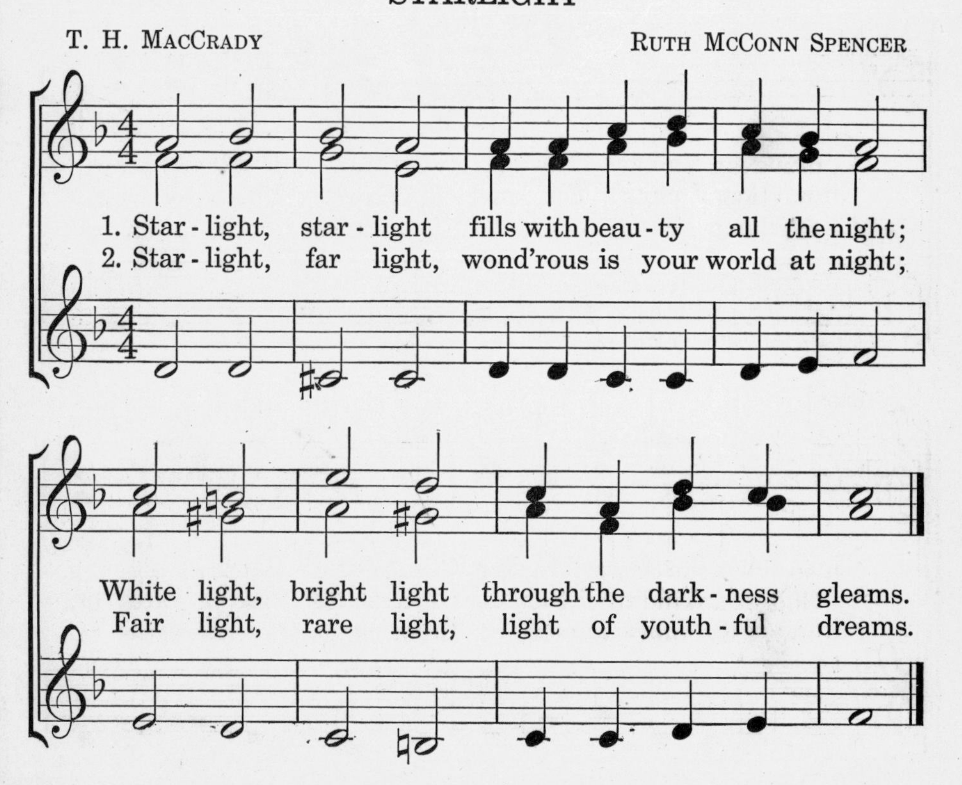

1. Star - light, star - light fills with beau - ty all the night;
2. Star - light, far light, wond'rous is your world at night;

White light, bright light through the dark - ness gleams.
Fair light, rare light, light of youth - ful dreams.

F. W. FABER
H. F. HEMY

Adagio

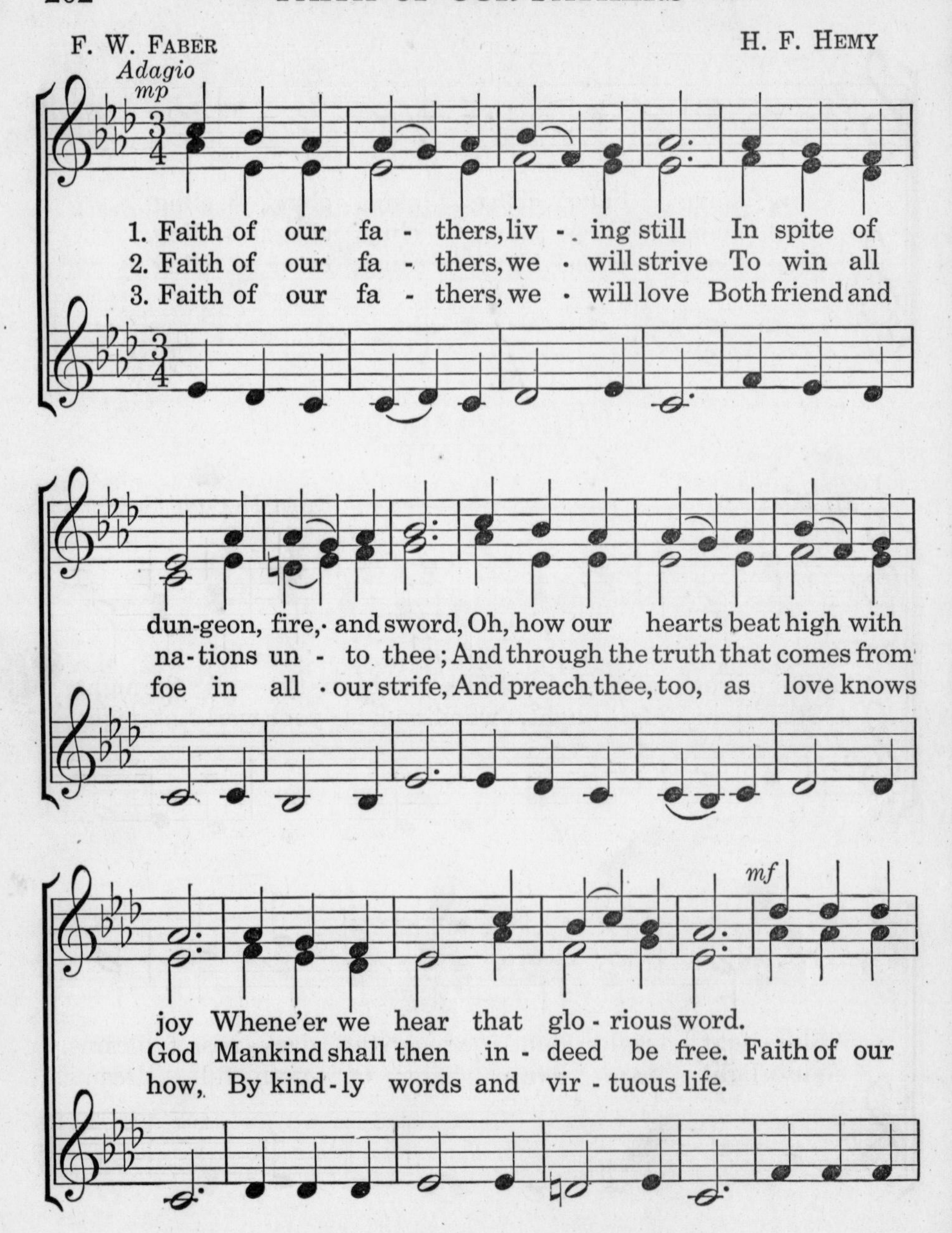

1. Faith of our fa - thers, liv - ing still In spite of
2. Faith of our fa - thers, we - will strive To win all
3. Faith of our fa - thers, we - will love Both friend and

dun-geon, fire, and sword, Oh, how our hearts beat high with
na - tions un - to thee; And through the truth that comes from
foe in all our strife, And preach thee, too, as love knows

joy Whene'er we hear that glo - rious word.
God Mankind shall then in - deed be free. Faith of our
how, By kind - ly words and vir - tuous life.

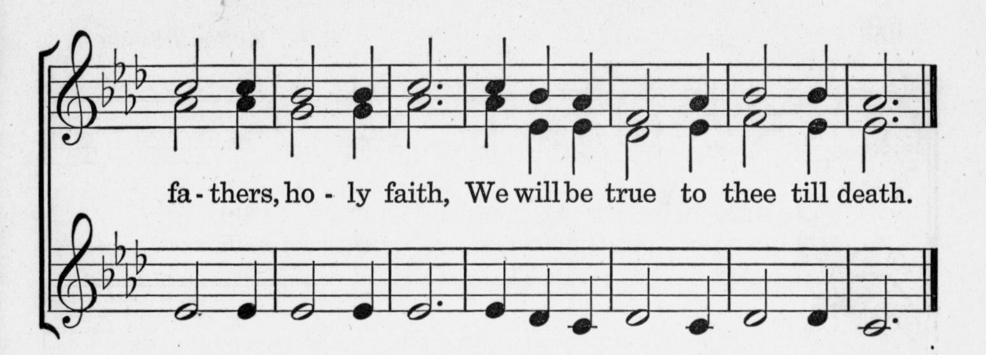

fa - thers, ho - ly faith, We will be true to thee till death.

THE SEASHORE

English Version by
LOUISE STICKNEY

SCANDINAVIAN FOLK SONG

Dolce
mp

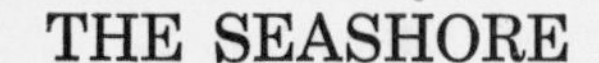

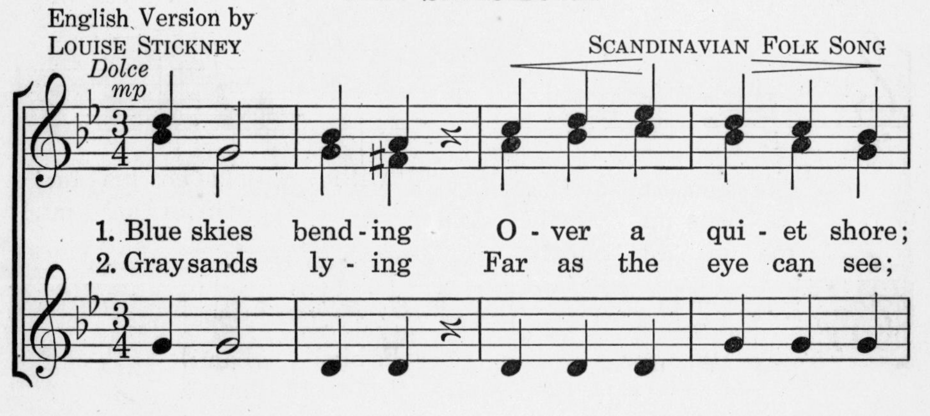

1. Blue skies bend - ing O - ver a qui - et shore;
2. Gray sands ly - ing Far as the eye can see;

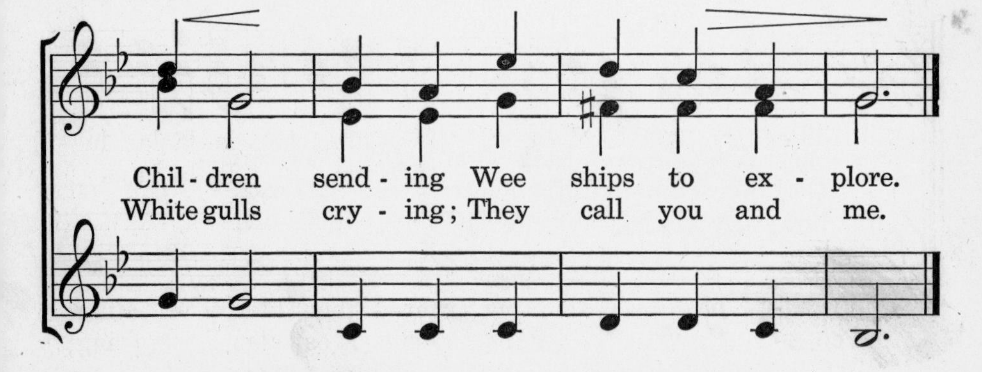

Chil - dren send - ing Wee ships to ex - plore.
White gulls cry - ing; They call you and me.

THE STREET BAND

Robert Brigham

Ruth McConn Spencer

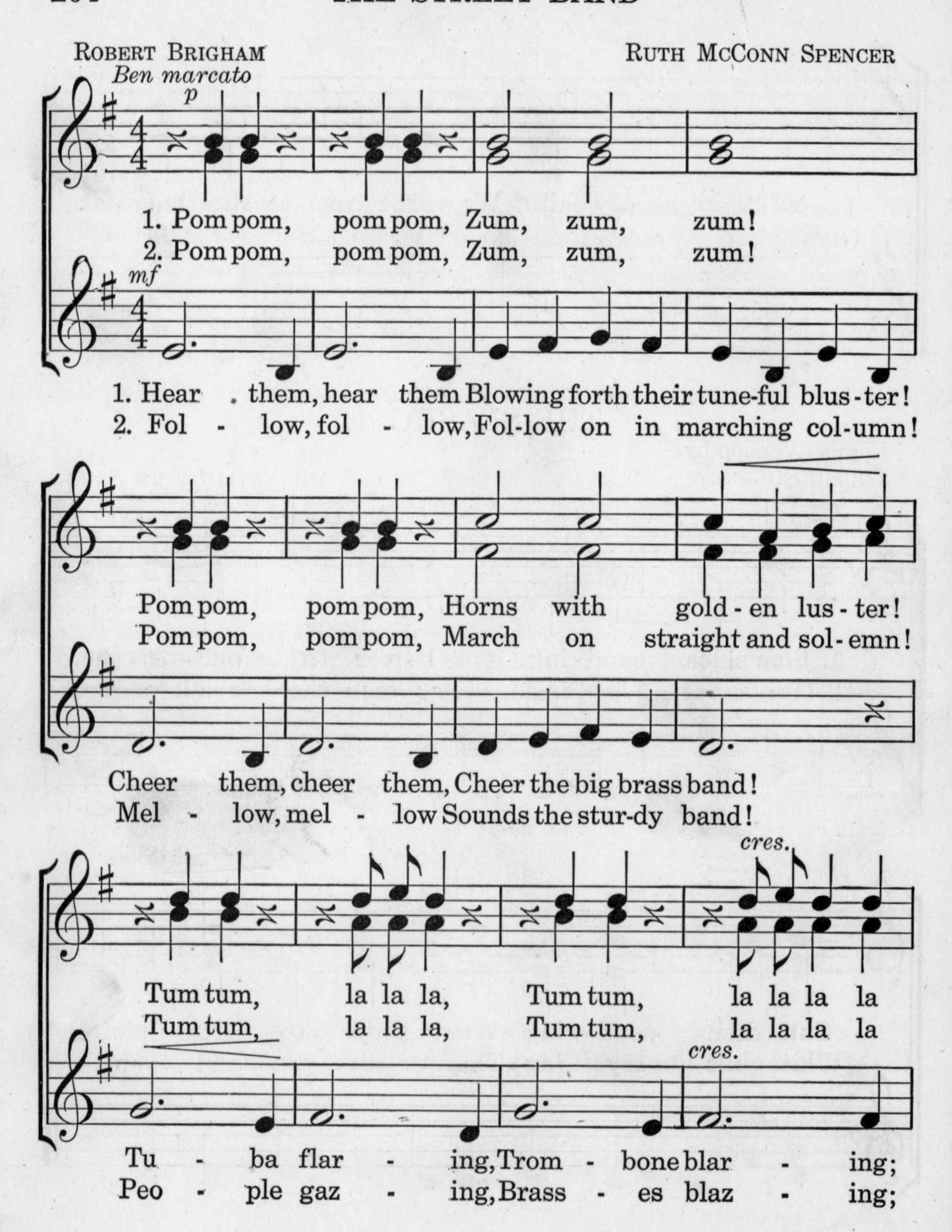

1. Pom pom, pom pom, Zum, zum, zum!
2. Pom pom, pom pom, Zum, zum, zum!

1. Hear them, hear them Blowing forth their tune-ful blus-ter!
2. Fol - low, fol - low, Fol-low on in marching col-umn!

Pom pom, pom pom, Horns with gold - en lus - ter!
Pom pom, pom pom, March on straight and sol - emn!

Cheer them, cheer them, Cheer the big brass band!
Mel - low, mel - low Sounds the stur-dy band!

Tum tum, la la la, Tum tum, la la la la
Tum tum, la la la, Tum tum, la la la la

Tu - ba flar - ing, Trom - bone blar - ing;
Peo - ple gaz - ing, Brass - es blaz - ing;

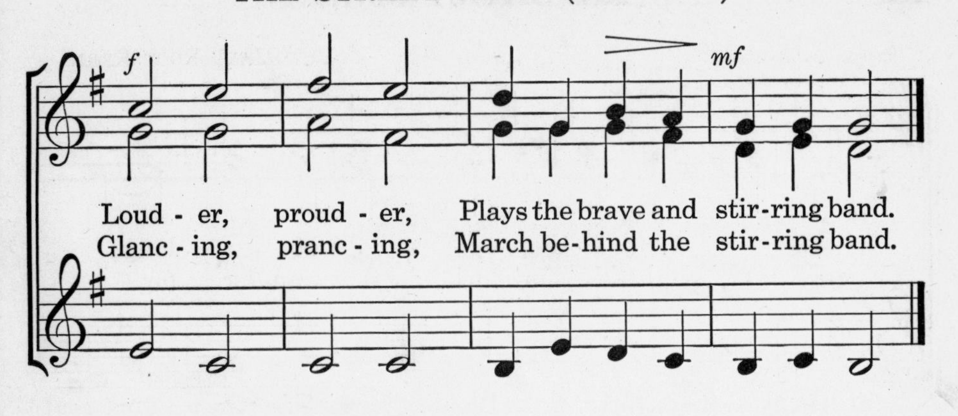

Loud - er,   proud - er,   Plays the brave and   stir-ring band.
Glanc - ing,   pranc - ing,   March be-hind the   stir-ring band.

THE ROBIN

NIXON WATERMAN

RUTH McCONN SPENCER

Cantabile

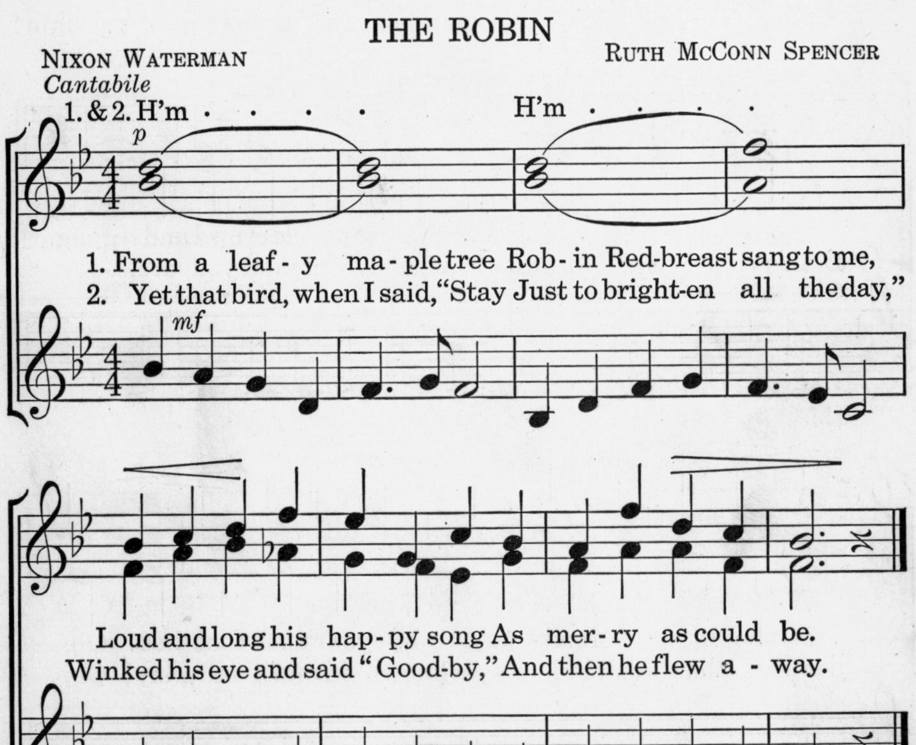

1. & 2. H'm . . . .   H'm . . . .

1. From a leaf - y   ma - ple tree Rob - in Red-breast sang to me,
2.   Yet that bird, when I said, "Stay Just to bright-en   all   the day,"

Loud and long his   hap - py song As   mer - ry   as could be.
Winked his eye and said " Good-by," And then he flew a - way.

THE ROAD TO HAPPINESS

DENIS A. McCARTHY

MARY ROOT KERN

Con anima
mf

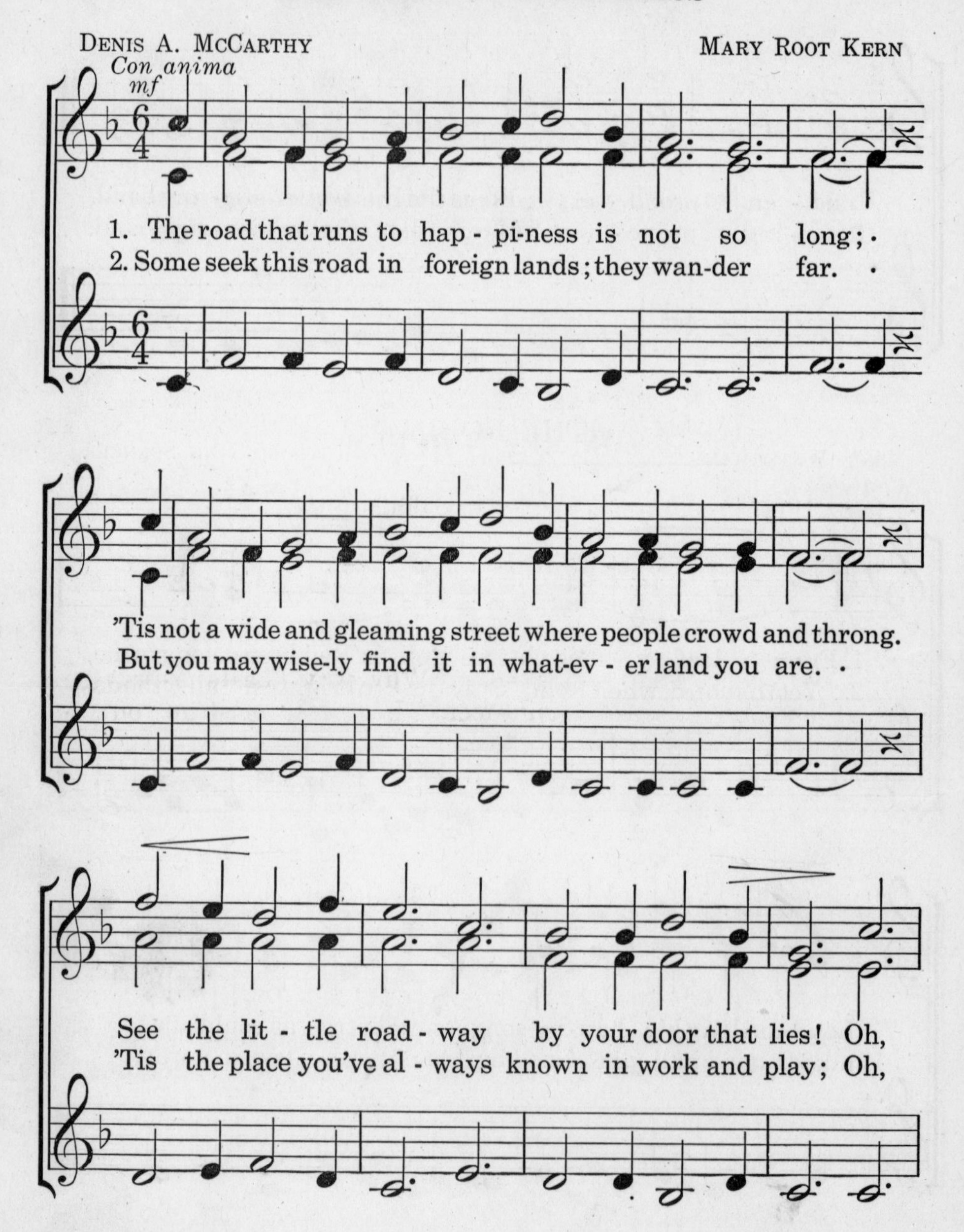

1. The road that runs to hap - pi-ness is not so long; .
2. Some seek this road in foreign lands; they wan-der far. .

'Tis not a wide and gleaming street where people crowd and throng.
But you may wise-ly find it in what-ev - er land you are. .

See the lit - tle road - way by your door that lies! Oh,
'Tis the place you've al - ways known in work and play; Oh,

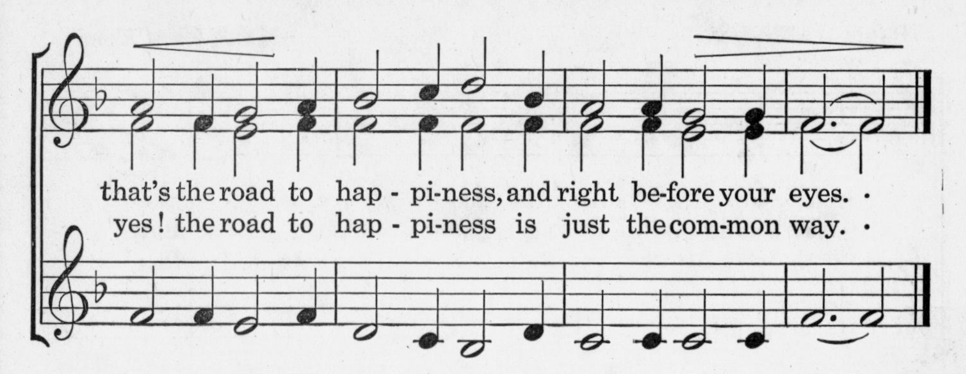

that's the road to hap - pi-ness, and right be-fore your eyes. ·
yes! the road to hap - pi-ness is just the com-mon way. ·

SUMMER'S REPLY

T. H. MacCrady

Evelyn Sprague

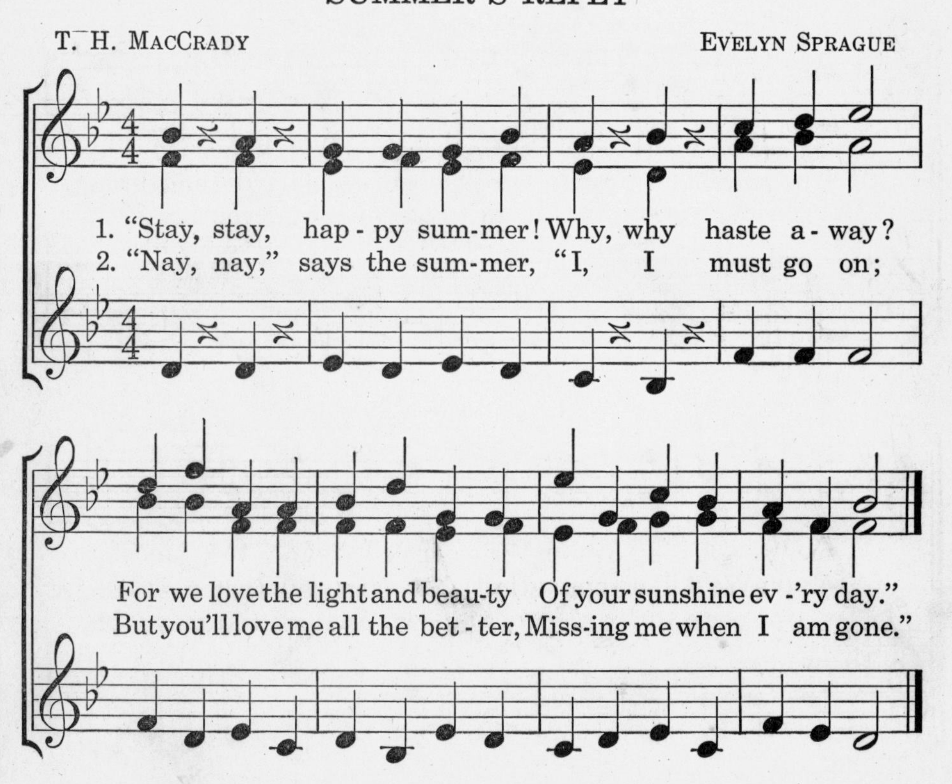

1. "Stay, stay, hap - py sum-mer! Why, why haste a - way?
2. "Nay, nay," says the sum-mer, "I, I must go on;

For we love the light and beau-ty Of your sunshine ev -'ry day."
But you'll love me all the bet - ter, Miss-ing me when I am gone."

CHRISTMAS CHEER

Nixon Waterman

Carl Engel

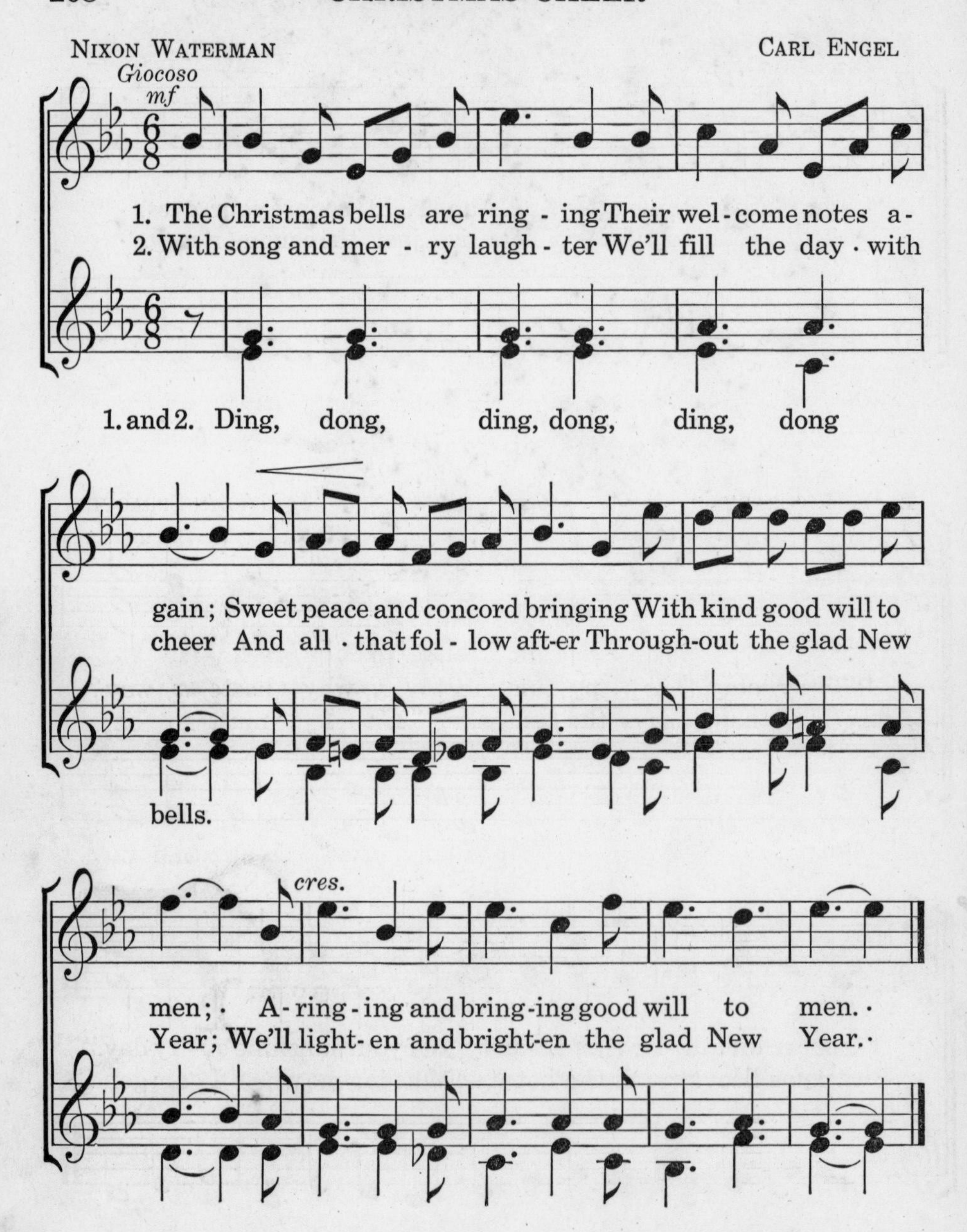

Giocoso

1. The Christmas bells are ring - ing Their wel - come notes a-
2. With song and mer - ry laugh - ter We'll fill the day - with

1. and 2. Ding, dong, ding, dong, ding, dong

gain; Sweet peace and concord bringing With kind good will to
cheer And all · that fol - low aft-er Through-out the glad New

bells.

men; · A - ring - ing and bring-ing good will to men. ·
Year; We'll light- en and bright-en the glad New Year. ·

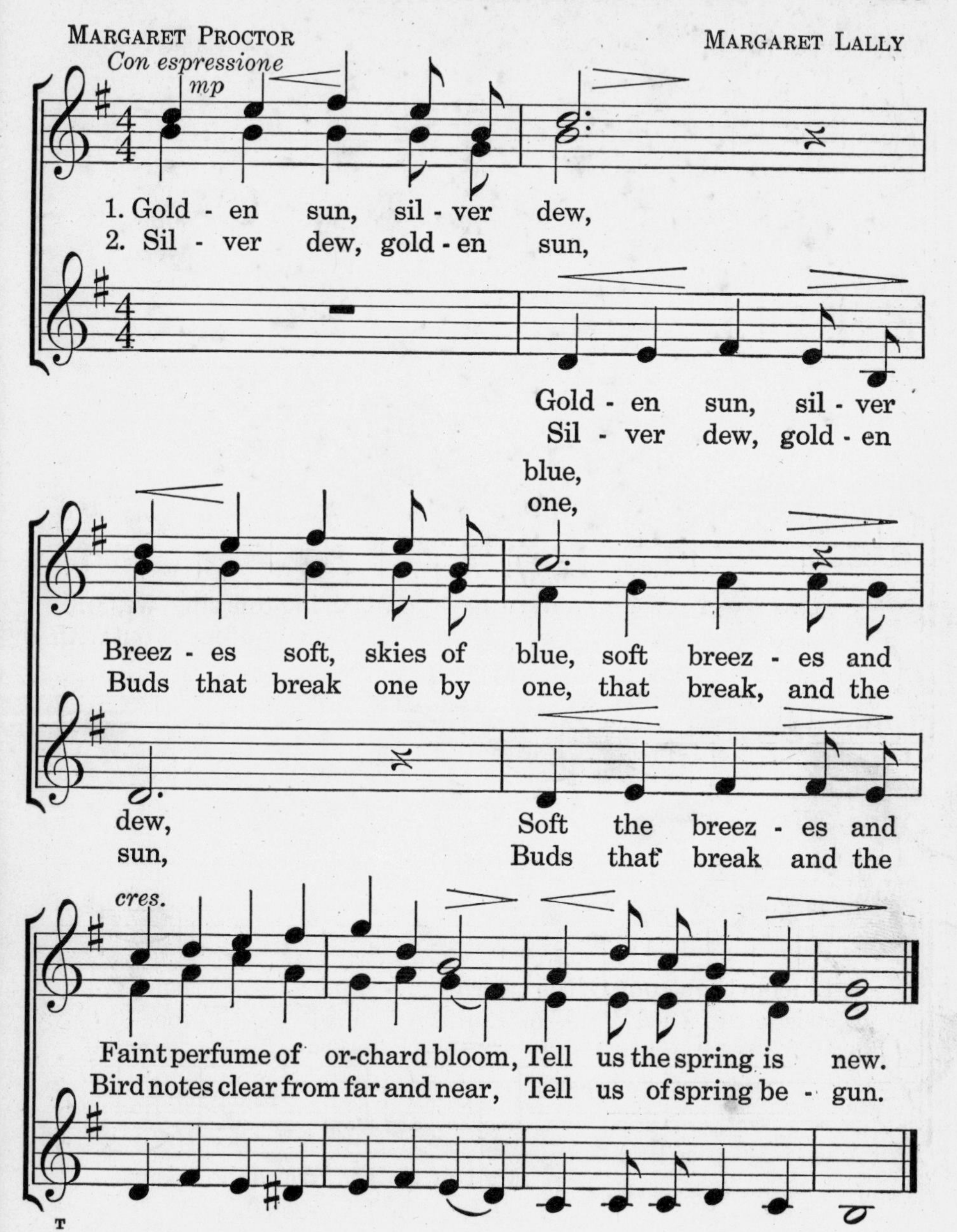

M. LOUISE BAUM

EARL TOWNER

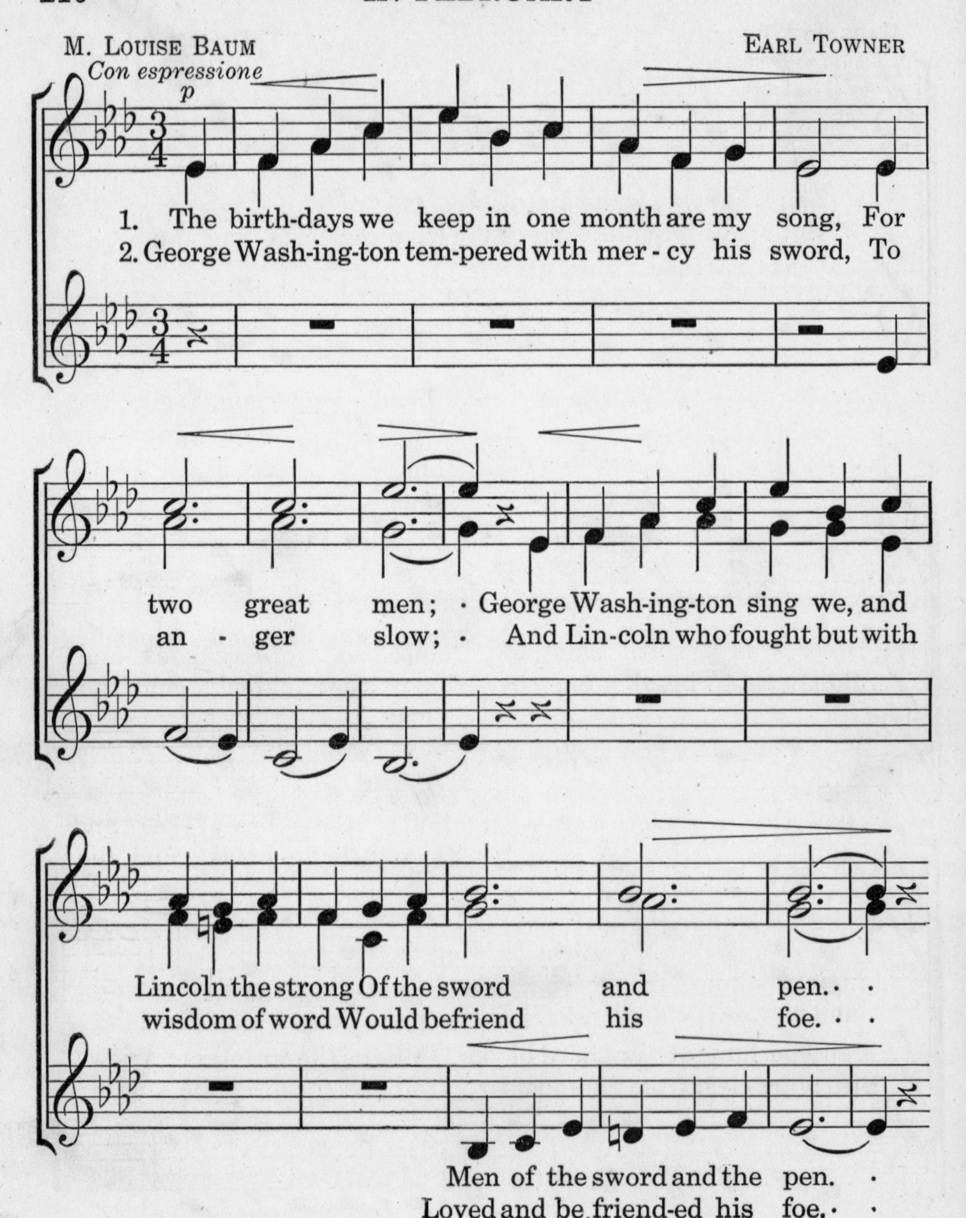

1. The birth-days we keep in one month are my song, For
2. George Wash-ing-ton tem-pered with mer - cy his sword, To

two great men; · George Wash-ing-ton sing we, and
an - ger slow; · And Lin-coln who fought but with

Lincoln the strong Of the sword and pen. · ·
wisdom of word Would befriend his foe. · ·

Men of the sword and the pen. ·
Loved and be.friend-ed his foe. · ·

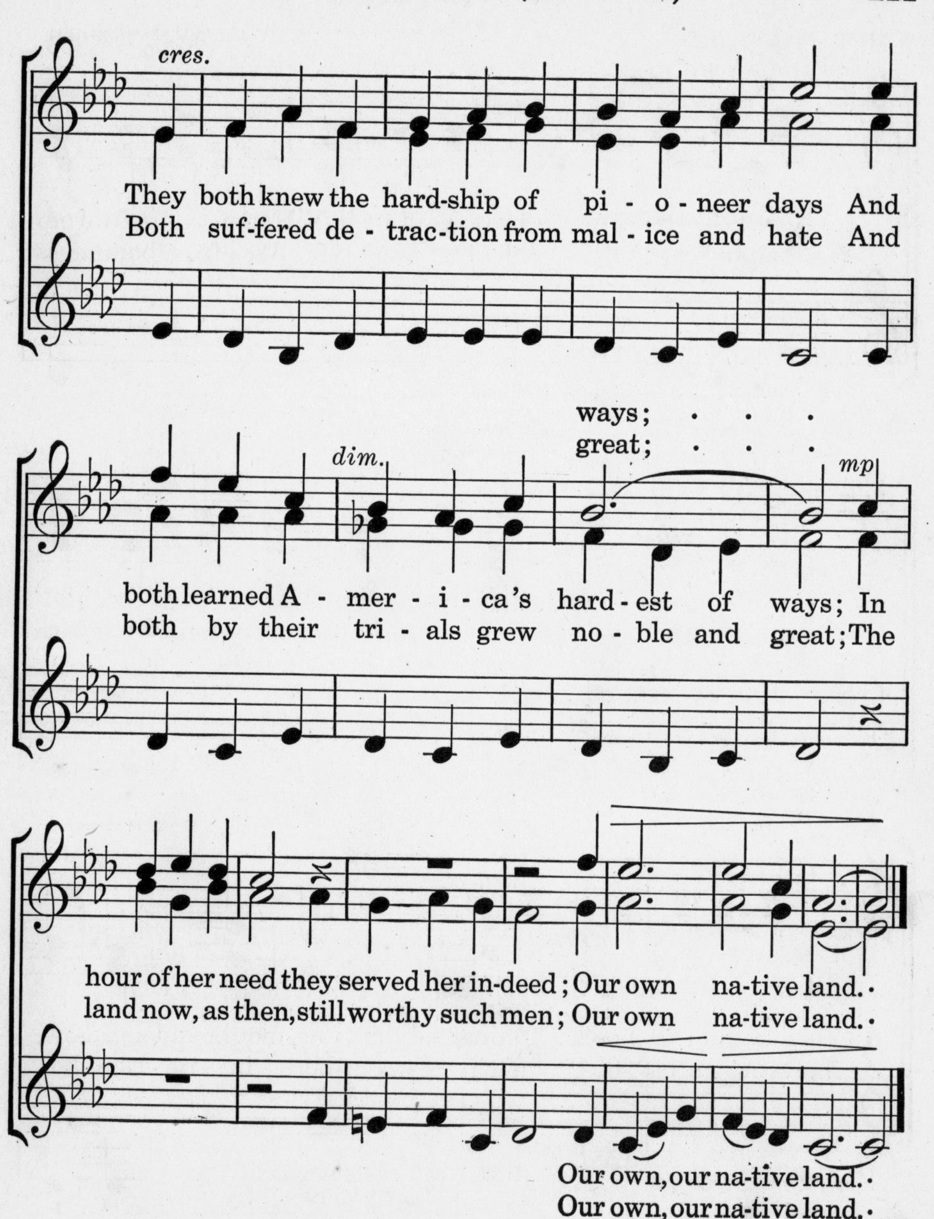

cres.

They both knew the hard-ship of pi - o - neer days And
Both suf-fered de - trac-tion from mal - ice and hate And

dim.   *mp*

ways;   . . .
great;   . . .

both learned A - mer - i - ca's hard - est of ways; In
both by their tri - als grew no - ble and great; The

hour of her need they served her in-deed; Our own na-tive land.
land now, as then, still worthy such men; Our own na-tive land.

Our own, our na-tive land.
Our own, our na-tive land.

BACK TO SCHOOL

DENIS A. McCARTHY

WILLIAM E. BROWN

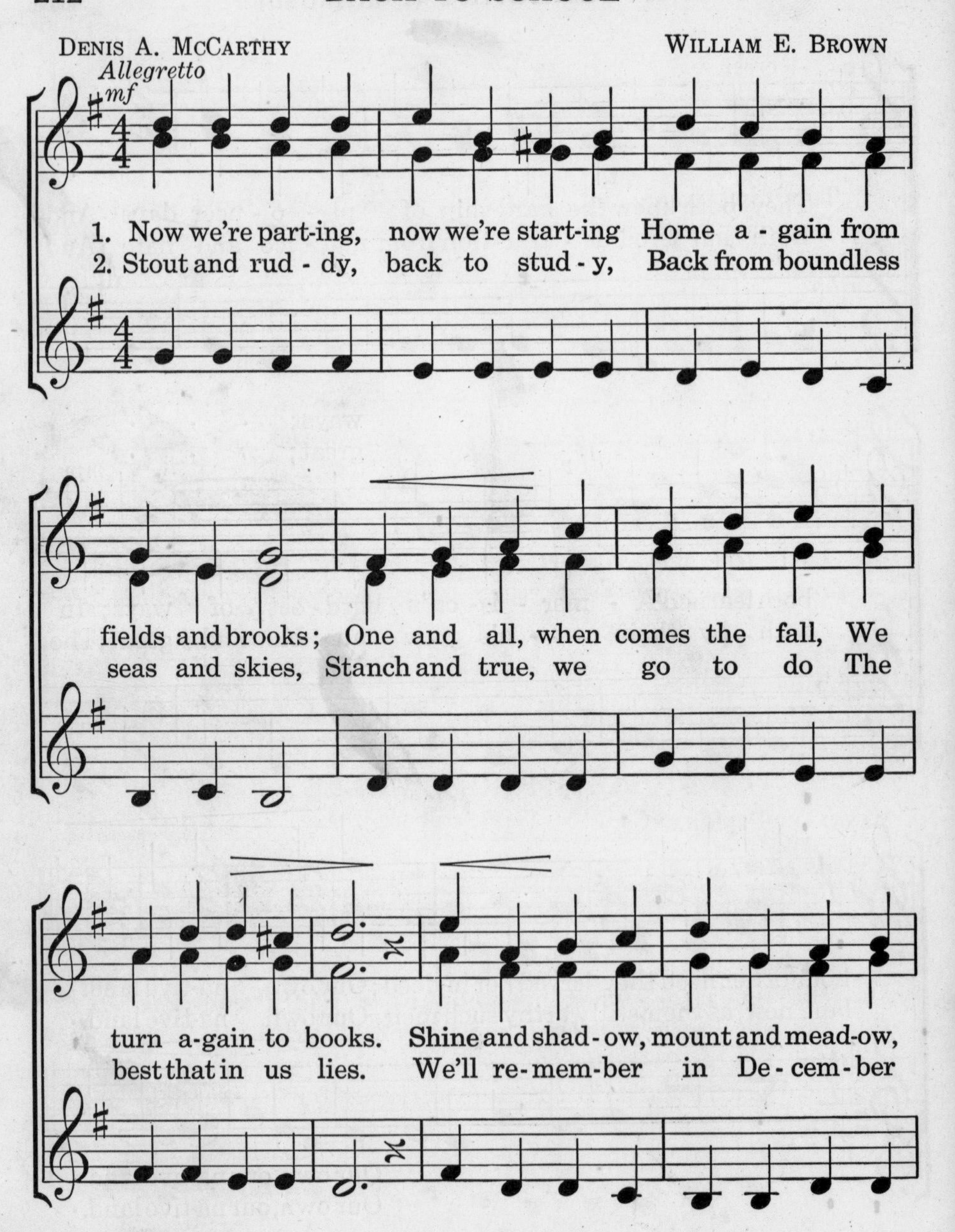

1. Now we're part-ing, now we're start-ing Home a - gain from
2. Stout and rud - dy, back to stud - y, Back from boundless

fields and brooks; One and all, when comes the fall, We
seas and skies, Stanch and true, we go to do The

turn a-gain to books. Shine and shad-ow, mount and mead-ow,
best that in us lies. We'll re-mem-ber in De-cem-ber

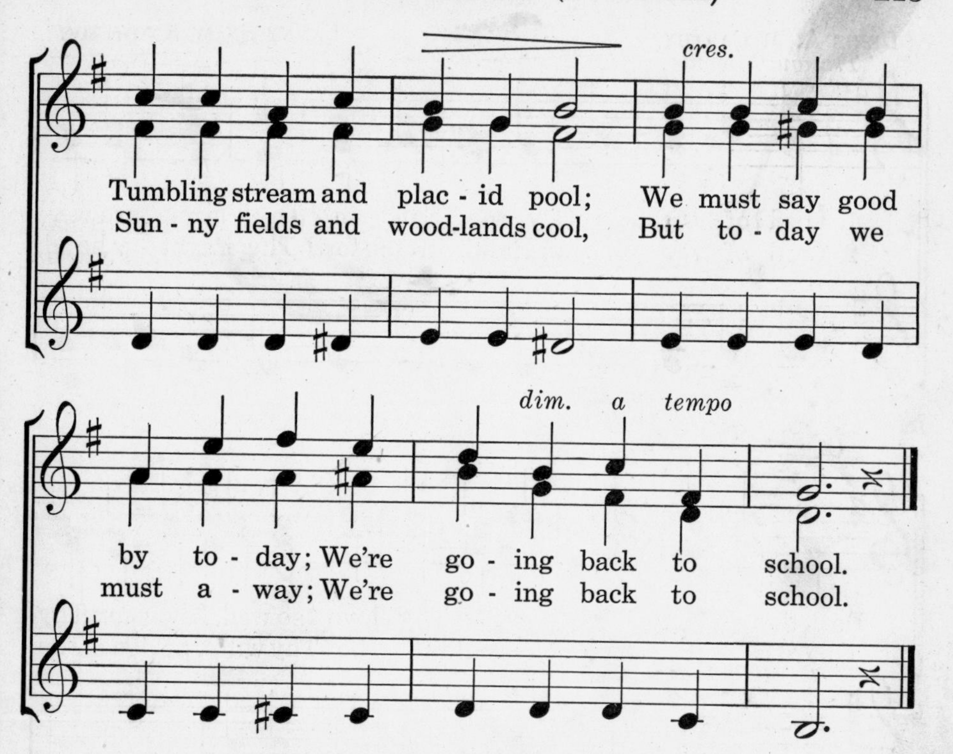

Tumbling stream and plac - id pool; We must say good
Sun - ny fields and wood-lands cool, But to - day we

by to - day; We're go - ing back to school.
must a - way; We're go - ing back to school.

BALTIMORE ORIOLES

MARGARET CONNOLLY

RUTH MAYNARD

Andante

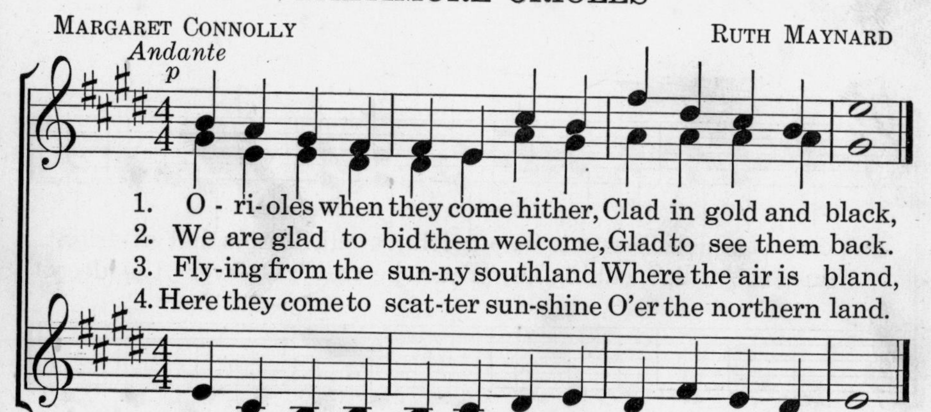

1. O - ri-oles when they come hither, Clad in gold and black,
2. We are glad to bid them welcome, Glad to see them back.
3. Fly-ing from the sun-ny southland Where the air is bland,
4. Here they come to scat-ter sun-shine O'er the northern land.

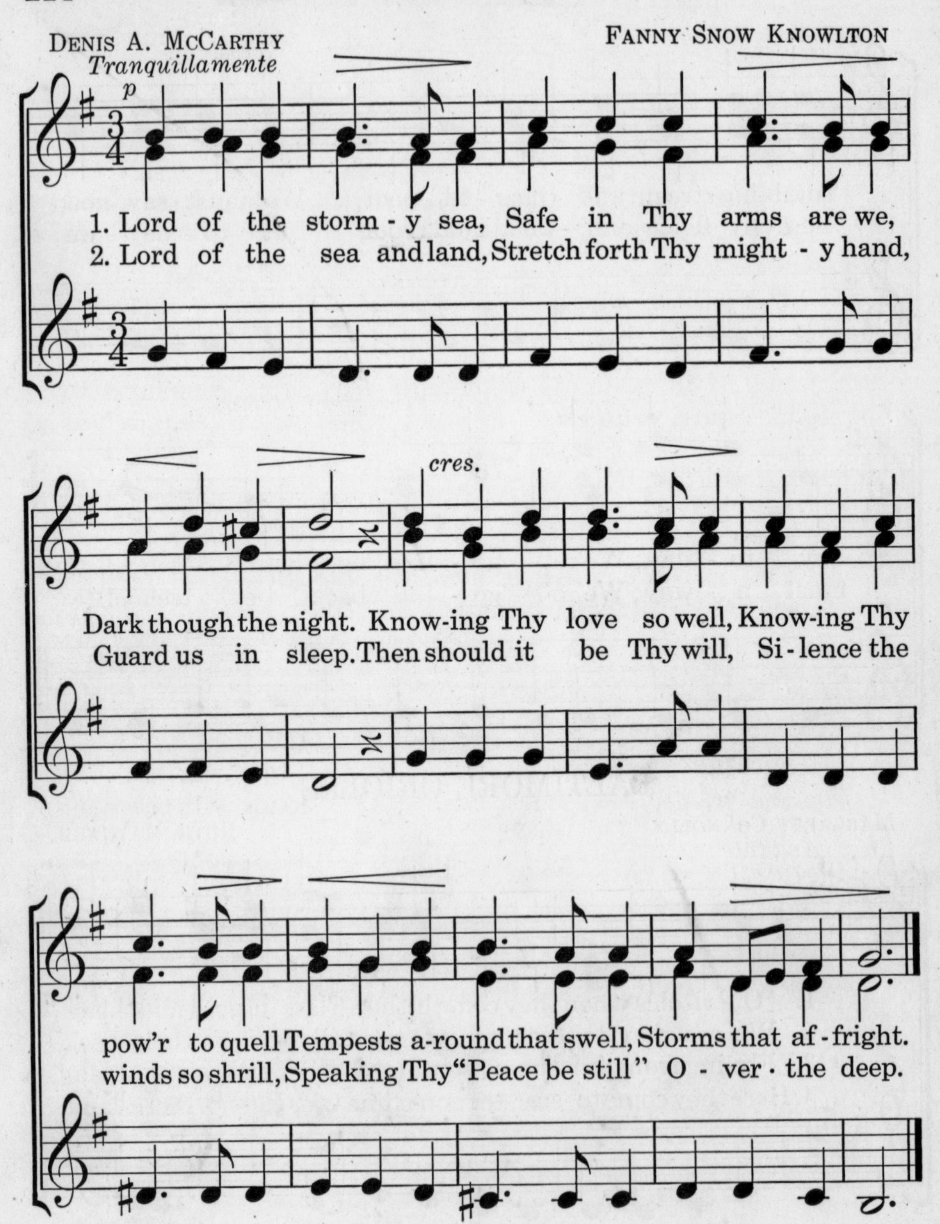

DENIS A. McCARTHY

FANNY SNOW KNOWLTON

Tranquillamente

1. Lord of the storm - y sea, Safe in Thy arms are we,
2. Lord of the sea and land, Stretch forth Thy might - y hand,

cres.

Dark though the night. Know-ing Thy love so well, Know-ing Thy
Guard us in sleep. Then should it be Thy will, Si - lence the

pow'r to quell Tempests a-round that swell, Storms that af - fright.
winds so shrill, Speaking Thy "Peace be still" O - ver - the deep.

WATERMAN-McCARTHY

JOHN WARD

Maestoso

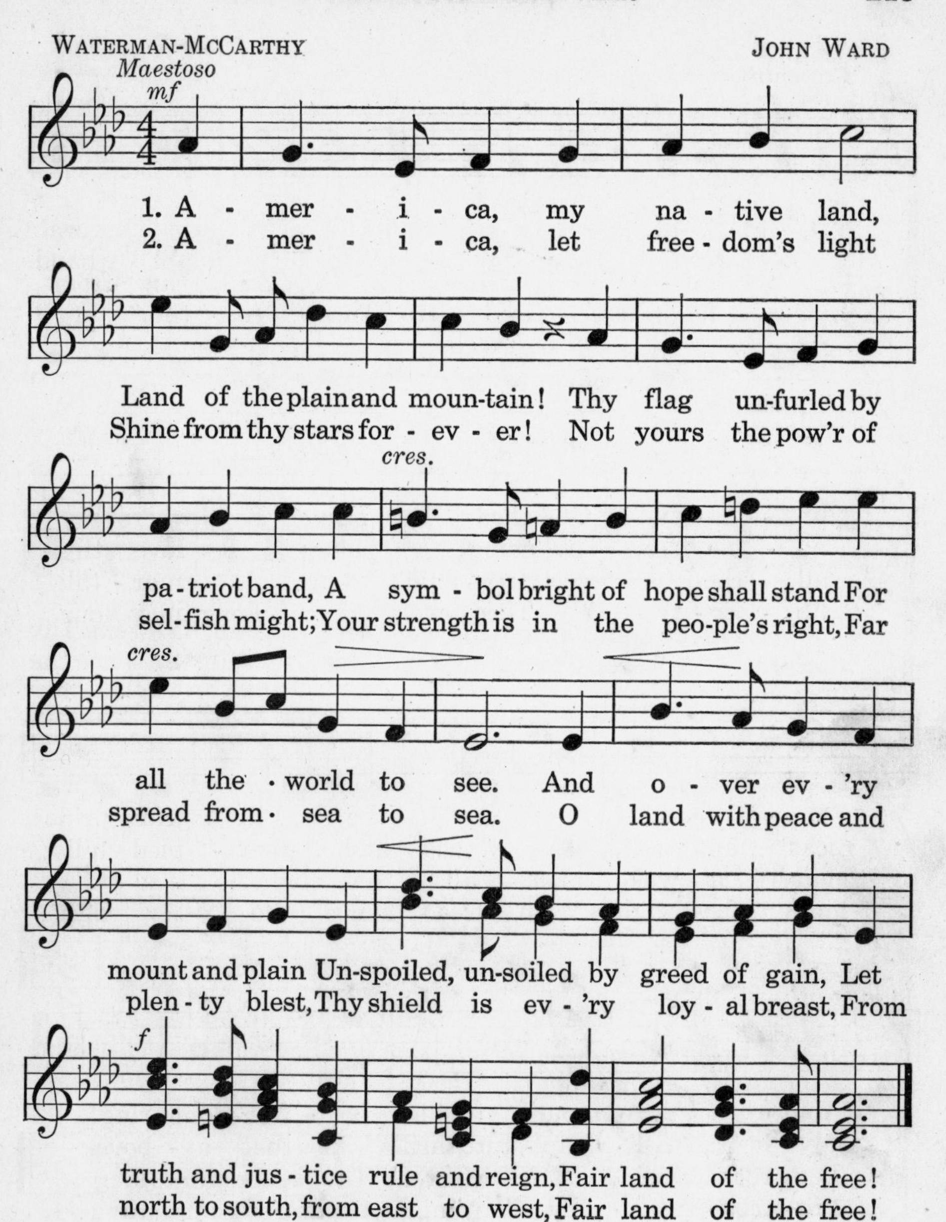

1. A - mer - i - ca, my na - tive land,
2. A - mer - i - ca, let free - dom's light

Land of the plain and moun-tain! Thy flag un-furled by
Shine from thy stars for - ev - er! Not yours the pow'r of

cres.

pa - triot band, A sym - bol bright of hope shall stand For
sel-fish might; Your strength is in the peo-ple's right, Far

cres.

all the world to see. And o - ver ev - 'ry
spread from sea to sea. O land with peace and

mount and plain Un-spoiled, un-soiled by greed of gain, Let
plen - ty blest, Thy shield is ev - 'ry loy - al breast, From

f

truth and jus - tice rule and reign, Fair land of the free!
north to south, from east to west, Fair land of the free!

S. F. SMITH   HENRY CAREY

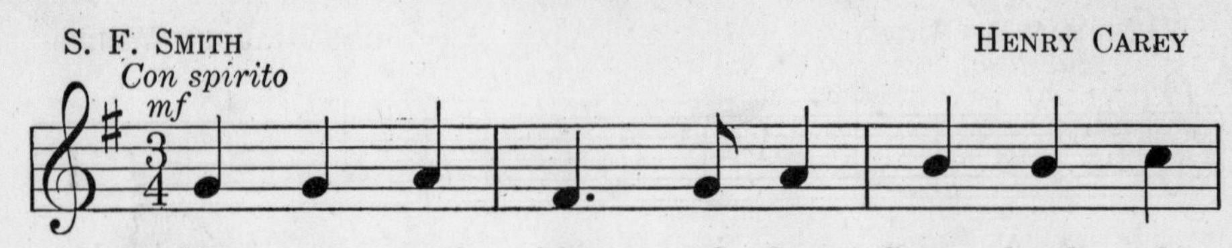

1. My coun - try! 'tis of thee, Sweet land of
2. My na - tive coun - try, thee — Land of the
3. Let mu - sic swell the breeze, And ring from
4. Our fa - thers' God! to Thee, Au - thor of

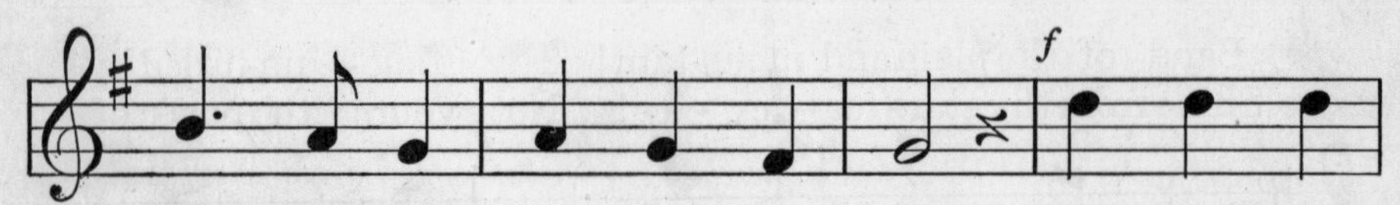

lib - er - ty, Of thee I sing; Land where my
no - ble free, Thy name I love; I love thy
all the trees Sweet free - dom's song; Let mor - tal
lib - er - ty, To Thee we sing; Long may our

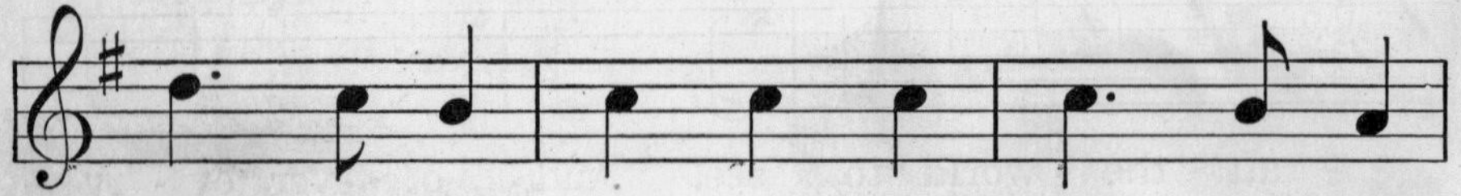

fa - thers died! Land of the Pil - grims' pride!
rocks and rills, Thy woods and tem - pled hills;
tongues a - wake, Let all that breathe par - take,
land be bright With free - dom's ho - ly light!

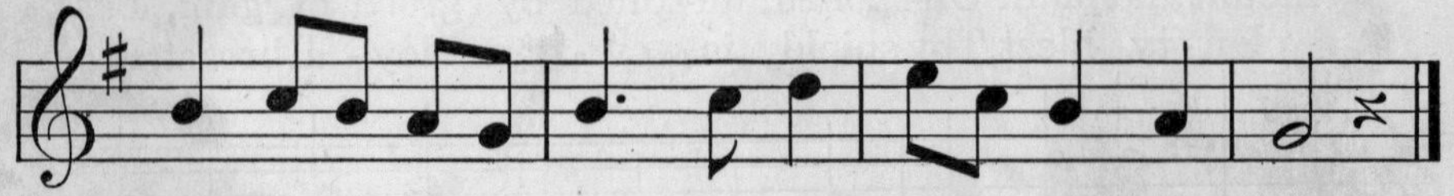

From ev - 'ry moun - tain side Let free - dom ring!
My heart with rap - ture thrills Like that a - bove.
Let rocks their si - lence break, The sound pro - long.
Pro - tect us by Thy might, Great God, our King!

FRANCIS SCOTT KEY

JOHN STAFFORD SMITH

Con spirito

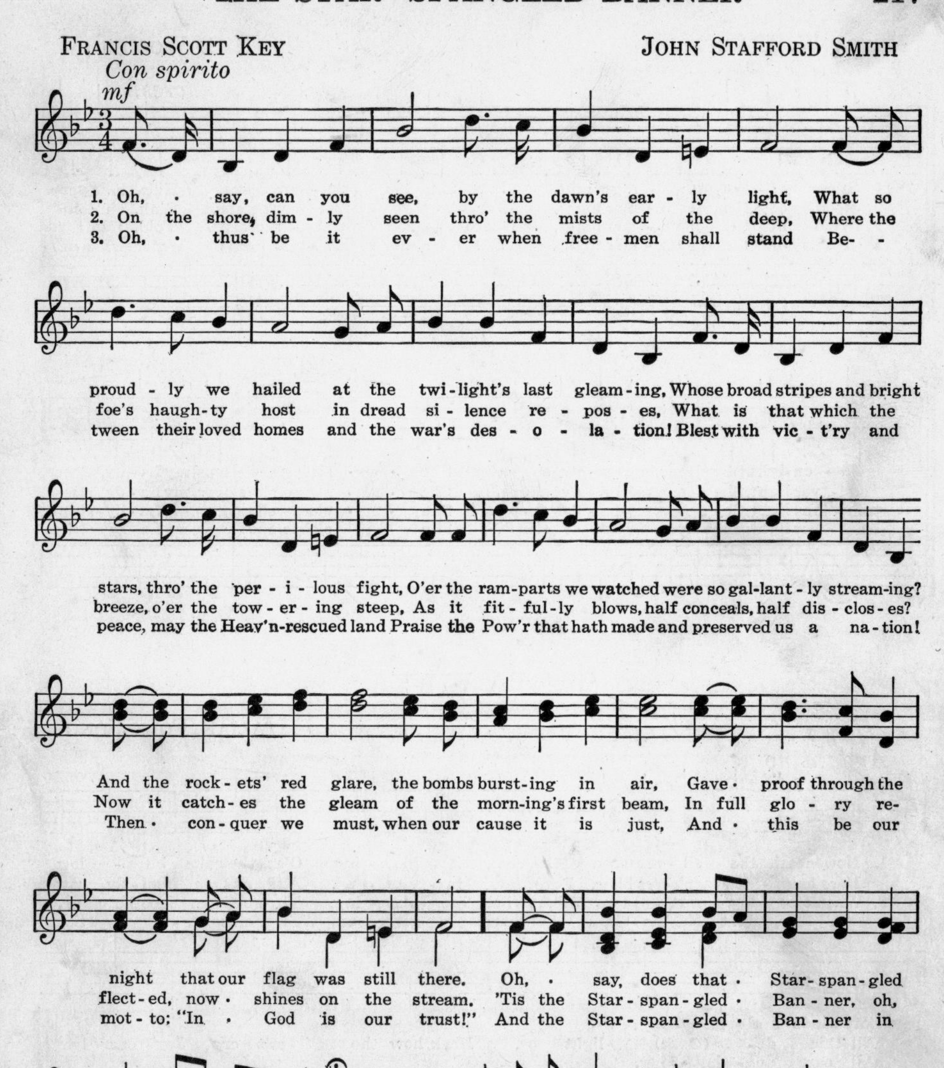

1. Oh, · say, can you see, by the dawn's ear-ly light, What so
2. On the shore, dim-ly seen thro' the mists of the deep, Where the
3. Oh, · thus · be it ev-er when free-men shall stand Be- -

proud-ly we hailed at the twi-light's last gleam-ing, Whose broad stripes and bright
foe's haugh-ty host in dread si-lence re-pos-es, What is that which the
tween their loved homes and the war's des-o-la-tion! Blest with vic-t'ry and

stars, thro' the per-i-lous fight, O'er the ram-parts we watched were so gal-lant-ly stream-ing?
breeze, o'er the tow-er-ing steep, As it fit-ful-ly blows, half conceals, half dis-clos-es?
peace, may the Heav'n-rescued land Praise the Pow'r that hath made and preserved us a na-tion!

And the rock-ets' red glare, the bombs burst-ing in air, Gave · proof through the
Now it catch-es the gleam of the morn-ing's first beam, In full glo-ry re-
Then · con-quer we must, when our cause it is just, And · this be our

night that our flag was still there. Oh, · say, does that · Star-span-gled
flect-ed, now · shines on the stream. 'Tis the Star-span-gled · Ban-ner, oh,
mot-to: "In · God is our trust!" And the Star-span-gled · Ban-ner in

Ban-ner · yet · wave O'er the land · of the free and the home of the brave!
long may · it · wave O'er the land · of the free and the home of the brave!
tri-umph shall wave O'er the land · of the free and the home of the brave!

STARS OF THE SUMMER NIGHT

HENRY W. LONGFELLOW

I. B. WOODBURY

Andante

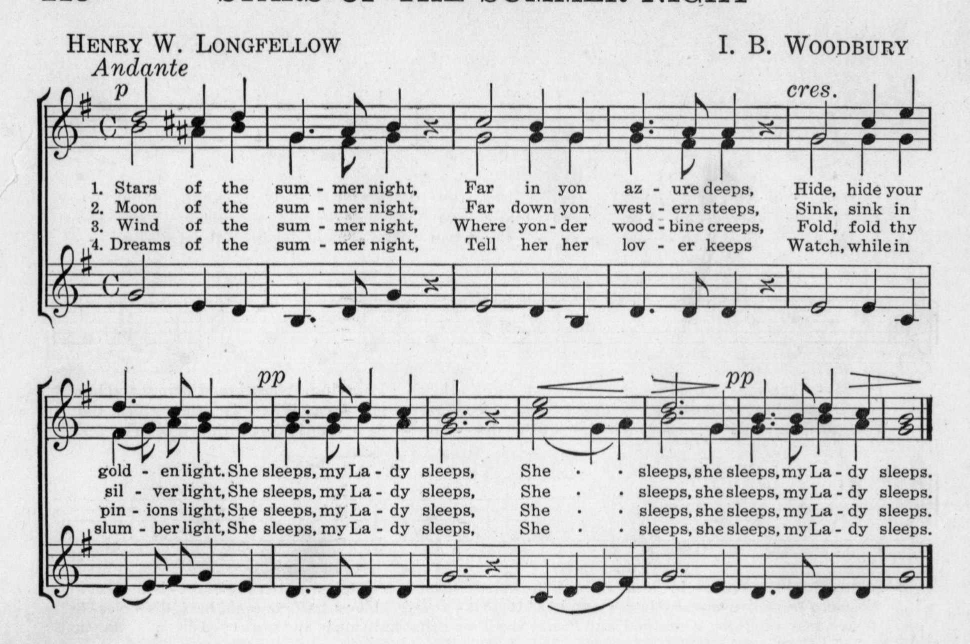

1. Stars of the sum - mer night, Far in yon az - ure deeps, Hide, hide your
2. Moon of the sum - mer night, Far down yon west - ern steeps, Sink, sink in
3. Wind of the sum - mer night, Where yon - der wood - bine creeps, Fold, fold thy
4. Dreams of the sum - mer night, Tell her her lov - er keeps Watch, while in

gold - en light. She sleeps, my La - dy sleeps, She sleeps, she sleeps, my La - dy sleeps.
sil - ver light, She sleeps, my La - dy sleeps, She sleeps, she sleeps, my La - dy sleeps.
pin - ions light, She sleeps, my La - dy sleeps, She sleeps, she sleeps, my La - dy sleeps.
slum - ber light, She sleeps, my La - dy sleeps, She sleeps, she sleeps, my La - dy sleeps.

SANTA LUCIA

ITALIAN FOLK SONG

Andantino

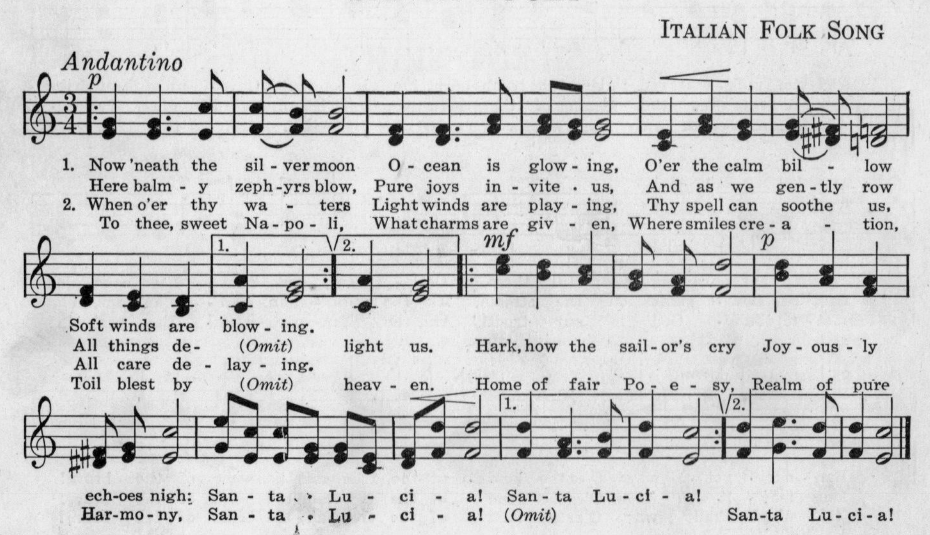

1. Now 'neath the sil - ver moon O - cean is glow - ing, O'er the calm bil - low
   Here balm - y zeph - yrs blow, Pure joys in - vite us, And as we gen - tly row
2. When o'er thy wa - ters Light winds are play - ing, Thy spell can soothe us,
   To thee, sweet Na - po - li, What charms are giv - en, Where smiles cre - a - tion,

Soft winds are blow - ing.
All things de - (Omit) light us. Hark, how the sail - or's cry Joy - ous - ly
All care de - lay - ing.
Toil blest by (Omit) heav - en. Home of fair Po - e - sy, Realm of pure

ech - oes nigh: San - ta Lu - ci - a! San - ta Lu - ci - a!
Har - mo - ny, San - ta Lu - ci - a! (Omit) San - ta Lu - ci - a!

ANCIENT OF DAYS

219

WILLIAM C. DOANE

J. ALBERT JEFFERY

Maestoso

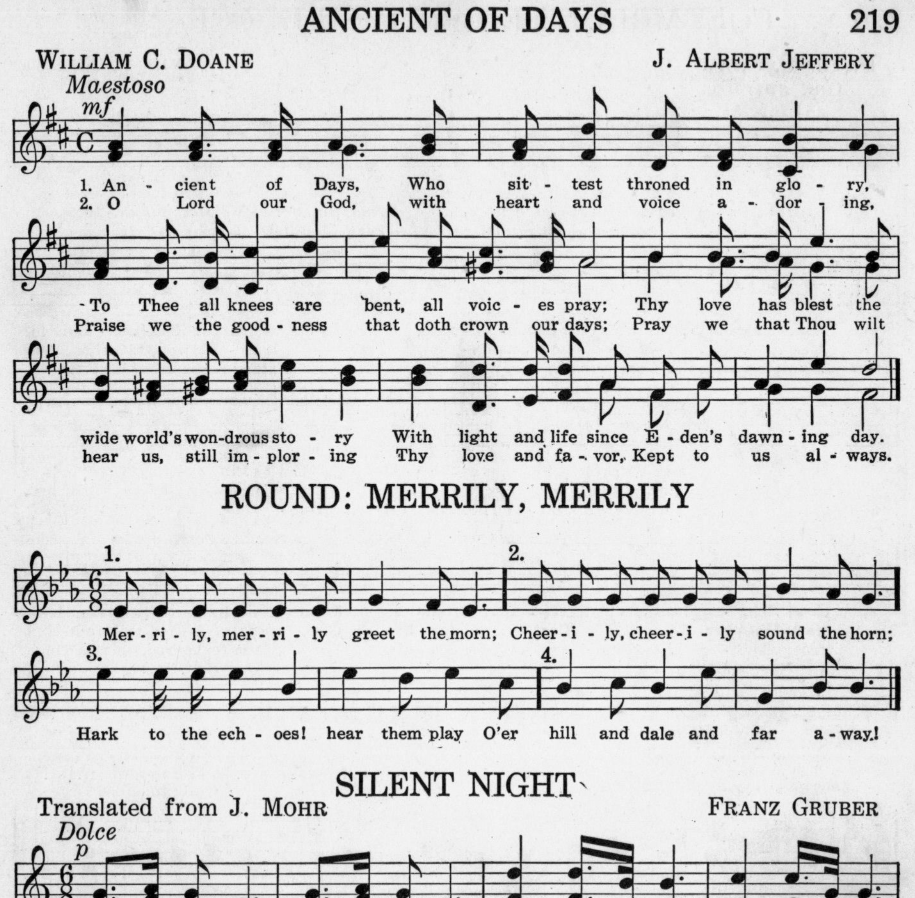

1. An - cient of Days, Who sit - test throned in glo - ry,
2. O Lord our God, with heart and voice a - dor - ing,

- To Thee all knees are bent, all voic - es pray; Thy love has blest the
Praise we the good - ness that doth crown our days; Pray we that Thou wilt

wide world's won-drous sto - ry With light and life since E - den's dawn - ing day.
hear us, still im - plor - ing Thy love and fa - vor, Kept to us al - ways.

ROUND: MERRILY, MERRILY

Mer - ri - ly, mer - ri - ly greet the morn; Cheer - i - ly, cheer - i - ly sound the horn;

Hark to the ech - oes! hear them play O'er hill and dale and far a - way!

SILENT NIGHT

Translated from J. MOHR

FRANZ GRUBER

Dolce

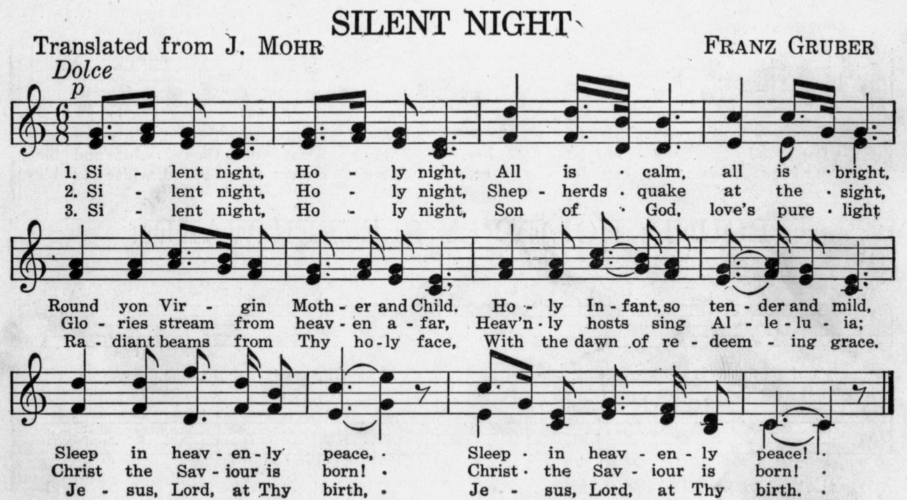

1. Si - lent night, Ho - ly night, All is calm, all is bright,
2. Si - lent night, Ho - ly night, Shep - herds quake at the sight,
3. Si - lent night, Ho - ly night, Son of God, love's pure light

Round yon Vir - gin Moth - er and Child. Ho - ly In - fant, so ten - der and mild,
Glo - ries stream from heav - en a - far, Heav'n - ly hosts sing Al - le - lu - ia;
Ra - diant beams from Thy ho - ly face, With the dawn of re - deem - ing grace.

Sleep in heav - en - ly peace, Sleep in heav - en - ly peace!
Christ the Sav - iour is born! Christ the Sav - iour is born!
Je - sus, Lord, at Thy birth. Je - sus, Lord, at Thy birth.

COLUMBIA, THE GEM OF THE OCEAN

David F. Shaw

David F. Shaw

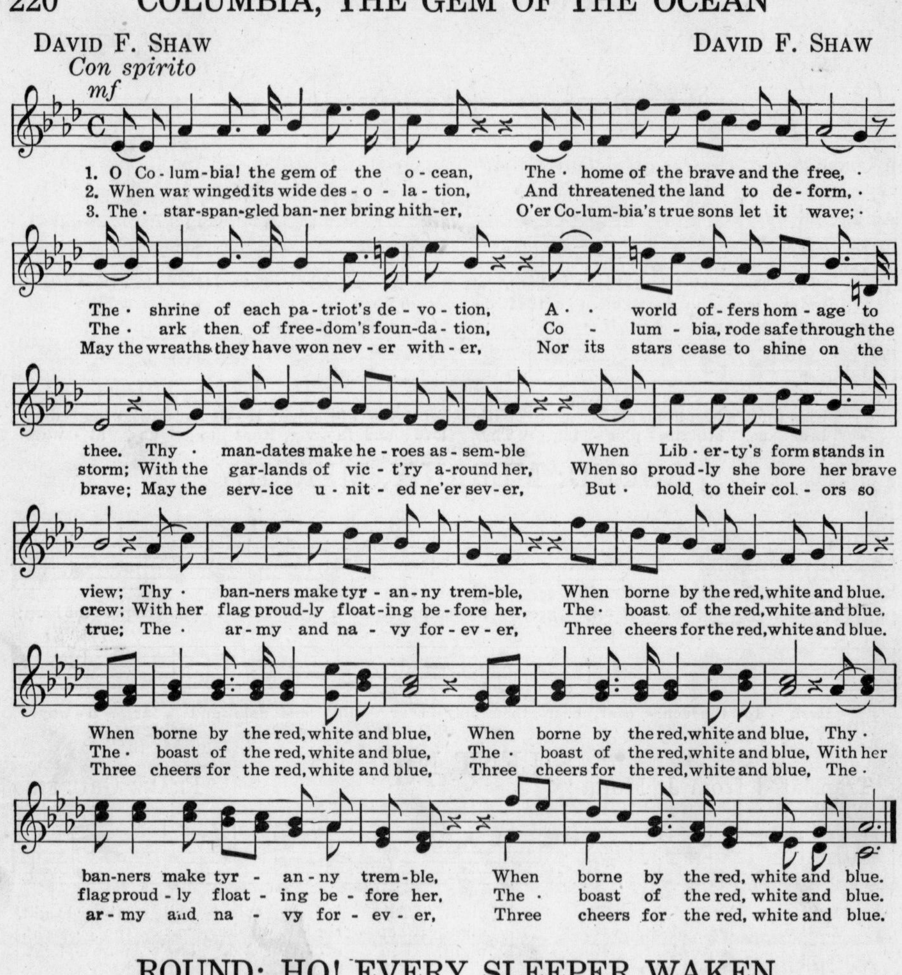

Con spirito

1. O Co-lum-bia! the gem of the o-cean, The home of the brave and the free,
2. When war winged its wide des-o-la-tion, And threatened the land to de-form,
3. The star-span-gled ban-ner bring hith-er, O'er Co-lum-bia's true sons let it wave;

The shrine of each pa-triot's de-vo-tion, A world of-fers hom-age to
The ark then of free-dom's foun-da-tion, Co-lum-bia, rode safe through the
May the wreaths they have won nev-er with-er, Nor its stars cease to shine on the

thee. Thy man-dates make he-roes as-sem-ble When Lib-er-ty's form stands in
storm; With the gar-lands of vic-t'ry a-round her, When so proud-ly she bore her brave
brave; May the serv-ice u-nit-ed ne'er sev-er, But hold to their col-ors so

view; Thy ban-ners make tyr-an-ny trem-ble, When borne by the red, white and blue.
crew; With her flag proud-ly float-ing be-fore her, The boast of the red, white and blue.
true; The ar-my and na-vy for-ev-er, Three cheers for the red, white and blue.

When borne by the red, white and blue, When borne by the red, white and blue, Thy
The boast of the red, white and blue, The boast of the red, white and blue, With her
Three cheers for the red, white and blue, Three cheers for the red, white and blue, The

ban-ners make tyr-an-ny trem-ble, When borne by the red, white and blue.
flag proud-ly float-ing be-fore her, The boast of the red, white and blue.
ar-my and na-vy for-ev-er, Three cheers for the red, white and blue.

ROUND: HO! EVERY SLEEPER WAKEN

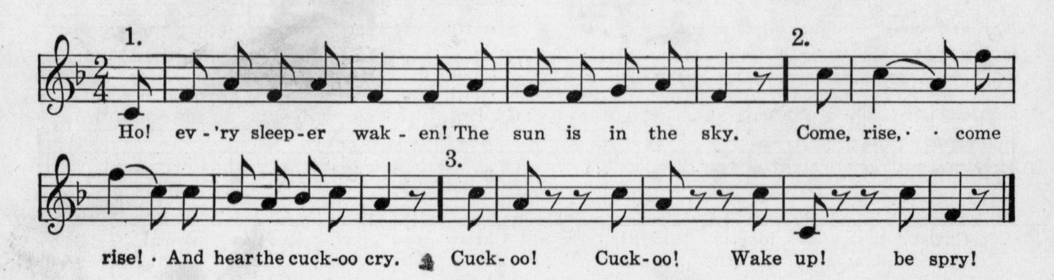

1.
Ho! ev-'ry sleep-er wak-en! The sun is in the sky. **2.** Come, rise, come

3.
rise! And hear the cuck-oo cry. Cuck-oo! Cuck-oo! Wake up! be spry!

TERMS OF EXPRESSION[1]

A tempo (ä tĕm′pō) : return to first rate of speed

Ad libitum (ăd lĭb′ĭ-tŭm) : at the pleasure of the performer

Adagio (ȧ-dä′jō) : slow; *literally*, at leisure

Allegretto (äl′lä-grĕt′tō) : less quick than *allegro*; diminutive of *allegro*

Allegro (äl-lā′grō) : quick, lively ; *literally*, cheerful

Andante (än-dän′tä) : slow, graceful ; moving at a moderate pace ; *literally*, walking

Andantino (än′dän-tē′nō) : the diminutive of *andante*, and indicating quicker tempo

Animato (ä′nĕ-mä′tō) : animated

Ben marcato (bĕn mär-kä′tō) : well marked

Cantabile (kän-tä′bĕ-lā) : in a singing style, or very *legato*

Con anima (kŏn ä′nĕ-mä) : with animation

Con brio (kŏn brē′ō) : with vigor, spirit, force

Con espressione (kŏn ĕs′prĕs-sĕ-ō′nä) : with expression

Con grazia (kŏn grä′tsĕ-ä) : with grace

Con moto (kŏn mō′tō) : with spirited movement

Con spirito (kŏn spē′rĕ-tō) : with spirit, energy

Crescendo (krĕ-shĕn′dō) : gradually increasing the tone

Diminuendo (dĭ-mĭn′u̇-ĕn′dō) : gradually lessening the tone

Dolce (dŏl′chä) : sweet, soft

Energico (ĕn-ĕr′jĕ-kō) : energetic, forcible

Espressivo (ĕs′prĕs-sē′vō) : with expression

f, forte (fôr′tä) : loud

ff, fortissimo (fôr-tĭs′ĭ-mō) : very loud

Giocoso (jō-kō′sō) : humorous, playful

Giojoso (jō-yō′sō) : joyous

Grazioso (grä-tsĕ-ō′sō) : graceful, elegant

Larghetto (lär-gĕt′tō) : rather slow ; the diminutive of *largo*, slow, *or*, *literally*, large

Largo (lär′gō) : slow, broad

Legato (lā-gä′tō) : even, continuous, flowing ; *literally*, tied

Leggiero (lĕd-jä′rō) : light

Lento (lĕn′tō) : *literally*, slow

Maestoso (mä′ĕs-tō′sō) : with dignity, majesty

Marcato (mär-kä′tō) : distinct, emphasized ; *literally*, marked

Meno mosso (mä′nō môs′sō) : less speed, less fast

mf, mezzo forte (mĕd′zō fôr′tä) : half loud

Misterioso (mĕs-tē′rĕ-ō′sō) : mysterious

Moderato (mŏd′ĕ-rä′tō) : moderate

Molto (mōl′tō) : much, very

mp, mezzo piano (mĕd′zō pĕ-ä′nō) : half soft

p, piano (pĕ-ä′nō) : soft

pp, pianissimo (pē′ȧ-nĭs′ĭ-mō) : very soft

Poco più moto (pō′kō pyoo mō′tō) : somewhat faster

Rallentando (räl′lĕn-tän′dō) : becoming slower ; *literally*, abating. Abb. *rall.*

Ritardando (rē′tär-dän′dō) : slower ; *literally*, retarding. Abb. *rit.*

Semplice (sĕm′plĕ-chä) : simple

Sforzando (sfôr-tsän′dō) (>) : with special emphasis

Sostenuto (sōs′tȧ-noo′tō) : sustained

Tranquillamente (trän-kwēl′lä-män tä) : calmly, quietly

Vivace (vē-vä′chä) : gay ; *literally*, lively

---

[1] Webster's Dictionary symbols of pronunciation used throughout.

SIGNS OF EXPRESSION

1. ≡ **Staff:** five horizontal lines and four equal spaces
2. ≡ **Leger Lines** *or* **Added Lines:** light lines above and below staff
3. **Pitch Names:** A, B, C, D, E, F, G, the first seven letters of the alphabet, by which tones are designated
4. 𝄞 **G Clef:** fixes G upon the second line, around which it turns and establishes the treble staff
5. ≡ **Bars:** vertical lines upon the staff
6. **Measure:** the space between two bars, representing a group of strong and weak beats
7. **Notes:**
   a. 𝅝 *Whole note:* an open notehead without stem
   b. 𝅗𝅥 *Half note:* an open notehead with stem
   c. 𝅘𝅥 *Quarter note:* a closed notehead with stem
   d. 𝅘𝅥𝅮 *Eighth note:* a closed notehead with stem and *one* hook
   e. 𝅘𝅥𝅯 *Sixteenth note:* a closed notehead with stem and *two* hooks
8. **Rests:**
   a. ▬ *Whole rest*   d. 𝄾 *Eighth rest*
   b. ▬ *Half rest*   e. 𝄿 *Sixteenth rest*
   c. 𝄽 *Quarter rest*
9. ⌢ **The Tie:** a curved line joining two notes of the *same* pitch
10. (•) **The Dot:** placed after a note lengthens it one half of its original value. Thus:
   𝅝• is equal to a 𝅝 and a 𝅗𝅥 tied
   𝅗𝅥• is equal to a 𝅗𝅥 and a 𝅘𝅥 tied
   𝅘𝅥• is equal to a 𝅘𝅥 and a 𝅘𝅥𝅮 tied
   𝅘𝅥𝅮• is equal to a 𝅘𝅥𝅮 and a 𝅘𝅥𝅯 tied
   The dot after a rest lengthens it one half, thus:
   ▬• is equal to ▬ 𝄽
   𝄽• is equal to 𝄽 𝄾
   𝄾• is equal to 𝄾 𝄿
11. ⌢ **The Slur:** a curved line joining two or more notes of different pitch. It indicates that notes so joined are to be sung to one syllable
12. ⌢ **The Hold or Pause:** a dot, under or over a small curved line, indicates

that the note or rest over or under which it is placed is to be held longer than usual

13. **Chromatic Characters:**
   a. ♯ *The Sharp:* represents a pitch a half-step above the staff degree
   b. 𝄪 *The Double Sharp:* represents a pitch a half-step above a sharped staff degree
   c. ♭ *The Flat:* represents a pitch a half-step below the staff degree
   d. ♭♭ *The Double Flat:* represents a pitch a half-step below a flatted staff degree
   e. ♮ *The Natural* or *Cancel:* removes the effect of a sharp or flat
   ♮♭ removes the effect of one of the two flats in ♭♭
   ♮♯ removes the effect of one of the two sharps in 𝄪
14. **Measure Signatures:**
   2-4, 2-2 two-quarter measure and two-half measure, meaning that two quarter notes or their equivalent fill one measure; that two half notes or their equivalent fill the measure
   3-4, 3-2 three-quarter and three-half measure
   4-4, ₵ four-quarter measure
   6-8, 6-4 six-eighth measure and six-quarter measure
   9-8, 12-8 nine-eighth measure and twelve-eighth measure
15. **Cantata:** a short sacred or secular musical work consisting of choruses and solos with instrumental accompaniment
16. **Folk Song:** a song whose words and music have originated among the people
17. **Folk Tune:** a melody which has originated among the people.
18. **Opera:** a drama or play set to music.
   Comic Opera: an opera made up entirely of gayety and farce
   Grand Opera: a serious opera in which there is no spoken dialogue
19. **Oratorio:** a large musical work with text founded on scriptural narrative, performed without scenery and action

INDEX